WORKSHOP MANL

for

TRIUMPH VITESSE GT 6 RANGE

COMPILED AND WRITTEN
BY

CHRIS CAFFREY

intereurope

PUBLISHED BY
INTEREUROPE LIMITED
NICHOLSON HOUSE
MAIDENHEAD
BERKSHIRE
ENGLAND

SBN 0 - 85666 - 040 - X

Technical Data

	VITESSE 2 LITRE	G.T.6.	G.T.6 Mk 3
Engine type	6-cylinder 1,998 cc (Vitesse 6 - 1,596 cc)	6-cylinder 1,998 cc	
Overall length	3,885 (152.95)	3,685 (145.10)	3,885 (152.95)
Overall width	1,525 (60.05)	1,448 (57.0)	1,490 (58.66)
Overall height	1,403 (55.25)	1,195 (47.05)	
Turning circle dia. metres (feet)	7.6 (25.0)		
Track - front	1,245 (49.02)		
- rear	1,220 (49.05)		1,245 (49.02)
Wheelbase	2,325 (91.55)	2,119 (83.05)	2,110 (83.07)
Ground clearance	171 (6.75)	102 (4.0)	
Weight (dry)	876 (1,932)	813 (1,793)	878 (1,936)
Fuel tank capacity	8.7 (10.6)	9.7 (11.6)	
Fuel consumption	23.7 (19.8)	25.7 (21.4)	
Maximum speed	161 (100)	172 (107)	177 (110)

NOTE:- mm (inches), kg (lbs), km/h (m.p.h.), cu. metres (cu. feet), imp galls (U.S. galls), miles/imp. gal (miles/U.S. gal)

Contents

Introduction

Our intention in writing this Manual is to provide the reader with all the data and information required to maintain and repair the vehicle. However, it must be realised that special equipment and skills are required in some cases to carry out the work detailed in the text, and we do not recommend that such work be attempted unless the reader possesses the necessary skill and equipment. It would be better to have an **AUTHORISED DEALER** to carry out the work using the special tools and equipment available to his trained staff. He will also be in possession of the genuine spare parts which may be needed for replacement.

The information in the Manual has been checked against that provided by the vehicle manufacturer, and any peculiarities have been mentioned if they depart from usual workshop practice. We have tried to cover the wide range of models on the market for this particular car and cross-references can normally, be made. Where in some instances this cannot be done, references are included in the Technical Data sections.

A fault finding and trouble shooting chart has been inserted at the end of the Manual to enable the reader to pin point faults and so save time. As it is impossible to include every malfunction, only the more usual ones have been included.

Brevity and simplicity have been our aim in compiling this Manual, relying on the numerous illustrations and clear text to inform and instruct the reader. At the request of the many users of our Manuals, we have slanted the book towards repair and overhaul rather than maintenance.

Although every care has been taken to ensure that the information and data are correct we cannot accept any liability for inaccuracies or omissions, or for damage or malfunctions arising from the use of this book, no matter how caused.

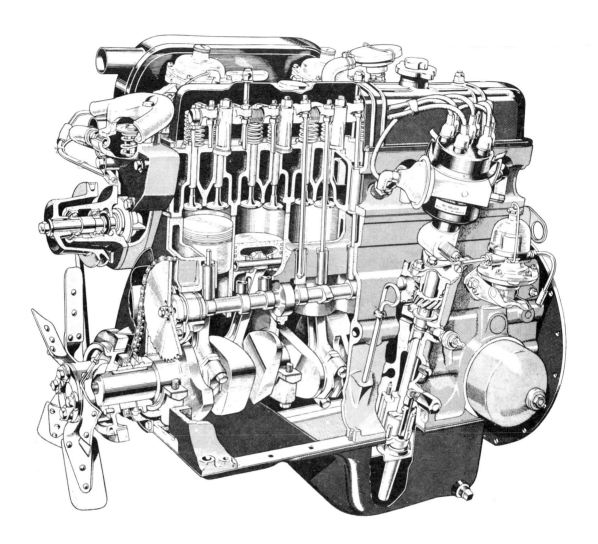

Fig.A.1   Cut-away view of the engine

Engine

GENERAL

A six cylinder, in-line engine with twin carburettors is used in both Vitesse and GT6 models. The engine in the Vitesse Six has a capacity of 1596 cc, and that in the Vitesse 2 litre and GT6 series has a capacity of 1998 cc . The engine incorporates a chrome cast-iron cylinder block and head, aluminium alloy pistons, high tensile steel connecting rods with floating gudgeon pins and a robust, integrally balanced crankshaft with four main bearings, aluminium bearing shells and cross-drilled oilways. The overhead valves are push rod operated by a five-bearing camshaft which is chain driven from the crankshaft.

The engine serial number is stamped on the left-hand side of the cylinder block and is the same as the model commission number with the addition of HE or LE to denote high or low compression engine.

The Vitesse Mk 2 and the GT6 Mk 2 both have a wider cylinder head on the engine to accommodate larger valves and improve the cylinder breathing which, together with a new cam-shaft, gives an increase in power.

VALVE CLEARANCES - Measurement and Adjustment

1. Disconnect breather pipe where fitted, and remove rocker cover. Renew gasket if damaged or distorted.

2. Rotate crankshaft clockwise and, with screwdriver and spanner (Fig.A.4), adjust and lock the adjusting screw to give a gap of 0.25 mm (0.010 in.) at each valve when the engine is cold and the following sequence followed:-

Adjust Nos. 1 and 3 valves with Nos. 10 and 12 valves open
Adjust Nos. 8 and 11 valves with Nos. 2 and 5 valves open.
Adjust Nos. 4 and 6 valves with Nos. 7 and 9 valve open.
Adjust Nos. 10 and 12 valves with Nos. 1 and 3 valves open.
Adjust Nos. 2 and 5 valves with Nos. 8 and 11 valves open.
Adjust Nos. 7 and 9 valves with Nos. 4 and 6 valves open.

NOTE.- Recheck each valve clearance after locking adjust-ing screw.

3. Refit rocker cover with gasket and connect breather pipe.

CYLINDER HEAD - Removal and Installation
Removal

1. Isolate battery

2. Drain cooling system (see COOLING SYSTEM).

3. Disconnect radiator hoses at thermostat housing and water pump inlet and disconnect water temperature gauge cable.

4. Remove radiator header tank (Early Vitesse Six only).

5. Disconnect heater hoses at engine.

6. Remove air filter assembly.

7. Slacken generator/alternator bolts and remove fan belt.

8. Remove water pump bolts and move pump away from engine.

9. Disconnect fuel pipe and throttle and choke controls at carburettors.

10. Disconnect breather pipe or emission control valve hoses from rocker cover and servo-vacuum pipe and front hose, where applicable, from manifold.

11. Remove HT leads and sparking plugs.

12. Disconnect exhaust down-pipe and remove inlet and exhaust manifolds.

13. Remove rocker cover.

14. Evenly slacken and remove rocker pedestal nuts and lift off rocker assembly. Withdraw push rods and cam followers and keep in correct order.

15. Remove cylinder nuts, initially in small increments, in the reverse sequence to that shown in Fig.A.5. Lift off cylin-der head complete with gasket.

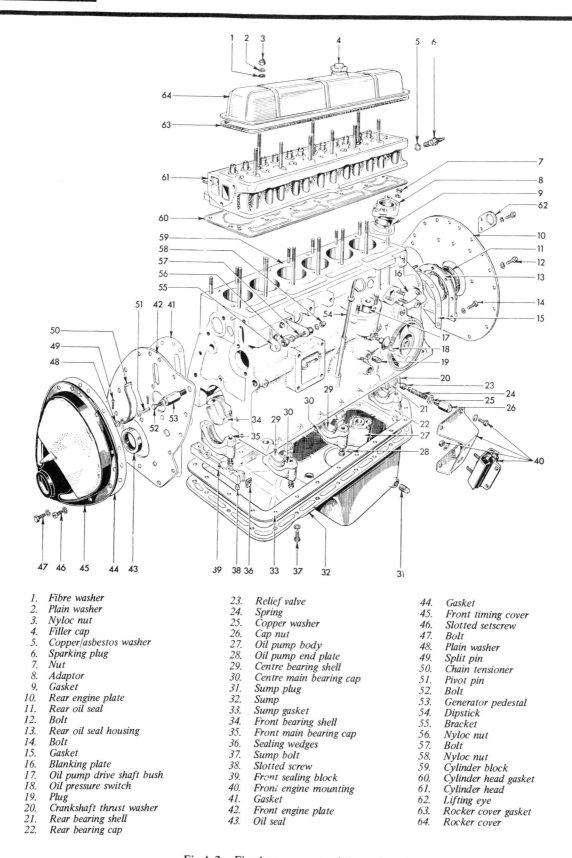

1. Fibre washer
2. Plain washer
3. Nyloc nut
4. Filler cap
5. Copper/asbestos washer
6. Sparking plug
7. Nut
8. Adaptor
9. Gasket
10. Rear engine plate
11. Rear oil seal
12. Bolt
13. Rear oil seal housing
14. Bolt
15. Gasket
16. Blanking plate
17. Oil pump drive shaft bush
18. Oil pressure switch
19. Plug
20. Crankshaft thrust washer
21. Rear bearing shell
22. Rear bearing cap

23. Relief valve
24. Spring
25. Copper washer
26. Cap nut
27. Oil pump body
28. Oil pump end plate
29. Centre bearing shell
30. Centre main bearing cap
31. Sump plug
32. Sump
33. Sump gasket
34. Front bearing shell
35. Front main bearing cap
36. Sealing wedges
37. Sump bolt
38. Slotted screw
39. Front sealing block
40. Front engine mounting
41. Gasket
42. Front engine plate
43. Oil seal

44. Gasket
45. Front timing cover
46. Slotted setscrew
47. Bolt
48. Plain washer
49. Split pin
50. Chain tensioner
51. Pivot pin
52. Bolt
53. Generator pedestal
54. Dipstick
55. Bracket
56. Nyloc nut
57. Bolt
58. Nyloc nut
59. Cylinder block
60. Cylinder head gasket
61. Cylinder head
62. Lifting eye
63. Rocker cover gasket
64. Rocker cover

Fig. A.2   Fixed components of the engine

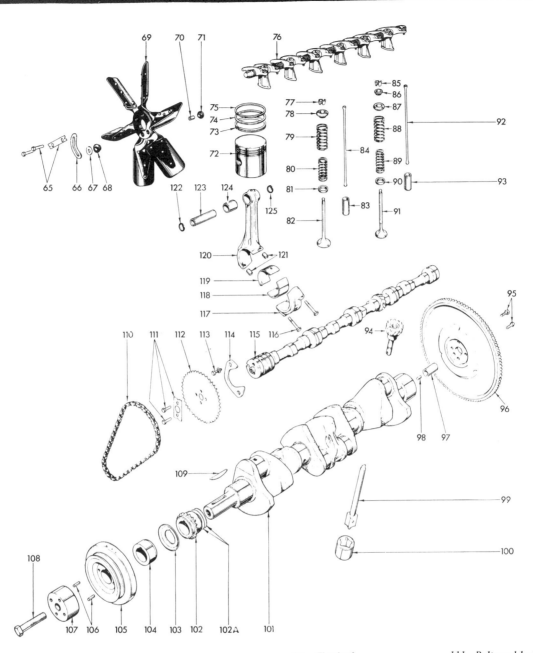

65.	Bolts and lock tabs	
66.	Balance weight	
67.	Washer	
68.	Rubber bush	
69.	Fan assembly	
70.	Steel bush	
71.	Rubber bush	
72.	Piston	
73.	Oil control ring	
74.	Compression ring tapered	
75.	Compression ring parallel	
76.	Rocker shaft assembly	
77.	Split collets	
78.	Collar	
79.	Spring - outer	
80.	Spring - inner	

81.	Lower collar
82.	Inlet valve
83.	Tappet
84.	Push rod
85.	Split collets
86.	Inner collar (exhaust)
87.	Outer collar (exhaust)
88.	Spring - outer
89.	Spring - inner
90.	Lower collar
91.	Exhaust valve
92.	Push rod
93.	Tappet
94.	Distributor and oil pump drive gear
95.	Bolts

96.	Flywheel
97.	Bush
98.	Dowel
99.	Inner rotor and spindle
100.	Outer rotor
101.	Crankshaft
102.	Sprocket
102A	Shim
103.	Flinger
104.	Seal extension
105.	Crankshaft pulley
106.	Dowels
107.	Fan boss
108.	Bolt
109.	Key
110.	Timing chain

111.	Bolts and lock plate
112.	Camshaft sprocket
113.	Bolt
114.	Keeper plate
115.	Camshaft
116.	Bolt
117.	Con-rod cap
118.	Con-rod bearing shell-lower
119.	Con-rod bearing shell-upper
120.	Con-rod
121.	Dowels
122.	Circlip
123.	Gudgeon pin
124.	Gudgeon pin bush
125.	Circlip

Fig.A.3   Moving components of the engine

Fig.A.4   Setting the valve clearances

Fig.A.6   Engaging the push rods in the rocker arms

Fig.A.5   Cylinder head nut tightening sequence

Fig.A.7   Compressing the valve springs

EXHAUST   INLET

Fig.A.8   Valve assemblies

Installation

1. Ensure faces of head and block are clean.

2. Smear serviceable cylinder head gasket with grease before assembling head. Fit washers and tighten nuts in small increments in sequence (Fig.A.5).

3. Install push rods and cam followers in correct order. Fit rocker shaft assembly to engage with the push rod caps (Fig.A.6). Fit washers and tighten nuts evenly. Check and if necessary, adjust valve clearances. Install rocker cover with serviceable gasket.

4. Secure water pump and connect water temperature gauge cable. Fit fan belt. Adjust and secure generator with total lateral movement of 19.05 - 25.4 mm (0.75 - 1.0 in.) midway on longest run of belt.

5. Assemble manifolds, connect pipes and controls to carburettors.

6. Connect hoses and install air filter assembly.

7. Install radiator header tank (Early Vitesse Six only)

8. Fill cooling system and connect battery.

9. Check valve clearances as described above and adjust if necessary.

10. Start engine, bring to normal operating temperature and check for leaks.

CYLINDER HEAD - Decarbonising

1. Plug all push rod, water-way and oil-way apertures in the cylinder head and also in the block. Bring pistons to top of cylinders in turn.

2. With suitable tool scrape all carbon deposits from cylinder head and block faces, valve heads, combustion chambers and piston crowns. Avoid scratch damage to all surfaces - particularly the piston crowns. Remove all particles of carbon and dirt from cylinder head and block. For valve grinding refer to CYLINDER HEAD - Inspection and Overhaul.

CYLINDER HEAD - Inspection and Overhaul

1. Remove thermostat elbow and thermostat.

2. Using valve spring compressor (Fig.A.7) remove split collets and then top collars, outer and inner springs, lower collars and valves.

3. Clean all parts.

4. Check valves for wear or distortion, reface or renew as necessary. A valve must be renewed if, after refacing, the head edge thickness is less than 0.8 mm (0.03 in.) (Fig.A.9).

5. Check valve springs for cracks and distortion. Check fitted length (1) and load (2), (Fig.A.10). See Technical Data for specifications. If any springs are defective a new set is recommended.

6. Check valve collars, spring seats and collets for damage and distortion. Renew as necessary.

7. Inspect cylinder head for cracks and scratches or burrs on the machined face. Renew if cracked, Remove stratches or burrs with oilstone. Out-of-true machined faces may be skimmed within specified limits.

8. Inspect valve seats for wear, scores or pitting. Reface or recut as necessary. When recutting seat ensure that the cutter pilot is a good fit in the valve guide. Valve seat dimensions are given in Fig.A.11 and it is particularly important that dimension "B" is not exceeded when using 15° cutter to reduce seat width. When valve seats cannot be restored by refacing, new inserts may be fitted to pocket dimensions given in Fig.A.12. If both inserts are replaced, fit inlet insert before boring for the exhaust insert. Remove all swarf after boring, drive insert squarely into pocket and secure by careful peening of cylinder head metal.

9. Check valve guides for wear with a new valve raised 3.2 mm (0.125 in.) approx. from its seat and moved diametrically in the guide (Fig.A.13). If movement of the valve head across the seat exceeds 0.5 mm (0.020 in.) the guide should be renewed. Use a good fitting drift to remove the guide and tool No. S60A, for fitting new guides which should project by 19.05 mm (0.75 in.) ('X' Fig.A.14). Limiting distance pieces to ensure correct protrustion are available.

   NOTE:- Guide protrusion should be 16.002 mm (0.63 in.) on Mk 2 and GT6 - Plus models.

10. After valve and seat refacing, grind the valves in their respective positions (Fig.A.15). Remove all traces of grinding paste and swarf before beginning assembly.

11. Lubricate valve stem, enter in guide and place support under valve head. Place lower collars, springs and upper collars over stem. compress springs and insert split collets into groove on valve stem. Carefully release compressor. Repeat for all valves.

    NOTE:- Exhaust valves have inner and outer top collars (Fig.A.8).

12. Remove cotter pin at end of rocker shaft and slide off rockers, springs, pedestals and washers from front end noting location and position of components (see Fig.A.16 Vitesse Six and Mk 1 models; Fig.A.17 Mk 2 models). Clean all parts. Renew rocker shafts if worn or scored and rockers if pivot holes or tips are worn. Tips are chill hardened to a depth of 1.525 mm (0.060 in.) and grinding to restore profile is not recommended. Renew adjusters if ball ends are worn or screwdriver slots or threads damaged Renew nuts with worn corners or damaged threads. Rebuild rocker gear as shown in Figs. A.16 or A.17 ensuring all oilways are clear, components are in correct order and rockers move freely on shaft.

OIL SUMP - Removal and Installation

1. Isolate battery, drain cooling system, drain sump and remove dipstick.

2. Disconnect top hoses from thermostat housing and from

9

A

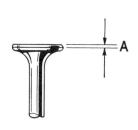

Fig.A.9 Valve head thickness

1
2

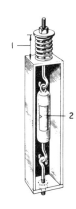

Fig.A.10 Checking the load (2) on the valve spring at its fitted length (1)

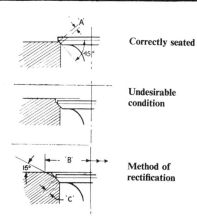

'A'
45°
Correctly seated
Undesirable condition
'B'
15°
'C'
Method of rectification

Fig.A.11 Valve seat conditions

A - 1.5 mm (0.06 in.)
B - Inlet 35 mm (1.375 in.)
Exhaust 32 mm (1.25 in.)
C - 2.5 mm (0.10 in.) max.

1
2
3
4

Fig.A.12 Valve seat insert dimensions

1. *5.563 - 5.689 mm (0.219 - 0.224 in.)*
2. *1.12 mm (0.044 in.) X 89° included.*
3. *31.75 - 31.775 mm (1.250 - 1.251 in.)*
4. *34.925 - 34.95 mm (1.375 - 1.376 in.)*

A

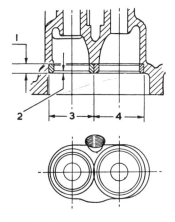

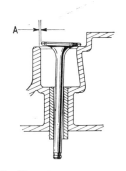

Fig.A.13 Checking the valve guide wear.

A - 0.5 mm (0.020 in.) max.

1
2
3
4
5
6
7
X

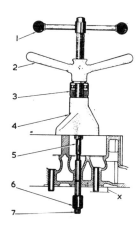

Fig.A.14 Replacing the valve guides

1. *Handle*
2. *Threaded handle*
3. *Thrust race*
4. *Tool body (Tool No. S.60 A)*
5. *Adaptor*
6. *Distance collar*
7. *Knurled nut*

X - 19.03 - 19.07 mm (0.749 - 0.751 in.)

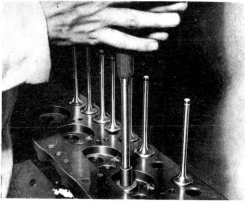

Fig.A.15 Grinding in the valves

radiator header tank (where fitted).

3. Attach lifting tackle to lifting eyes and take weight of engine.

4. Slacken right-hand engine mounting bolts and remove left-hand bolts.

5. Remove sump bolts

6. Raise engine slightly, lever towards rear to enable sump to clear front cross-member and withdraw sump complete with gasket.

7. Remove all traces of gasket from joint faces and replace in reverse order using new gasket and tightening bolts to specified torque only.

8. Refill cooling system and oil sump;

9. Connect battery, run engine and check for leaks.

OIL PUMP - Removal and Installation

1. Remove sump - see previous paragraph.

2. Remove three attachment bolts and pump.

3. Clean and inspect as described in LUBRICATION SYSTEM section.

4. Secure pump to crankcase.

5. Install sump.

TIMING COVER OIL SEAL AND/OR TENSIONER - Replacement

1. Isolate battery.

2. Remove radiator (See COOLING SYSTEM).

3. Slacken generator/alternator bolts and remove fan belt.

4. Remove securing bolt and withdraw crankshaft pulley and fan assembly (Fig.A.18).

5. Remove attachment bolts and washers (Fig.A.19) and cover and gasket.

6. Carefully lever oil seal out avoiding damage to timing cover.

7. Press new seal evenly in housing with seal lip towards sprocket.

8. Remove worn tensioner by opening blade and springing over pin and fit new tensioner in reverse manner.

9. Lubricate seal lip and pulley running surface.

10. Position serviceable gasket on front plate and check oil flinger is in position.

11. Position timing cover with tensioner compressed with bent wire (Fig.A.20) on locating dowels and evenly tighten attachment bolts.

12. Fit and secure crankshaft pulley and fan assembly, install and tension fan belt.

13. Install and fill radiator (see COOLING SYSTEM section).

14. Connect battery.

TIMING CHAIN - Removal and Installation

1. Remove timing cover as previously described and straighten locking plate tabs on camshaft sprocket bolts.

2. Bring No. 1 piston to TDC on compression stroke. Timing marks on sprockets should now be in line (Fig.A.21).

3. Check timing chain wear, (Fig.A.22). Dimension "A" must not exceed 10 mm (0.4 in.).

4. Remove camshaft sprocket bolts, ease sprocket off camshaft and detach chain from crankshaft sprocket.

5. Install chain and sprocket with timing marks aligned.

   NOTE:- If new sprocket is being fitted, proceed as in VALVE TIMING - Engine Overhaul.

6. Install timing cover as previously described.

CAMSHAFT - Removal and Installation
Removal

1. Disconnect battery.

2. Remove overriders, disconnect lighting and horn connectors at bonnet, disconnect bonnet stay, remove four hinge bolts and remove bonnet.

3. Remove cylinder head, timing cover and camshaft sprocket and timing chain as previously described.

4. Remove distributor (see IGNITION SYSTEM section), and drive gear. Remove fuel pump.

5. Remove camshaft keeper plate.

6. Extract camshaft avoiding damage to cams and bushes.

Installation

1. Lubricate journals and bearings and insert camshaft with care to avoid damage.

2. Fit keeper plate and check camshaft end-float is within 0.10 - 0.20 mm (0.004 - 0.008 in.) (Fig.A.23). If necessary correct with new keeper plate.

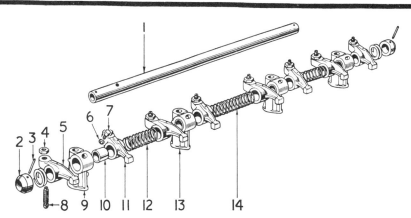

Fig.A.16 Rocker shaft details - Mk 1

1. Rocker shaft
2. End cup
3. Mills pin
4. Locknut
5. Rocker arm (R.H.)
6. Shakeproof washer
7. Lockscrew
8. Adjuster
9. Rocker pedestal (New)
10. Rocker bush
11. Rocker arm (L.H.)
12. Spring
13. Rocker pedestal
14. Spring

1. Rocker cover gasket
2. Rocker cover
3. Fibre washer
4. Plain washer
5. Nyloc nut
6. Oil filter cap
7. Stud- rocker pedestal
8. Stud - rocker cover
9. Rocker shaft
10. Valve guides
11 Cylinder head gasket
12. Cam-follower
13. Push rods
14. Exhaust valve
15. Inlet valve
16. Valve spring - inner
17. Valve spring - outer
18. Upper spring seat - exhaust valve
19. Valve cap - exhaust valve
20. Valve cotters
21. Valve cap - inlet valve
22. Valve spring seats
23. Rocker pedestal - outer
24. Cotter pin
25. Rocker shaft end plug
26. Rocker
27. Double spring washer - end rocker
    pedestal
28. Rocker
29. Nut
30. Washer
31. Rocker shaft spring
32. Rocker pedestal - intermediate
33. Tappet adjuster
34. Tappet adjuster locknut

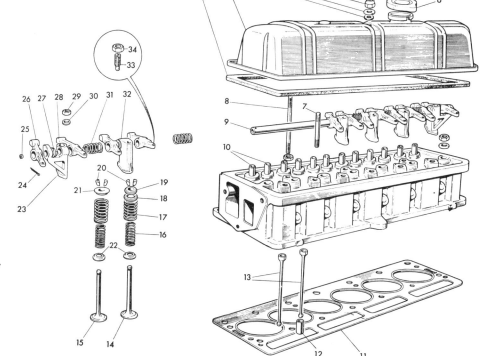

Fig.A.17 Cylinder head assembly- Mk 2

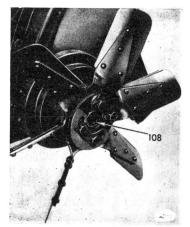

Fig.A.18 Fan blade and pulley attachment

Fig.A.19 Timing cover installation

Fig.A.20 Holding back the tensioner while fitting the timing cover.

3. Install fuel pump and distributor.

4. Fit cam followers.

5. Assemble camshaft sprocket, timing chain, cover and cylinder head.

6. Adjust valve timing and ignition timing as necessary.

7. Install bonnet and connect electrical connectors.

FRONT ENGINE PLATE - Removal and Installation

1. Remove timing cover, chain and sprocket as previously described.

2. Remove generator/alternator and attachment bracket.

3. Remove camshaft keeper plate.

4. Remove three bolts front engine plate and gasket.

5. Reverse procedure for installation using new front plate gasket.

CORE PLUG - Replacement

1. Remove old plug.

2. Clean plug seating groove.

3. Apply jointing compound to edge of plug, place in position and spread with large diameter punch against centre of plug. Avoid making too heavy a blow as this could distort plug.

NOTE:- To replace rear left-hand plug remove distributor, distributor pedestal and disconnect fuel pump; to replace front right-hand plug remove air-cleaner and disconnect water return pipe at water pump. For centre plugs remove manifold and for rear plug remove air-cleaner and water return pipe; to replace plug at rear of cylinder head remove head; for plug at rear of block gain access from inside vehicle by removing gearbox tunnel and remove front engine plate to replace front block plug.

FLYWHEEL AND STARTER RING GEAR - Removal and Installation

1. Remove gearbox and clutch (see relevant sections).

2. Remove attachment bolts and flywheel assembly.

3. Inspect flywheel assembly as detailed in "ENGINE - Inspection and Overhaul"

4. Reverse procedure to install flywheel assembly.

CONNECTING ROD BEARINGS - Replacement

1. Proceed in accordance with "SUMP - Removal".

2. Rotate crankshaft until required connecting rod is at BDC.

3. Remove bearing cap bolts and cap and remove shells. Do not intermix.

4. Renew shells as necessary and ensure that tab ends are correctly seated.

5. Fit caps and tighten bolts to specified torque.

6. Proceed in accordance with "SUMP - Installation".

CONNECTING RODS AND PISTONS - Removal and Installation

1. Proceed in accordance with "OIL SUMP - Removal".

2. Proceed in accordance with "CYLINDER HEAD - Removal".

3. Remove connecting rods bearing caps and shells. Do not intermix.

4. Push pistons and connecting rods through top of bores.

5. Check in accordance with "ENGINE - Inspection".

6. Replace pistons and connecting rods in their respective cylinders (see "ENGINE - Assembly").

7. Proceed in accordance with "CONNECTING ROD BEARINGS - Replacement".

8. Install cylinder head, oil pump and sump.

ENGINE UNIT - Removal and Installation
Removal

1. Isolate battery and drain cooling system, oil sump and gearbox. Remove air-cleaner.

2. Remove bonnet by disconnecting front lighting and horn cable connectors on top grille centre, removing overriders and stay bolt and then hinge bolt. Support bonnet while hinge bolts are removed.

3. Remove radiator assembly. Remove header tank on early Vitesse (see COOLING SYSTEM).

4. Remove engine bay side valances (GT6 only) or fan assembly (Vitesse Six only).

5. Disconnect and plug fuel inlet pipe at pump (1), disconnect oil pressure switch (3), generator leads (4), ignition lead (5) and tachometer drive cable (2) (GT6 and Vitesse 2 litre) (Fig.A.24).

6. Disconnect choke and throttle controls (9 and 10), starter motor lead (II), heater pipes (6 and 7) and water control valve cable (8) (Fig.A.25).

Fig.A.21 Valve timing alignment marks

A. Scribed lines
B. Punch mark opposite camshaft groove

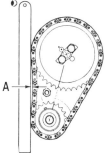

Fig.A.22 Checking the timing chain wear

A - 10 mm (0.4 in.) max.

A →

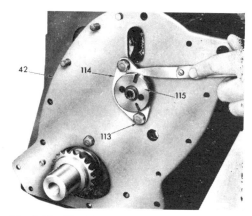

Fig.A.23 Checking the camshaft end-float

Fig.A.25 Right-hand view of the engine installation

(See Fig.A.24 for key)

Fig.A.24 Left-hand view of the engine installation

1. Fuel pipe
2. Tachometer drive cable
3. Oil pressure switch
4. Generator leads
5. Ignition lead
6. Heater pipe
7. Heater pipe
8. Water valve cable
9. Choke control
10. Throttle control
11. Starter cable
12. Earth cable

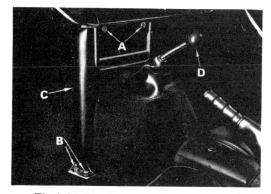

Fig.A.26 Fascia support bracket - G.T.6

NOTE:- On Vitesse, only heater pipes are fitted at rear of manifold.

7. Disconnect earth strap from left-hand side of engine front plate and from bell housing.

8. Disconnect water temperature transmitter cable at thermostat housing.

9. Separate exhaust front pipe from manifold and detach from clutch housing or gearbox.

10. Remove front carpets and seats. On GT6, remove fascia support (Fig.A.26).

11. Remove gear lever knob. On GT6, remove transmission tunnel cover (Fig.A.27).

12. Release speedometer drive connection (F) from right-hand side of gearbox extension, remove clutch slave cylinder attachment bolts (E) and move cylinder clear, remove rear mounting nuts (G) and front universal flange bolts (D) (Fig.A.28).

13. Select first gear, remove four nuts and remove gearchange extension. Fit cardboard cover to opening.

14. Disconnect overdrive solenoid cables if applicable.

15. Attach lifting gear to the engine lifting points, take weight of engine and remove front engine mounting bolts (2) (Fig.A.29).

16. Manoeuvre engine from vehicle. On Vitesse Six, lift engine and gearbox until sump is clear of front cross-member then move forward until gearbox clears bulkhead aperture (Fig. A.30). On Vitesse 2 Litre and GT6, raise engine sufficiently to place brake pipe protection plate in position on front crossmember (see Fig.A.32 for suggested protection plate and Fig.A.33 for installation of plate): carefully raise engine, tilting rearward and pulling forward (Fig.A.31).

Installation

1. Lower engine unit into position using brake pipe protection plate on Vitesse 2 Litre and GT6.

2. Attach gearchange extension and front universal flange to gearbox.

3. Install speedometer cable and clutch slave cylinder.

4. Connect overdrive solenoid cables, if applicable.

5. Fit gearbox cover and floor carpets. Fit fascia support on GT6. Install seats.

6. Connect starter cable and engine earth strap.

7. Secure exhaust down-pipe and clutch housing bracket.

8. Connect heater hoses, carburettor controls and install air cleaner.

9. Connect fuel pump supply pipe.

10. Connect electrical cables to coil, generator/alternator water temperature transmitter and oil pressure switch.

11. Fit fan assembly to Vitesse Six.

12 Install radiator and bonnet. Install header tank on early Vitesse.

13. Fill cooling system, engine and gearbox, and connect battery.

14. Run engine and tune carburettors.

ENGINE - Ancillary Equipment - Dismantling (Figs. A.34 and A.35)

The following items should be removed before despatch for reconditioning and as far as necessary before overhaul.

1. Remove gearbox and clutch, see relevant sections.

2. Disconnect fuel pipe (6) remove two nuts (7) and remove pump (5).

3. Disconnect HT leads from plugs and coil and LT leads from coil. Remove spark plugs.

4. Remove two bolts to remove distributor (4) and further two bolts to uncouple distributor pedestal and drive gear.

5. Remove two attachment bolts and remove coil (2).

6. Remove centre bolt (8) and remove oil filter. Remove dipstick (11).

7. Screw out oil pressure switch (II).

8. Remove domed nut, spring and plunger of oil pressure relief valve (12).

9. Remove two pivot bolts (14), adjuster bolt (17) and remove generator (13) and fan belt (15). Remove generator bracket.

10. Remove pipe clip (I)

11. Disconnect water hose (19) and return pipe at rear of pump, remove two bolts (18) and water pump assembly.

12. Disconnect and remove fuel and vacuum pipes from carburettor.

13. Remove bolt (16) and withdraw fan and pulley assembly. (Removed before engine removal on Vitesse Six).

14. Remove hoses (22 and 23), bolt (20) and emission valve (21). (Vitesse 2 Litre and GT6 only).

15. Remove four nuts (29), six clamps (27) and manifold assembly.

16. Remove engine mounting brackets (24), lifting eyes (28) and drain tap (26).

Fig.A.28 Right-hand view of the gearbox installation

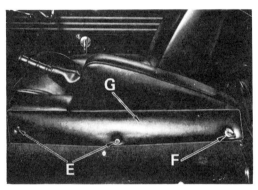

Fig.A.27 Transmission tunnel covers - G.T.6.

Fig.A.30 Removing/Installing the engine - Vitesse Six.

Fig.A.29 Front engine mounting attachment

Fig.A.31 Removing/installing the engine - Vitesse 2 Litre and GT6

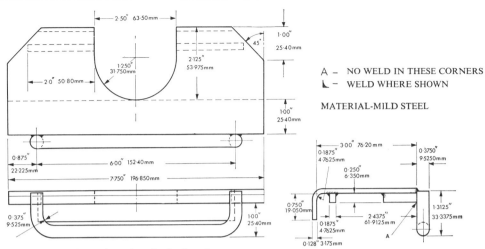

A — NO WELD IN THESE CORNERS
L — WELD WHERE SHOWN

MATERIAL-MILD STEEL

Fig.A.32 Dimensions for the brake pipe protection plate.

1. Clip bolt
2. Coil
3. Ignition lead
4. Distributor
5. Petrol pump
6. Fuel pipe
7. Nut
8. Bolt
9. Oil filter
10. *Oil pressure switch*
11. Dipstick
12. Domed nut
13. Generator
14. Pivot bolt
15. Fan belt
16. Fan bolt
17. Adjuster bolt
18. Bolt
19. Water hose
20. Bolt
21. Emission valve
22. Hose
23. Hose
24. Mounting bracket
25. Bolt
26. Drain tap
27. Clamp
28. Lifting eye
29. Nut

Fig.A.34 Left-hand view of the engine ancillary equipment

Fig.A.33 Brake pipe protection plate in position

Fig.A.35 Right-hand view of the engine ancillary equipment (See Fig.A.34 for key)

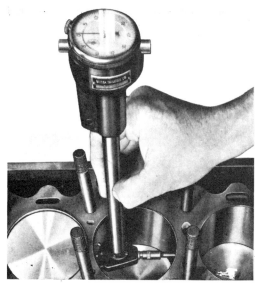

Fig.A.36 Measuring the cylinder bore for wear.

Fig.A.38 Main bearing cap location marks

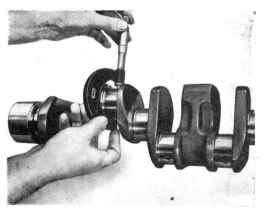

Fig.A.39 Measuring the crankshaft journals.

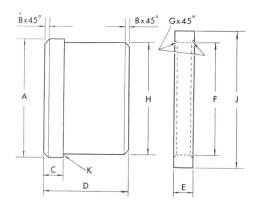

Fig.A.37 Mandrel and limiting ring for removal and installation of the cylinder liners - Vitesse 2 Litre and GT6

A (dia.) - 77.7621 mm (3.0615 in.)
         77.7367 mm (3.0605 in.)
B   - 3.175 mm (0.125 in.)
C   - 12.7 mm (0.5 in.)
D.   - 57.15 mm (2.25 in.)
E   - 12.7 mm (0.5 in.)
F (dia.) - 74.1934 mm (2.921 in.)
         - 74.2188 mm (2.922 in.)
G.   - 1.588 mm (0.0625 in.)
H. (dia.) - 74.1553 mm (2.9195 in.)
         - 74.1807 mm (2.9205 in.)
J. (dia.) - 88.90 mm (3.5 in.)
K.   - 0.254 mm (0.010 in.) max. radius.
NOTE;- Remove all sharp edges.

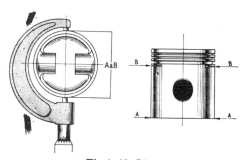

Fig.A.40 Piston measurement points

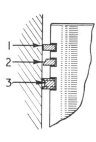

Fig.A.41 Piston ring locations

1. Upper compression ring (parallel)
2. Lower compression ring (tapered)
3. Oil control ring

ENGINE - Dismantling (Figs. A.2 and A.3)

Remove cylinder head, push rods and cam followers; also oil sump, oil pump and flywheel as described in "in position" procedures.

Backplate

1. Remove bolts (12) washers backplate (10), timing gear and camshaft.

2. Remove bolts washers timing cover (45) complete with tensioner and gasket (44). Remove oil seal (43).

3. Check chain for wear (Fig.A.22). Renew if necessary.

4. Straighten lock tabs on camshaft sprocket bolts and remove bolts. Ease camshaft sprocket (112) of camshaft and detach chain from crankshaft sprocket.

5. Remove seal extension (104), oil slinger (103), crankshaft sprocket (102) and shims (102A). Retain shims in pack and key (109).

6. Remove camshaft keeper plate bolts (113) and plate (114).

7. Remove attachment bolts, front plate (42) and gasket (41)

8. Carefully withdraw camshaft (115) to avoid damaging cams and journal bearings.

Connecting Rods and Pistons

1. Remove connecting rod bearing cap bolts (116), separate caps (117) and remove both half shell bearings (118 and 119).

   NOTE:- Connecting rod/piston assemblies must be kept together and identified with their respective cylinders.

2. Remove piston (72) and con-rod (120) through the top of the cylinder.

3. Remove gudgeon pins (123) by extracting circlips (112) and pushing pin from piston and con-rod. A tight pin is removed more easily when the piston is immersed in hot water.

Crankshaft

1. Remove rear oil seal housing (13) and gasket (15). Drive seal (11) from housing using a drift inserted in each of two holes alternately.

2. Remove front sealing block (39) and packing pieces (36).

3. Remove bearing cap bolts, bearing caps (22,30 and 35) and lower half shell bearings. Withdraw crankshaft and remove upper half shell bearings and thrust washers (20).

ENGINE - Inspection and Overhaul

Thoroughly clean all parts removing all traces of gasket and jointing material. Renew gaskets, inspect plugs and studs and renew as necessary.

Cylinder Block

1. Inspect cylinder bores for scores and check for wear by setting gauge in different positions in bore (Fig.A.36). Rebore for oversize pistons if necessary.

   NOTE:- On Vitesse 2 Litre and GT6, 0.508 mm (0.020 in.) oversize pistons are available and block should be rebored to 77.8 - 77.775 mm (2.9614 - 2.9609 in. diameter. On Vitesse Six, 0.250, 0.508 and 0.762 mm (0.010, 0.020 and 0.030 in.) oversize piston are available and bores should be opened to appropriately oversize dimension (see TECHNICAL DATA).

   Where maximum oversize piston dimension cannot be achieved, liners in sets of six may be fitted or renewed. On Vitesse 2 Litre and GT6, bores must be opened out to 77.8 - 77.775 mm (3.063 - 3.062 in.) diameter. On Vitesse Six to 69.6 - 69.61 mm (2.781 - 2.780 in.) diameter and surface finish of 45-60 micro-inches CLA should be achieved. A mandrel and limiting ring, similar to that illustrated in Fig.A.37 for Vitesse 2 Litre and GT6, will assist in installing or removing liners. Ensure bore lip is free from burrs and apply tallow to bore and liner. Assemble mandrel and ring to liner, ensure press ram is square to bore and has sufficient movement to press liner in with one continuous and even movement. Bore out liner to required bore size. Worn liners should be pressed out with mandrel in one continuous movement also. When new pistons or rings are fitted, light honing or careful use of medium grade carborun dum paste will assist bedding-in of rings.

2. Check camshaft bores for wear (see TECHNICAL DATA for specifications).

3. Insert distributor drive shaft into its bush and rock to check bush wear.. Remove a worn bush with stepped drift positioned in crankcase and carefully drive replacement bush into pedestal flange.

4. Clear oilways and water passages where necessary.

5. Smooth any burrs from joint faces.

Crankshaft

NOTE:- Main bearing housings with assembled bearing caps are line-bored at manufacture. Caps are not interchangeable and location markings are stamped on cap and block (Fig.A.38).

Undersize bearing sizes are 0.254 mm (0.010 in.), 0.508 mm (0.020 in.) and 0.762 mm (0.030 in.), with a further main bearing undersize of 1.016 mm (0.040 in.) on the

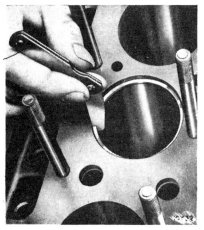

Fig.A.42 Measuring the piston ring gap

Fig.A.43 Measuring the run-out on the flywheel face

Fig.A.44 Fitting the thrust washers at the rear main bearing

Fig.A.45 Checking the crankshaft end-float with a dial gauge

Fig.A.46 Installing the wedge pieces in the front sealing block

Fig.A.47 Centralising tool installed in the rear oil seal housing

Vitesse Six. Undersize dimensions are stamped on back of bearing shells and on web of crankshaft when re-ground.

1. Inspect journals and crankpins for scores and check for wear, taper or ovality (Fig.A.39). If necessary, grind to next undersize and stamp web with undersize dimension.

2. Renew shell bearings if worn or scored, or if crankshaft is reground.

Camshaft

1. Check journal diameters for wear (see TECHNICAL DATA for specifications).

2. Inspect for cracks and burrs. Remove burrs with carborundum stone.

3. Check distributor drive gear for damage.

Connecting Rods and Pistons

The diameters of normal size pistons are graded "F" "G" and "H" with appropriate identification letter on piston crown and cylinder bore face. Grading is not applied to oversize pistons which are available in +0.010 in., +0.020 in. and +0.030 in. sizes for Vitesse Six and in +0.020 size for Vitesse 2 Litre and GT6. Piston diameter measurement points and the location of the piston rings are shown in Figs. A.40 and A.41 respectively.

Weight difference between the heaviest and lightest of a connecting rod set should not exceed 4 drams. Piston set weight difference is also 4 drams (7.09 grams). When building con-rod piston sets, assemble heaviest-to-lightest to reduce overall weight difference.

1. Inspect pistons for burning and damage and check for wear (Fig.A.40). See TECHNICAL DATA for specifications.

2. Check connecting rods for bowing and twist with suitable checking equipment. Rectify or renew if deformation exceeds 0.025 mm (0.001 in.) in gudgeon pin length.

3. Inspect piston rings for wear and damage. Renew if necessary.

4. On gudgeon pin assemblies, check that a thumb push will pass a dry pin through connecting rod bush. A pin passing through under its own weight is too loose and replacement bush is necessary. Use press and adaptor to press out old bush avoiding direct contact with con-rod. Ensure that oil holes are in alignment before pressing in new bush. Fine bore or broach new bush to pin size, see TECHNICAL DATA for specifications.

5. Insert each piston ring into cylinder in which it is to operate, and square-up with the head of a piston. Measure ring gap with feelers and check that gap is to the dimensions in TECHNICAL DATA (Fig.A.42).

Flywheel Assembly

1. Inspect flywheel clutch face for scores which may be removed by skimming in a lathe to a maximum thickness reduction of 0.762 mm (0.030 in.). Run out at 127.0 mm (5.0 in.) radius must not exceed 0.076 mm (0.003 in.) when checked in lathe or as shown in Fig.A.43. Balance should remain within 1 dram (1.8 g).

2. Inspect starter ring for damaged teeth and security. Renew if necessary by supporting flywheel on hard wood blocks with clutch side up and with no obstruction to ring gear. Evenly drive off ring in small movements. Reverse flywheel on blocks and thoroughly clean rim and new starter ring. Evenly heat ring in boiling water and, with chamfered edge of teeth towards clutch face, place ring on flywheel.

NOTE:- Do not flame-heat starter ring.

Timing Cover and Gears Assembly

1. Inspect timing cover for cracks or distortion. Rectify distortion and, with a straight edge, ensure flanges are flat.

2. Renew tensioner if damaged or distorted by opening the blade sufficiently to spring over the pin.

3. Renew oil seal by positioning lip towards cover and applying even pressure.

4. Inspect chain sprockets for worn or damaged teeth. Renew as necessary.

5. Renew timing chain if excessively slack when checked before dismantling, or if damaged or distorted.

ENGINE - Assembly (Figs. A.2 and A.3).

1. Fit main bearing shells to cylinder block housing and to bearing caps with tabs correctly located.

2. With clean engine oil, lubricate journals and bearings and position crankshaft in crankcase.

3. Fit a thrust bearing at each side of the rear main bearing with the thrust faces against crankshaft (Fig.A.44).

4. Assemble bearing caps in identified locations (Fig.A.38) and evenly tighten bolts.

5. Lever crankshaft in each direction to check if endfloat is 0.16 - 0.20 mm (0.006 - 0.008 in.).

Reduce excessive float with oversize thrust bearings. Check end float with feelers or dial gauge (Fig.A.45).

Front Sealing Block

1. Smear jointing compound on end of sealing block (39) and assemble to cylinder block. Do not fully tighten screws.

2. Smear wedge pieces (36) with jointing compound and drive into sealing block slots.

3. With a straight-edge align sealing block with front face and tighten screws (Fig.A.46).

4. Trim wedge pieces flush with crankcase.

Fig.A.48 Marking the T.D.C. position on the flywheel

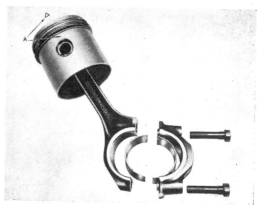

Fig.A.49 Piston and connecting rod assembly

Fig.A.50 Checking the alignment of the timing sprockets

Fig.A.52 Determining the point of balance at No. 6 cylinder

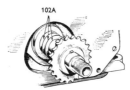

Fig.A.51 Crankshaft sprocket adjustment shims

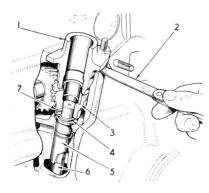

Fig.A.53 Determining the required packing thickness for the distributor pedestal

1. Pedestal
2. Feeler blade
3. Drive gear
4. Gauging washer (12.7 mm/0.5 in. I.D.)
5. Bush
6. Oil pump shaft
7. Pin

Fig.A.54 Assembling the distributor pedestal and packing

Crankshaft Rear Oil Seal - Lip Type

1. Coat new gasket (15) on both sides with jointing compound and position on housing joint face.

2. With lip facing forward press oil seal (II) into housing (13). Lubricate seal lip, slide carefully onto crankshaft and loosely attach housing to block. Centralise with Churchill tool No. S335, and evenly tighten attachment bolts (Fig.A.47). Remove tool.

Front and Rear Engine Plate

1. Position gasket (41) and front plate (42) on two dowels and secure to front face of cylinder block.

2. Fit rear plate to block and tighten attachment bolts evenly and in turn.

Flywheel

1. Ensure the mating faces of flywheel and crankshaft spigot are clean and free from burrs.

2. Smear spigot bush (97) with zinc oxide grease and insert into crankshaft.

3. Offer-up flywheel to engage crankshaft dowels.

4. Fit and tighten self-locking bolts.

NOTE:- When fitting a new flywheel, the T.D.C. position should be marked and is best done when pistons are fitted but before cylinder head is assembled. Set pistons 1 and 6 to T.D.C. and scribe a line across the periphery of flywheel in line with the marking on backplate. Accentuate scribe line with a small chisel, and mark "I" and "6" at each side of line (Fig.A.40).

Connecting Rods and Pistons

1. Using a ring handling tool or thin plaster strips to avoid breakage, assemble rings to piston beginning with oil control (bottom) ring (Fig.A.41).

2. Assemble connecting rod to piston as shown in Fig.A.49, lubricate pin and connecting rod bush, correctly align bush with piston boss, slide pin into position and secure with circlips. Pre-heating of piston in hot water or oil will facilitate gudgeon pin insertion.

3. With Nos. 1 and 6 crankpins at B.D.C. lubricate cylinder bore and piston with engine oil, fit piston ring sleeve or compressor and enter con-rod and piston into No.1 bore with arrow to front of engine. Press piston into bore until clear of compressor tool. Lubricate crankpin and bearing shells, fit shells to con-rod and bearing cap with tabs correctly located and assemble to crankpin. Install and secure remaining piston assemblies.

Oil Pump and Sump

1. Lubricate pump rotors assemble cover and secure to crankcase.

2. Use new gasket (33) and evenly tighten attachment bolts of sump.

Camshaft

Insert camshaft, secure with keeper plate and check and correct end-float if necessary (see "CAMSHAFT - Removal and Installation").

Cylinder Head Assembly

Carry out relevant operations of "CYLINDER HEAD - Assembly". Do not fit rocker cover.

Sprocket Installation

1. Mount sprockets on camshaft and crankshaft with the short hub boss outwards on the crankshaft pulley, and without key.

2. With straight-edge check alignment of sprockets (Fig.A.50

3. Shim crankshaft pulley as necessary (Fig.A.51).

4. Press crankshaft sprocket into position over key.

5. Assemble original (marked) camshaft sprocket with timing chain as shown in Fig.A.21.

6. Fit oil thrower (103) and timing cover with gasket (44).

7. Fit seal extension (104) to crankshaft with chamfered edge leading, position fan pulley assembly and secure with bolt (108).

Valve Timing

When an unmarked timing chain sprocket is installed, the following procedure should be followed:

1. Turn crankshaft until number 1 piston is at T.D.C. and camshaft until number 1 push rod is at highest point. Set number 12 valve clearance at 1.00 mm (0.040 in.)

2. Turn camshaft until number 2 push rod is at highest point. Set number 11 valve clearance at 1.00 mm (0.040 in.).

3. Turn camshaft until inlet valve of number 6 cylinder is about to open and exhaust valve is about to close; check with feelers that clearance at valves 11 and 12 are equal (Fig.A.52).

4. With camshaft and crankshaft positions unchanged, assemble timing chain on sprockets, fit crankshaft sprocket with keyway aligned and adjust camshaft sprockets inside chain until two attachment holes are aligned with camshaft holes. Four holes in the camshaft sprocket are offset from a tooth centre so that a 90° rotation gives half tooth adjustment, sprocket reversal gives a quarter tooth

difference, and reversal and 90º rotation give threequarter tooth variation.

5. Secure camshaft sprocket, re-check that clearances at valves 11 and 12 are equal and secure bolts with lockplate.

6. Adjust all valve clearances to 0.25 mm (0.010 in.), assemble oil thrower, timing cover and crankshaft pulley with fan assembly and fit rocker box.

Distributor Drive Gear and Pedestal

It is essential that an end-float of 0.076 - 0.178 mm (0.003-0.007 in.) exists between drive gear and bottom of pedestal after assembly. This is obtained by fitting packing washers under the pedestal. To determine packing thickness required, proceed as illustrated in Fig.A.52.

1. Set number 1 piston at T.D.C. on compression.

2. Place 12.7 mm (0.5 in.) inside diameter washer (4) of measured thickness over drive gear shaft and insert assembly into bush to mesh with camshaft gear and engage with oil pump shaft (6).

3. Place pedestal in position and measure pedestal to cylinder block gap. Subtract this from washer thickness to obtain end-float without packing washers, and determine packing washer thickness required to produce specified end-float.

   Example
   Thickness of gauging washer 1.57 mm (0.062 in.)
   Gap width   1.52 mm (0.060 in.)
   End-float without packing washers 0.05 mm (0.002 in.)

   This end-float is less than stipulated tolerance and packing washer thickness required to give nominal 0.12 mm (0.005 in.) float is 0.051 mm (0.003 in.).

4. Remove drive gear to extract gauging washer, replace gear to mesh with camshaft gear and engage oil pump shaft and fit pedestal with correct thickness of packing washers (Fig.A.53).

ENGINE - Preparation for Installation

Refit items removed in preparation for reconditioning following relevant section procedures.

Technical Data

GENERAL

Type:-	6 cylinder "in line" O.H.V.
Bore.	
Vitesse Six	66.8 mm (2.63 in.)
Vitesse 2 Litre/GT6	74.7 mm (2.94 in.)
Stroke.	76.0 mm (2.992 in.)
Cubic capacity.	
Vitesse Six	1596 cc. (97.39 cu. in.)
Vitesse 2 Litre/GT6	1998 cc. (122 cu in.)
Compression Ratio	
Vitesse Six	8.75 : 1 or 7.0 : 1
Vitesse 2 Litre/GT6	9.5 : 1
Vitesse 2 Litre/GT6 Mk .2	9.25 : 1

DIMENSIONS AND TOLERANCES
Crankshaft

Main bearing journal dia.	50.81-50.83 mm (2.0005-2.001 in.)
Crankpin dia.	47.625-47.638 mm (1.875 - 1.8755 in.)
Rear journal width	35.54-34.59 mm (1.360-1.362 in.)
Thrust washer thickness	2.31-2.36 mm (0.091-0.093 in.)
Oversize thrust washers	2.44-2.49 mm (0.096-0.098 in.)

Connecting rod

End-float on crankpin	0.218-0.317 mm (0.0086-0.0125 in.)
Small-end bush internal dia.	20.63-20.64 mm (0.8122-0.8126 in.)
Gudgeon pin dia.	20.64-20.63 mm (0.8125-0.8123 in.) Selective

Standard cylinder bore gradings.

Vitesse Six	
Grade F.	66.75-66.74 mm (2.6279-2.6276 in.)
Grade G.	66.76-66.71 mm (2.6283-2.6280 in.)
Grade H.	66.77-66.76 mm (2.6287-2.6284 in.)
Vitesse 2 Litre/GT6	
Grade F	74.70-74.69 mm (2.9408-2.9405 in.)
Grade G.	74.71-74.70 mm (2.9412-2.9409 in.)
Grade H.	74.72-74.71 mm (2.9416-2.9513 in.)

Piston ring widths

Compression ring	
Vitesse 2 Litre/GT6	1.956-1.999 mm (0.077-0.787 in.)
Vitesse Six	1.97-1.99 mm (0.077-0.787 in.)
Oil control ring.	
Vitesse Six	3.94-3.97 mm (0.1582-0.1563 in.)
Vitesse 2 Litre/GT6	3.945-3.970 mm (0.1553-0.1563 in.)
Piston Ring Grooves:	
Compression ring.	
Vitesse Six	2.02-2.06 mm (0.0797-0.0812 in.)
Vitesse 2 Litre/GT6	2.024-2.050 mm (0.0797-0.0807 in.)
Oil control ring.	
Vitesse Six	3.94-3.97 mm (0.1552-0.1562 in.)
Vitesse 2 Litre/GT6	3.99-4.01 mm (0.157-0.158 in.)

Piston Ring Clearance in Groove:

Compression ring	0.048-0.089 mm (0.0019-0.0035 in.)
Oil Control ring	0.0178-0.068 mm (0.0007-0.0027 in.)
Piston Ring Fitted Gap	0.20-0.33 mm (0.008-0.013 in.)

Camshaft

Journal diameter	46.74-46.75 mm (1.8402-1.8407 in.)
Bearing clearance	0.066-0.117 mm (0.0026-0.0046 in.)
End-float	0.20-0.11 mm (0.008-0.004 in.)

Tappets

Diameter	
Vitesse 6	17.46-17.45 mm (0.6871-0.6867 in.)
Vitesse 2 Litre/GT6	20.32-20.310 mm (0.8000-0.7996 in.)
Bore in cylinder. block	
Vitesse 6	17.47-17.46 mm (0.688-0.687 in.)
Vitesse 2 Litre/GT6	20.343-20.325 mm (0.8009-0.8002 in.)
Clearance in bore	0.0508-0.033 mm (0.002-0.0013 in.)

Rocker Assembly

Rocker arm bore	
Vitesse Six	14.27-14.30 mm (0.562-0.563 in.)
Vitesse 2 Litre/GT6	14.326-14.30 mm (0.564-0.563 in.)
Rocker shaft diameter	14.26-14.24 mm (0.5612-0.5607 in.)
Clearance	0.02-0.06 mm (0.0008-0.0023 in.)

Inlet Valves:

Head diameter	
Vitesse Six/2 Litre/GT6	33.045-33.147 mm (1.301-1.305 in.)
Mk 2/GT6 - Plus	36.6-36.7 mm (1.411-1.445 in.)
Stem diameter	
Vitesse Six	7.87-7.89 mm (0.310-0.311 in.)
Vitesse 2 Litre/GT6	7.891-7.905 mm (0.3107-0.3112 in.)
Stem to guide clearance	
Vitesse Six	0.025-0.075 mm (0.001-0.003 in.)
Vitesse 2 Litre/GT6	0.041-0.058 mm (0.0018-0.0023 in.)

Exhaust Valves

Head diameter	
Vitesse Six/2 Litre/GT6	29.87-29.972 mm (1.176-1.180 in.)
Mk 2/GT6 - plus	31.9-32.0 mm (1.256-1.26 in.)
Stem diameter	
Vitesse Six	7.85-7.82 mm (0.309-0.308 in.)
Vitesse 2 Litre/GT6	7.874-7.887 mm (0.310-0.3105 in.)
Stem to guide clearance	
Vitesse Six	0.075-0.13 mm (0.003-0.005 in.)
Vitesse 2 Litre/GT6	0.038-0.064 mm (0.0015-0.0025 in.)

Valve Guides:

Length	
Vitesse Six/2 Litre/GT6	69.088 mm (2.72 in.)
Mk 2/GT6 - plus - inlet	52.386 mm (2.0625 in.)
- exhaust	57.15 mm (2.25 in.)
Outside diameter	12.725-12.751 mm (0.501-0.502 in.)
Bore	7.925-7.950 mm (0.312-0.313 in.)

Protrusion above cylinder head

Vitesse Six/2 Litre/GT6	19.025-19.075 mm (0.749-0.751 in.)
Mk 2/GT6 - plus	16.002 mm (0.63 in.)

Valve Springs

Vitesse Six	
Fitted length at load	34.54 mm/12.25-13.61 kgs 1.36 in./27-30 lbs.
Total number of coils	7.25
Vitesse 2 Litre/GT6	
Inner - Free length	39.624 mm (1.56 in.)
- fitted length at load	28.956 mm/4.99-6.35 kgs. (1.14 in./11-14 lbs)
Outer - free length	40.894 mm (1.61 in.)
- fitted length at load	35.2 mm /12.247-13.608 kgs (1.386 in./27-30 lbs.)
Mk 2 /GT6 - plus	
Inner - Free length	39.624 mm (1.56 in.)
- Solid length (max)	18.542 mm (0.73 in.)
- Outer diameter	18.542 mm (0.73 in.)
- Wire diameter	1.9034 mm (0.076 in.)
- Rate fitted	28.5 lb/ in.)
Outer - Free length	39.878 mm (1.57 in.)
- Solid length (max)	23.32 mm (0.918 in.)
- Inner diameter	20.193 mm (0.795 in.)
- Wire diameter	3.454 mm (0.136 in.)
- Rate fitted	150 lb/ in.)

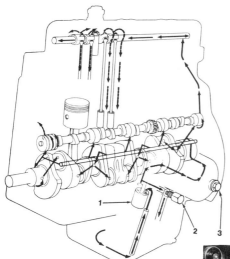

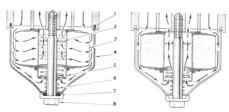

1. Rubber sealing ring
2. Locating washer
3. Filter element
4. Filter bowl
5. By-pass valve
6. Spring
7. Sealing ring
8. Attachment bolt

Fig.B.2   Sectional view of the oil filter assembly

Normal flow - Left: By-pass flow - Right

Fig.B.1   Engine lubrication system

1. Oil pump
2. Relief valve
3. Oil filter

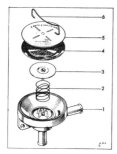

Fig.B.4   Removal/Installation of the oil filter assembly

1. Attachment bolt
2. Filter bowl
3. Filter element
4. Rubber sealing ring

Fig.B.3   Emission valve controlled engine breathing system

Fig.B.5   Details of the emission valve assembly

1. Valve body
2. Spring
3. Plate
4. Diaphragm
5. Cover
6. Retaining clip

Fig.B.6   Checking the clearance between the inner and outer rotors

Fig.B.9   Details of the oil pump assembly

1. Pump housing
2. Inner rotor
3. Outer rotor
4. Retaining bolts
5. End plate

Fig.B.7   Checking the clearance between the outer rotor and the pump housing

Fig.B.8   Checking the end-clearance of the rotors.

Lubrication System

GENERAL

Oil from the engine sump is pressurised by a rotor type oil pump and delivered to a filter via a passage in the block. A relief valve between the pump and filter regulates pressure and returns excess oil to the sump. Filtered oil is distributed through the main oil gallery to the crankshaft and camshaft bearings, and through drillings to the big-end bearings which splash-lubricate the cylinders. The rear camshaft journal meters oil to the rocker gear and valve gear (Fig.B.1). The timing gear is lubricated by mist from the crankcase and Seepage from the front camshaft journal. The crankshaft is sealed by lip-type seals at the front and rear. A full-flow sealed unit filter, screwed to the cylinder block, incorporates a relief valve which opens when filter blockage occurs and permits unfiltered oil to enter the supply line (Fig.B.2).

Crankcase ventilation on the Vitesse Six is through an open pipe to the atmosphere, whilst closed circuit system is incorporated on other models where a pipe from the rocker cover to an emission valve on the inlet manifold is provided. The emission control valve responds to induction manifold depression to restrict crankcase gas flow when the depression is greatest, and non-return valve in the oil filler cap balances crankcase and ambient pressures (Fig.B.3).

ROUTINE MAINTENANCE

Every 250 miles (400 km) or before beginning a long journey, check the oil level. Allow oil to settle with vehicle on level ground, remove and clean dipstick, insert fully and withdraw again. Read level on dipstick and replenish if necessary through the filler hole on the rocker cover, until top mark on dipstick is reached.

Every 6,000 miles (10,000 km) or six months, whichever is earlier, drain engine at sump drain plug, replace plug and refill through rocker cover filler cap. Change oil more frequently if dusty roads are used or short journeys made.

Every 12,000 miles (20,000 km), unscrew oil filter from the block and fit new unit ensuring the mating faces are clean and smeared with oil. (Fig.B.4).

Where an emission valve is installed, release clip (1), remove cover, diaphragm (2), valve pin and spring, wash parts in methylated spirits and inspect for serviceability before re-assembly (Fig.B.5).

Clean oil filler cap and ensure vent hole is clean.

OIL PUMP - Inspection

1. Remove pump as detailed in engine dismantling.

2. With pump components cleaned and dry and assembled without cover/intake pipe assembly, check clearances are as given in TECHNICAL DATA. (Figs. B.6, B.8). Renew worn parts.

3. Assemble and install pump.

RELIEF VALVE - Inspection

1. Remove cap nut, copper washer, spring and valve.

2. Clean parts, examine washer and valve for wear or damage and check spring rate (see TECHNICAL DATA). Renew parts as necessary.

3. Assemble relief valve.

Technical Data

Sump Capacity - Total	8 Imp. pts.	(9.6 U.S. pts; 4.6 Litres)
- Refill	7 Imp. pts.	(8.4 U.S. pts; 4.0 Litres)

Recommended Oils
British Isles:

B.P.	Super Visco - Static 20 W -50
Castrol	G.T.X.
Duckhams	Q 20 - 50
Esso	Extra Motor Oil 20 W/50
Mobil	Mobiloil Super SAE 10W/40 or Special 20 W/50.
Petrofina	Fina Multigrade Motor Oil SAE 20 W/50.
Regent	Havoline Motor Oil 20W/50.
Shell	Super Motor Oil 100

Overseas:
Over 30ºC (80ºF) A.P.I. MM or MS S.A.E. 30
0ºC to 30ºC (30ºF + 80ºF) A.P.I. MM or MS S.A.E. 20
Below 0ºC (30ºF) A.P.I. MM or MS S.A.E. 10

Single or Multigrades to specification may be used
Oil pump:
Type. Hobourn - Eaton double eccentric rotor.
Pressure at 2,000 r.p.m. (engine hot). 40 - 60 p.s.i. (4.2 kg/sq.cm)
Permissible clearances.

Outer rotor to body	0.190 mm (0.0075 in.).
Outer to inner rotor	0.254 mm (0.010 in.) max.
Rotor end clearance	0.102 mm (0.004 in.) max.

Oil Filter

Type	Full-flow "throw away" unit (Purolator, A.C. Delco or Tecalemit)
Relief valve pressure	3.16-3.87 kg/cm^2 (45-55 lbs/sq. ins.)

Relief valve spring
Free length	39.37 mm (1.55 in.)
Fitted length	31.75 mm (1.25 in.)
Load at fitted length	6.58 kg (14.5 lbs)

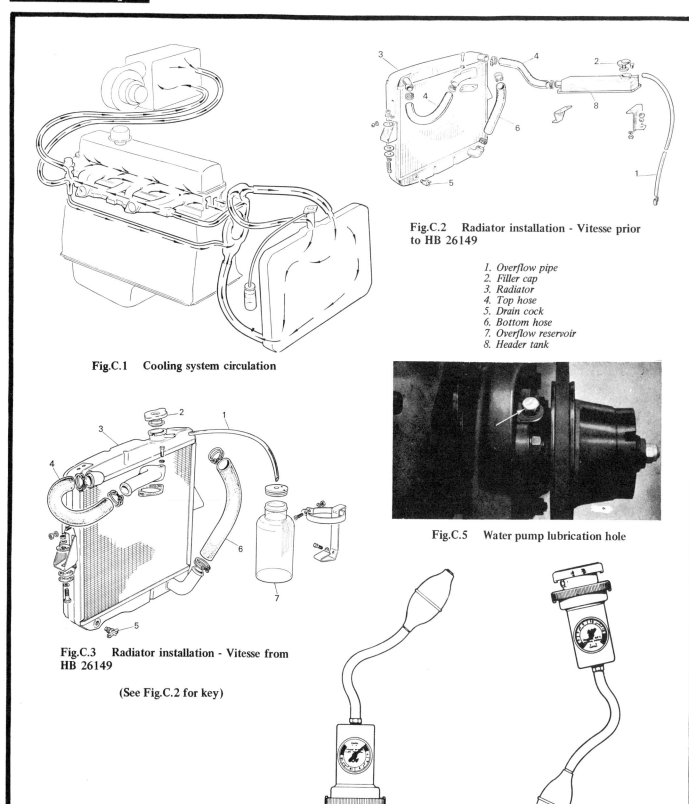

Fig.C.1   Cooling system circulation

Fig.C.2   Radiator installation - Vitesse prior to HB 26149

1. *Overflow pipe*
2. *Filler cap*
3. *Radiator*
4. *Top hose*
5. *Drain cock*
6. *Bottom hose*
7. *Overflow reservoir*
8. *Header tank*

Fig.C.3   Radiator installation - Vitesse from HB 26149

(See Fig.C.2 for key)

Fig.C.5   Water pump lubrication hole

Fig.C.6   Testing the cooling system with a pressure tester

Fig.C.7 Testing the radiator filler cap

Cooling System

GENERAL

Circulation of coolant through radiator and cylinder block is assisted by a centrifugal water pump at the front of the cylinder head which is belt driven from the crankshaft pulley (Fig.C.1). A filler cap, incorporating pressure relief and recuperating valves, seals the system, relieves excess pressure during heat expansion and relieves inwardly during cooling contraction. Excess coolant relieves into a translucent coolant reservoir, making a closed-circuit, self-recuperating system, except on the Vitesse Six up to HB26149 where a separate header tank was mounted alongside the cylinder head. A thermostat isolates and then controls flow to the radiator during the warming-up period and a fan on the water pump pulley assists air flow through radiator. Drain cocks are fitted at the bottom of the radiator and at the right-hand side of the cylinder block and the heater pipe is fed from the rear cylinder head.

On the Vitesse 2 Litre and GT6, hot water from the cooling system is directed to heat the inlet manifolds.

ROUTINE MAINTENANCE

CAUTION: If the engine is hot, rotate filler cap one half-turn only to allow pressure to dissipate before fully removing cap.

Weekly

Check water level by removing filler cap or examining translucent reservoir, as applicable. If required, replenish with soft water until the level is one inch below the filler neck or the reservoir is at least half full. Should reservoir become empty, fill radiator before replenishing reservoir.

Annually

1. Remove plug at water pump, screw in 1/8 in. taper Briggs grease nipple and apply grease gun until grease exudes from a release hole in pump. Replace plug (Fig.C.5).

2. Flush out the system at least once a year when adding anti-freeze. Remove drain cocks completely and use plenty of clean running water. Add anti-freeze to required concentration (see TECHNICAL DATA), run engine and check for leaks at all joints. See draining and filling.

3. Remove thermostat from water pump (Fig.C.6).

   Inspect for wear, damage or corrosion. If accuracy is suspect, check as described in "THERMOSTAT - Testing", replace thermostat.

4. Examine filler cap for damage, wear and corrosion and check fastening device for correct functioning. Filler cap and radiator can be checked with a pressure tester as detailed, in "FILLER CAP - Testing".

COOLING SYSTEM - Draining

1. Set heater control to "HOT" and remove radiator or header tank filler cap.

2. Open drain cocks at bottom of radiator and on cylinder block.

   NOTE:- Draining does not completely empty the heating system and is therfore not a safeguard against frost damage

COOLING SYSTEM - Filling

1. Set heater control to "HOT" and ensure drain cocks are closed.

2. Remove filler cap and fill system with clean soft water. Replace cap.

3. Run engine until warmed up to circulate water. Stop engine.

4. Check level and replenish as necessary.

5. Half fill overflow reservoir where applicable.

COOLING SYSTEM - Pressure testing

1. Ensure water system level is correct and run engine until coolant is warm.

2. Remove filler cap and attach AC pressure tester or equivalent to filler neck (Fig.C.6).

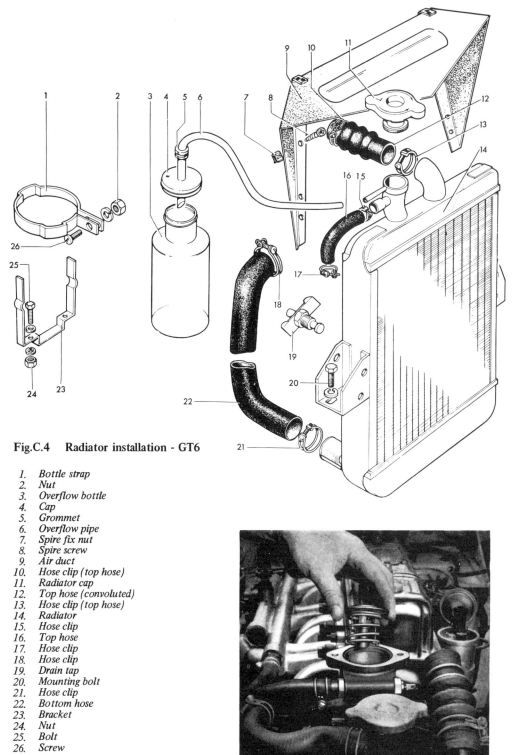

Fig.C.4 Radiator installation - GT6

1. Bottle strap
2. Nut
3. Overflow bottle
4. Cap
5. Grommet
6. Overflow pipe
7. Spire fix nut
8. Spire screw
9. Air duct
10. Hose clip (top hose)
11. Radiator cap
12. Top hose (convoluted)
13. Hose clip (top hose)
14. Radiator
15. Hose clip
16. Top hose
17. Hose clip
18. Hose clip
19. Drain tap
20. Mounting bolt
21. Hose clip
22. Bottom hose
23. Bracket
24. Nut
25. Bolt
26. Screw

Fig C.8 Thermostat installation

3. Pump tester until 7 p.s.i. (0.492 kg/cm) is indicated on dial. This pressure should be maintained for 10 seconds. Rectify leakage if necessary.

4. Remove tester and replace filler cap.

   NOTE:- This test is more stringent if carried out with engine running. With this procedure, pressure fluctuation with no evidence of external leakage points to defective cylinder head gasket.

FILLER CAP - Pressure testing

1. Clean filler cap with water and, while still wet, attach pressure tester.

2. Pump tester until relief valve operates. Indicator should read within one p.s.i. of 7 p.s.i. (0.492 kg/sq. cm) and maintain pressure for 10 seconds. Reject cap if requirements are not met.

3. Remove tester and refit cap if serviceable.

RADIATOR - Removal and Installation (Figs. C2,C3,C4).
Removal

1. Drain system and, on GT6, remove air duct (9).

2. Disconnect top and bottom radiator hoses and pull off overflow pipe

3. Remove two bolts, nuts and washers. Tilt radiator rearwards and carefully lift out without fouling fan blades.

Installation

1. Place radiator in position without fouling fan blades, and secure with nuts, bolts and washers.

2. Connect top and bottom radiator hoses and overflow pipe.

3. Install air duct on GT6, fill system, run engine and check for leaks.

THERMOSTAT - Removal and Installation
Removal

1. Drain system sufficiently to empty cylinder head water jacket.

2. Remove both attachment bolts, remove outlet elbow with gasket and remove thermostat (Fig.C.8).

Installation

1. Place thermostat in position.

2. Assemble elbow with serviceable gasket.

3. Replenish system

THERMOSTAT - Testing

1. Immerse the thermostat in water with a thermometer and apply heat to the vessel. Move thermostat to circulate water around bellows.

2. On the thermometer read off the temperature at which the valve begins to open. This should be within 5°F of temperature marked on the thermostat flange and should be fully open with a valve lift of 6.35 mm (0.25 in.) when the temperature rises a further 25°F.

WATER PUMP - Removal and Installation

1. Isolate battery and drain coolant system

2. Slacken generator/alternator bolts, pivot unit towards engine and remove fan belt.

3. Disconnect hoses from pump and top elbow. Remove elbow and thermostat.

4. Disconnect temperature transmitter cable.

5. Disconnect vacuum pipe at distributor and manifold and fuel pipe at carburettor and fuel pump; remove water pump bolt securing pipe clip and remove pipes together with clip.

6. Remove bolt retaining upper generator bracket.

7. Remove remaining bolt and lift pump from engine. Remove gasket.

8. Reverse removal procedure to install pump with new gasket.

9. Run engine and check for leaks.

WATER PUMP - Reconditioning
Dismantling (Fig.C.9)

1. Remove nut (19) with washer and extract pulley (21). Retain key.

2. Detach bearing housing (13) and gasket from body.

3. Using Churchill tool S4221A with adaptor FTS 127 withdraw impeller (9) from spindle (Fig.C.10).

4. Remove seal (11) from impeller.

5. Remove circlip (22) and drift out spindle complete with bearing assembly.

6. Remove spinner (15), circlip (22) and washer (16).

7. Press bearings and spacer (17) from spindle.

Inspection

1. Clean all parts and examine for wear, damage and corrosion.

1. Bolt
2. Elbow
3. Gasket
4. Bolt
5. Temperature transmitter
6. Thermostat
7. Gasket
8. Body
9. Impeller
10. Stud
11. Seal
12. Gasket
13. Bearing housing
14. Spindle
15. Spinner
16. Washer
17. Spacer
18. Ball race
19. Nut
20. Washer
21. Pulley
22. Circlip
23. Circlip
24. Woodruff key
25. Grease plug
26. Bolt
27. Bolt
28. Bolt
29. Union

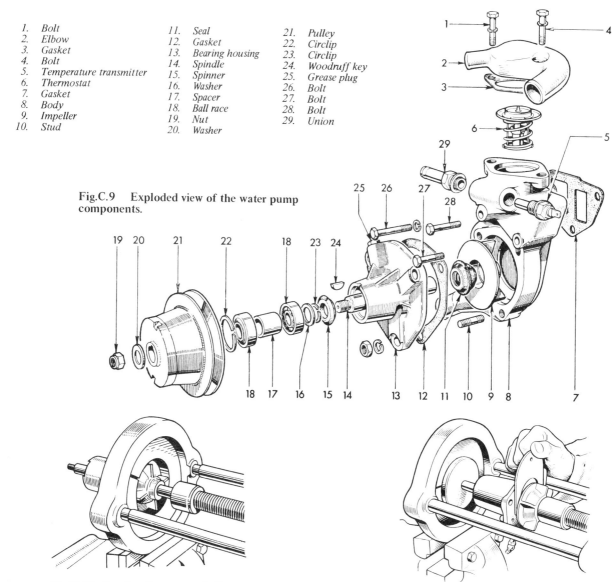

Fig.C.9   Exploded view of the water pump components.

Fig.C.10 Pressing the sump spindle out of the impeller

Fig.C.11 Using a 0.030 in. gauge to set the correct impeller clearance

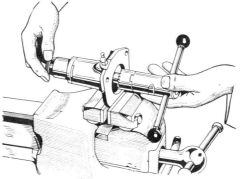

Fig.C.12 Recutting the pump sealing gland face.

2. Examine bearings for cracks, rough rotation, and excessive play. Renew if in doubt.

3. Renew seals if damaged or deformed.

4. Renew spindle if scored or worn.

5. Inspect gland face of bearing housing for scores - particularly if pump has been leaking, and, if necessary, re-cut the face with Churchill tool S.126.

6. Renew gaskets.

Assembly (Fig.C.9)

1. Fit circlip (22) and washer (16) to spindle and press on ball races with distance piece (17) between them. The sealed faces on the ball races must be away from distance piece. Fit spinner (15) next to circlip.

2. Pack the space between bearings with high melting point grease and press spindle and races into housing (13). Use a tube on the outer race of the bearing to insert assembly and secure with circlip (22).

3. With sealing gland (II) in the rear recess, press impeller onto spindle until a clearance of 0.76 mm (0.030 in.) is obtained between impeller and rear face of bearing housing (see Fig.C.11).

4. Solder impeller to end of spindle to prevent water leakage.

5. Key and attach pulley to the spindle, and secure with nut (19).

6. Smear grease on new gasket (12) and secure bearing housing assembly to pump body.

7. Install serviceable thermostat (see 'THERMOSTAT - Testing") fit new gasket and secure elbow. Install temperature transmitter.

WATER PUMP - Restoring Sealing Gland Face (Fig.C.12)

1. Insert pilot of Churchill tool S126 into gland side of housing, until protruding at pulley side.

2. Slide bush-with small diameter leading-on pilot and follow with tool bearing and then knurled nut.

3. Turn knurled nut to bring cutter against gland face and steadily turn tommy bar-simultaneously applying light even pressure on cutter with knurled nut. Continually remove tool to discard swarf and check gland face surface. Remove only sufficient material to produce a score-free and polished surface.

IMPORTANT:- Gland face depth from mounting face of housing must not exceed 6.7 mm (0.256 in.)

Technical Data

Cooling System Capacity (including heater)			
Vitesse Six	14.0 Imp. pts (7.4 Litres 15.6 U.S. pts.)		
Vitesse 2 Litre and GT6	11.0 Imp. pts (6.2 Litres 13.2 U.S. pts.)		
System Working Pressure	7 p.s.i.		
Anti-freeze Solution Specification	B.S.I. 3151 or 3152		
Anti-freeze Protection Concentration	25%	30%	35%
1.Complete protection Vehicle may be driven away immediately from cold.	10ºF (-12ºC)	3ºF(-16ºC)	-4ºF(-20ºC)

2. Safe limit: Coolant in mushy state. Short warm-up before driving away.	0ºF(-17ºC)	-8ºF(-22ºC)	-18ºF(-28ºC)
3. Lower protection limit: Frost damage prevented. Engine should NOT be starter until thawed out.	-14ºF(-26ºC)	-22ºF(-30ºC)	-28ºF(-33ºC)
Pump drive belt Tension	26 mm (1 in.) total deflection.		

Fig.D.1   Distributor lubrication points -
Lucas

1. Cam screw
2. Pivot
3. Timing mechanism
4. Cam

Fig.D.3   Contact breaker point adjustment -
Lucas

1. Lock screw
2. Fixed contact
3. Moving contact pivot
4. Adjustment slot

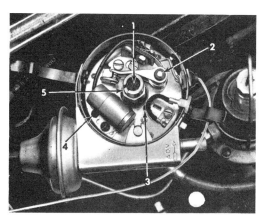

Fig.D.2   Distributor lubrication points -
Delco

1. Cam screw
2. Pivot
3. Oil hole
4. Oil hole
5. Cam

Fig.D.4   Contact breaker point adjustment -
Delco

1. Lock screw
2. Eccentric screw

Ignition System

GENERAL
ROUTINE MAINTENANCE
CONTACT BREAKER POINTS - Adjustment
CONTACT (LUCAS) - Replacement
CONTACT (DELCO-CONVENTIONAL) Replacement
CONTACT (DELCO-EMISSION CONTROL) - Replacement
IGNITION TIMING - Adjustment
DISTRIBUTOR - Removal and Installation
DISTRIBUTOR (LUCAS) - Overhaul
DISTRIBUTOR (DELCO-CONVENTIONAL) - Overhaul
DISTRIBUTOR (DELCO-EMISSION CONTROL) - Overhaul
TECHNICAL DATA

GENERAL

The coil ignition system includes a Lucas coil on all models: a Lucas distributor on early Vitesse Six and Vitesse 2 Litre models, and a Delco distributor on later Vitesse Six and G.T.6 models. Micro adjustment of the vacuum control unit is provided on the distributor, except on the later Vitesse Six and on the G.T.6 with emission control which also has a double-acting vacuum control unit (Fig.D.15).

NOTE:- The ignition timing on emission control models can only be adjusted dynamically, and should be done by an Authorised Dealer.

ROUTINE MAINTENANCE

Interior and exterior of distributor cap, high tension leads, ..d sparking plug ceramics should be kept clean to prevent tracking.

Every 6,000 miles (10,000 km)

1. Remove distributor cap and rotor arm, and apply a few drops of thin oil to screw (1), pivot (2), and centrifugal control (3), and lightly grease cam (4), or lightly oil (1), (2) and (3); inject 5 c.c of engine oil at hole (4), and lightly grease cam (5), (Fig.D.1 - Lucas, or D.2 - Delco).

2. Remove contact breaker points, and clean up faces evenly with fine carborundum stone. Renew contacts if excessively worn or pitted.

3. Refit contacts, and adjust gap between points.

4. Remove and clean sparking plugs, inspect for worn electrodes and cracked or loose ceramic insulators, and renew if necessary. Set plug gaps to 0.64 mm (0.025 in.)

Every 12,000 miles (20,000 km)

Fit replacement sparking plugs with correct gap setting.

CONTACT BREAKER POINTS - Adjustment
(Fig.D.3 - Lucas, or D.4 - Delco)

1. Remove distributor cap and rotor arm, and rotate crankshaft until moving contact is on cam peak.

2. Slacken fixed contact screw (1).

3. With screwdriver in slot (4), or at eccentric screw (2), as applicable, and with feeler gauge between contacts, adjust fixed contact until 0.35-0.40 mm (0.014-0.016 in.) is obtained.

4. Tighten fixed contact screw, and re-check gap.

5. Replace rotor arm and distributor cap.

CONTACT BREAKER POINTS (LUCAS) -
(Replacement (Fig.D.5).

1. Remove distributor cap and rotor arm.

2. Remove nut, insulation bush, and L.T and capacitor terminals.

3. Remove moving contact and large and small fibre washers.

4. Remove lock screw with washer, and remove fixed contact.

5. Clean preservative from faces of new contacts.

6. Position fixed contact, and fit lock screw and washer.

7. Fit insulation washers, and position moving contact.

8. Connect L.T. and capacitor leads, insulator, and secure with nut.

9. Adjust contact breaker points.

10. Assemble rotor arm and distributor cap.

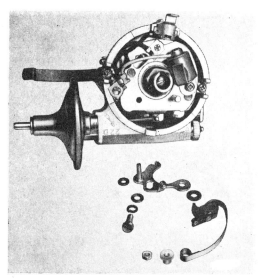

Fig.D.5   Details of the contact breaker assembly - Lucas

Fig.D.6   Details of the contact breaker assembly Delco (conventional).

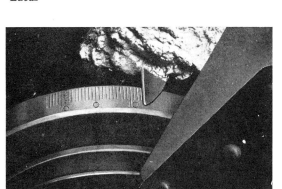

Fig.D.7   Ignition timing scale on the crankshaft pulley - Vitesse Six and 2 Litre.

Fig.D.8   Ignition timing scale on the crankshaft pulley - Vitesse Mk 2 and G.T.6

Fig.D.9   Checking the distributor setting with a test lamp

Fig.D.10 Installing the distributor - Lucas

Fig.D.11 Installing the distributor - Delco

Fig.D.12 Distributor position with No. 1 cylinder at T.D.C. on the firing stroke - Lucas

Fig.D.13 Distributor position with No. 1 cylinder at T.D.C. on the firing stroke - Delco

Fig.D.15 Distributor with double acting vacuum unit fitted to emission control models

1. *Vacuum retard connection*
2. *Vacuum advance connection*

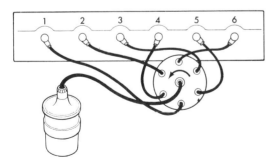

Fig.D.14 High tension lead connections

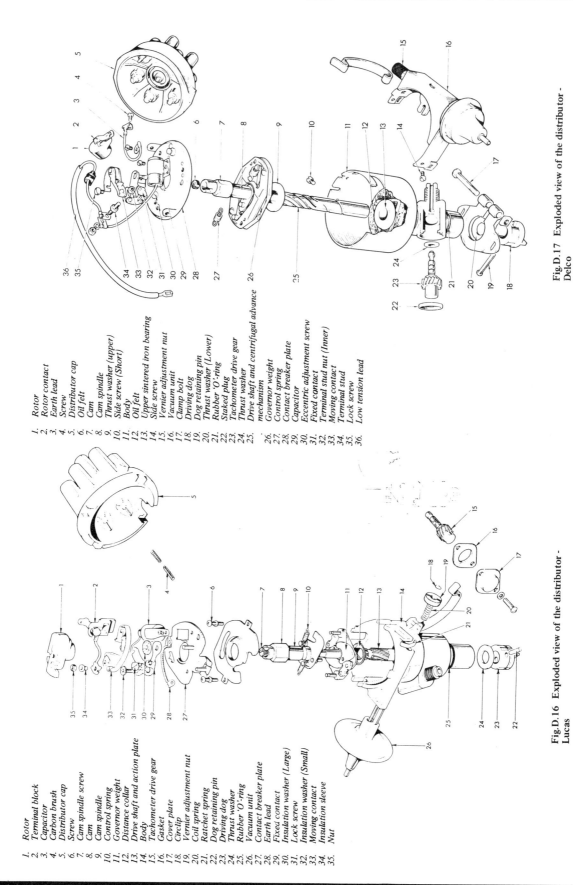

Fig.D.17 Exploded view of the distributor -
Delco

1. Rotor
2. Rotor contact
3. Earth lead
4. Screw
5. Distributor cap
6. Oil felt
7. Cam
8. Cam spindle
9. Thrust washer (upper)
10. Side screw (Short)
11. Body
12. Oil felt
13. Upper sintered iron bearing
14. Side screw
15. Vernier adjustment nut
16. Vacuum unit
17. Clamp bolt
18. Driving dog
19. Dog retaining pin
20. Thrust washer (Lower)
21. Rubber 'O'-ring
22. Tachometer drive gear
23. Staked plug
24. Thrust washer
25. Drive shaft and centrifugal advance
      mechanism
26. Governor weight
27. Control spring
28. Contact breaker plate
29. Capacitor
30. Eccentric adjustment screw
31. Fixed contact
32. Terminal stud nut (Inner)
33. Moving contact
34. Terminal stud
35. Lock screw
36. Low tension lead

Fig.D.16 Exploded view of the distributor -
Lucas

1. Rotor
2. Terminal block
3. Capacitor
4. Carbon brush
5. Distributor cap
6. Screw
7. Cam spindle screw
8. Cam
9. Cam spindle
10. Control spring
11. Governor weight
12. Distance collar
13. Drive shaft and action plate
14. Body
15. Tachometer drive gear
16. Gasket
17. Cover plate
18. Circlip
19. Vernier adjustment nut
20. Coil spring
21. Ratchet spring
22. Dog retaining pin
23. Driving dog
24. Thrust washer
25. Rubber 'O'-ring
26. Vacuum unit
27. Contact breaker plate
28. Earth lead
29. Fixed contact
30. Insulation washer (Large)
31. Lock screw
32. Insulation washer (Small)
33. Moving contact
34. Insulation sleeve
35. Nut

38

CONTACT BREAKER POINTS (DELCO CONVENTIONAL)-
Replacement (Fig. D.6).

1. Remove distributor cap and rotor arm.

2. Slacken terminal stud inner nut, and remove moving contact.

3. Remove lock screw and fixed contact.

4. Clean preservative from faces of new contacts.

5. Secure fixed contact to terminal stud with nut finger-tight only, and to base plate with lock screw.

6. Position moving contact on pivot with spring on outside of fixed contact insulating strip, and tighten terminal stud nut.

7. Adjust contact breaker points.

8. Assemble rotor arm and distributor cap.

CONTACT BREAKER POINTS (DELCO-EMISSION CONTROL) - Replacement (Fig. D.18)

1. Remove distributor cap and rotor arm

2. Disengage moving contact spring from terminal block, and remove moving contact.

3. Remove L.T. lead and condenser lead from terminal block.

4. Remove lock screw and fixed contact.

5. Clean preservative from faces of new contacts.

6. Secure fixed contact to base plate with lock screw.

7. Locate L.T. lead and condenser lead on terminal block.

8. Position moving contact on pivot, and locate moving contact spring on terminal block. Ensure both leads are correctly secured by spring.

9. Adjust contact breaker points.

10. Assemble rotor arm and distributor cap.

IGNITION TIMING - Adjustment

1. Remove distributor cap, loosen pedestal clamp bolt, and where applicable, set vacuum micro adjuster to midway position.

2. Turn crankshaft until pointer on timing chain case is aligned with correct degree marking on crankshaft pulley (Figs. D.7 and D.8) and rotor arm is pointing towards No.1 segment of cap (Figs. D.12 and D.13).

NOTE:- This is 10° B.T.D.C. for Vitesse Six, Vitesse 2 Litre Mk 2, and G.T.6 Mk 2 and 13° B.T.D.C. for Mk I models.

3. With ignition switched on, rotate distributor until contact breaker points begin to open. Check by observing spark, or when test lamp connected to distributor L.T. terminal and good earth illuminates (Fig.D.9).

4. Re-tighten pedestal clamp bolt, and replace distributor cap.

NOTE:- This setting is nominal, and should be further adjusted if necessary to give best performance.

Emission Control Models

On the crankshaft pulley a notch is provided which when aligned with the pointer on the timing chain case gives the T.D.C. position for No. 1 piston. Two further marks on the crankshaft pulley, one on either side of the notch, indicate the static ignition point (6° B.T.D.C.) and the idling timing point (4° A.T.D.C.). However, on some early models, these may be absent, and in this case the points should be determined and marked with white paint. Using a pair of dividers set to 7.62 mm (0.30 in.), mark the 6° B.T.D.C. position on the periphery of the pulley CLOCKWISE of the notch (Fig.D.21). Similarly mark the 4° A.T.D.C. point 5.08 mm (0.20 in.) ANTICLOCKWISE of the notch.

1. Remove distributor cap, and loosen pedestal clamp bolt.

2. Turn crankshaft until static ignition mark (mark CLOCKWISE of notch) is aligned with pointer on timing chain case, and rotor arm is pointing towards No. 1 segment of cap.

3. With ignition switched on, rotate distributor until contact breaker points begin to open. Check by observing spark at points, or connecting a test lamp between distributor L.T. terminal and good earth, and observing point at which lamp illuminates. Re-tighten clamp bolt and re-check setting. This gives static ignition setting.

4. Apply white paint to leading edge of pointer, and paint a fine line on crankshaft pulley at idling timing point (point ANTICLOCKWISE of notch).

5. Refit distributor cap.

6. Connect a stroboscopic timing light and tachometer to the engine in accordance with equipment manufacturer's instructions.

7. Start engine and run up to normal operating temperature.

8. Set idling speed to 800 - 850 rev/min by turning both carburettor throttle stop screws an equal amount.

9. With engine running at this speed, point timing light at crankshaft pulley, and observe position of idling timing mark in relation to pointer. If timing is correctly set, mark should be in line with pointer. If otherwise, loosen pedestal clamp bolt, and rotate distributor body until this condition is obtained. This may necessitate re-adjustment of throttle stop screws to maintain correct idle speed.

10. Re-tighten clamp bolt, and re-check timing. If satisfactory, remove timing light and tachometer.

11. Finally, reset idle speed to specified figure.

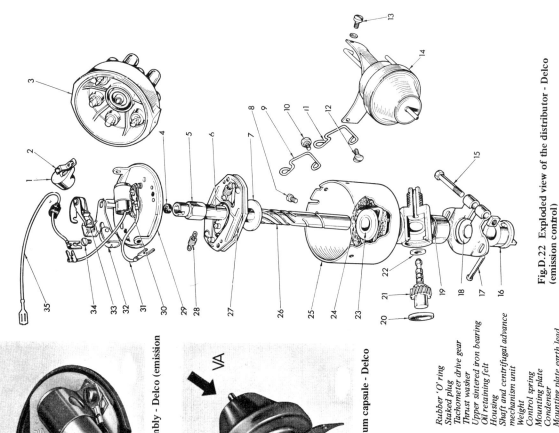

Fig.D.22 Exploded view of the distributor - Delco (emission control)

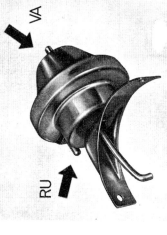

Fig.D.19 Mounting plate assembly - Delco (emission control)

Fig.D.20 Double-acting vacuum capsule - Delco (emission control)

VA Vacuum Advance
RU Retard unit

1.	Rotor	19.	Rubber 'O' ring
2.	Rotor contact	20.	Staked plug
3.	Cap	21.	Tachometer drive gear
4.	Oil retaining felt	22.	Thrust washer
5.	Cam	23.	Upper sintered iron bearing
6.	Cam spindle	24.	Oil retaining felt
7.	Upper thrust washer	25.	Housing
8.	Side screw	26.	Shaft and centrifugal advance mechanism unit
9.	Clip	27.	Weight
10.	Side screw - clip securing	28.	Control spring
11.	Clip	29.	Mounting plate
12.	Side screw - clip securing	30.	Condenser
13.	Side screw - with washer	31.	Mounting plate earth lead
14.	Double acting vacuum capsule	32.	Fixed contact
15.	Clamp bolt	33.	Moving contact
16.	Coupling	34.	Lock screw
17.	Coupling pin	35.	Low tension wire
18.	Lower thrust washer		

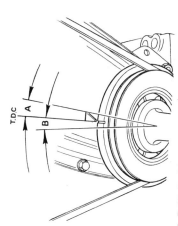

Fig.D.18 Details of the contact breaker assembly Delco (emission control)

Idle Speed	Ignition Static		Ignition at Idle	
	Crank-shaft Degrees	Equiv-alent Distance "A" (Fig. 2)	Crank-shaft Degrees	Equiv-alent Distance "B" (Fig. 2)
(R.P.M.)	6° B.T.D.C.	·3″	4° A.T.D.C.	·2″
800/850				

Fig.D.21 Ignition timing marks on the crankshaft pulley - GT6 (emission control)

T.D.C
A
B

A - 7.62 mm (0.30 in.)
B - 5.08 mm (0.20 in.)

DISTRIBUTOR - Removal and Installation

1. Disconnect L.T. lead to distributor.

2. Disconnect H.T. cables from sparking plugs and coil, or remove distributor cap.

3. Disconnect tachometer drive cable from distributor.

4. Disconnect vacuum pipe from distributor.

NOTE:- On emission control models, two vacuum pipes are connected to the distributor and their respective positions should be noted before removal as one controls advance and the other retard action of the vacuum unit.

5. Remove rear bolt securing distributor clamp to pedestal, and forward bolt together with distributor (Figs. D.10 and D.11).

NOTE:- Do not slacken clamping bolt unless dismantling.

6. Install in reverse order. If clamping bolt has been released or pedestal drive gear disturbed, set number 1 piston at T.D.C. on compression stoke, and proceed as described in "IGNITION TIMING - Adjustment"

NOTE:- On emission control models, the ignition timing MUST be checked after installation.

DISTRIBUTOR (LUCAS) - Overhaul (Fig.D.16)

1. Remove distributor cap and rotor arm.

2. Remove contact breaker points, capacitor (3), and L.T. terminal (2).

3. Disconnect vacuum control spring from moving plate (27), remove two screws (6), and take out moving plate and base plate.

4. Remove circlip (18), adjuster (19), and spring taking care to retain ratchet spring (21). Withdraw vacuum control unit (26).

5. Remove cover (17), gasket (16), and tachometer drive gear (15).

6. Release springs (10) from base of cam (8) and from action plate. Remove screw (7), and draw cam from shaft.

7. Before driving out pin (22) to release driving dog (23) washer (24) and shaft from distributor body, check shaft end-float which should not exceed 0.8 mm (0.31 in.)

8. With new shaft or checking bar of 12.45 mm (0.49 in.) check sleeve in body (14) for wear. Renew sleeve if worn. Reduce excessive end-float by renewing collar (12) under action plate and washer (24). Clean all parts, inspect for wear or damage, and renew as necessary.

9. Fit collar (12) under action plate, and assemble weights, springs and cam to action plate. Secure cam with screw (7).

10. Fit washer (24), driving dog (23), insert pin (22), and peen over ends.

11. Lubricate tachometer drive gear (15) with engine oil insert in body, and secure with cover (17) using new gasket (16).

12. Assemble moving plate (27) to base plate by springing clip over base plate slot edge, inserting moving plate peg into a slot on base plate and turning it slightly clockwise. Secure assembly to body with screws (6).

13. Insert vacuum control unit (26) into body, and assemble ratchet spring, spring, adjuster (19), and circlip (18). Hook spring onto lug.

14. Assemble capacitor L.T. lead and contact breaker points to contact plate, and adjust points.

15. Refit rotor arm and cap.

DISTRIBUTOR (DELCO-CONVENTIONAL)- Overhaul (Fig.D.17)

1. Remove distributor cap and rotor arm.

2. Remove vacuum control unit (16)

3. Remove mounting plate (28), complete with contact breaker assembly, condenser, and L.T. lead.

4. With a 0.218 in dia. steel bar turned down at one end to 0.15 in. dia. by 0.125 in. drive out tachometer gear (23), thrust washer (24), and end cap (22).

5. Remove clamp and oil seal ring (21).

6. Remove securing pin (19), and withdraw coupling (18), and spacer (20).

NOTE:- Driving dog teeth are offset to left when facing rotor arm locating slot.

7. Remove shaft assembly (25) with spacer (9) from distributor. Release spring at bottom of distributor bowl, and remove oil retaining felt (12).

8. Clean all parts, inspect for wear or damage, and renew as necessary. Soak felt in clean engine oil, shake off surplus and secure felt in position with spring clip.

9. Fit shaft spacer washer (9) on shaft, and thread shaft (25) into distributor. Fit coupling washer (20), correctly position coupling (18) and secure with pin.

10. With thrust washer (24) on tachometer drive gear shaft, cover assembly with petroleum jelly and push into position. Fit new end cover (22), and secure with four equi-spaced centre punch indentations at edge of bore.

11. Fit oil seal ring (21) and clamp to bottom of shaft.

12. Fit mounting plate assembly (28), complete with contact breaker points, condenser and L.T. lead.

13. Fit vacuum control unit (16), ensuring that mounting plate earth lead terminal is secured by appropriate screw.

14. Refit rotor arm and distributor cap.

Overhaul is performed in the same manner as described above for the conventional unit.

Technical Data

Coil	Lucas HA12
Distributor - Vitesse Six to engine HB15000	Lucas 25D6
Vitesse Six, from engine HB15001	Delco 200
Vitesse Six, from engine HB16302	Delco 202
Vitesse 2 Litre and Mk 2	Lucas 22D6
G.T.6 Mk 1 (conventional)	Delco 202
G.T.6 Mk 1 (emission control)	Delco 204
G.T.6 Mk 1 (emission control)	Delco 200
G.T.6.- plus (emission control)	Delco 204
Moving contact spring tension	
- Lucas	18 - 24 oz.
- Delco	17 - 21 oz.
Firing angle	$60^o \pm 1^o$
Dwell angle - Lucas	$35^o \pm 3^o$
- Delco	$41^o \pm 1^o$
- Delco (Vitesse Six)	$36^o \pm 1^o$
Open angle - Lucas	$25^o \pm 3^o$
- Delco	$19^o \pm 1^o$
- Delco (Vitesse Six)	$24^o \pm 1^o$
Firing order	1 - 5 - 3 - 6 - 2 - 4
Sparking plugs (conventional)	Champion N - 9Y
(emission control)	Champion UN12Y
Sparking plug gap	0.64 mm (0.025 in.)

Fuel System

GENERAL

The fuel system main components are the fuel tank, fuel pump, air cleaner and carburettors. The fuel tank is located in the luggage compartment and incorporates a filler neck with cap and overflow pipe, a fuel gauge transmitter and a fuel feed/ drain connection. On the Vitesse, the fuel tank contains a reserve fuel compartment controlled by a tap on top of the tank.

The mechanical type fuel pump is mounted on the left-hand side of the engine and is rocker arm operated from the crankshaft.

Twin Stromberg, side-draught carburettors are fitted to all models except the early Vitesse Six where Solex, semi-down-draught units were provided. On the G.T.6. - plus model the carburettors are produced to a stringent anti-pollution standard and must not be replaced by units not to this standard.

ROUTINE MAINTENANCE
Every 6,000 miles (10,000 km)

1. Top-up carburettor damper with seasonal grade of engine oil until threaded plug of damper is 6 mm (0.25 in.) above dashpot before resistance is felt (Fig.E.1).

2. Lubricate throttle and choke control linkages.

3. Remove and clean air cleaner elements with low pressure air line or soft brush (see 'AIR CLEANER for removal and installation).

Every 12,000 miles (20,000 km)

1. Renew paper type air cleaner element.

2. Clean fuel pump as follows (Fig.E.2):-

   (a) Disconnect and plug inlet pipe to cut off fuel supply from tank.

   (b) Remove bolt (I), washer and cap (2) with gasket.

   (c) Remove gauze filter (3) and clean in petrol using fingers to remove dirt.

   (d) Loosen sediment in bowl with small screwdriver and blow out with air pump.

   (e) Renew gasket if damaged or deteriorated.

   (f) Assemble with filter gauze face downwards and connect inlet pipe.

   NOTE:- On Vitesse Six and early Mk 1. models, a glass sediment bowl secured by a stirrup is fitted.

3. Adjust idling control if necessary.

4. Check exhaust system for deterioration, leakage and security. Rectify or renew parts as necessary.

AIR CLEANER - Removal and Installation (Fig.E.4)

1. Remove air intake tubes from cover

2. Unscrew attachment bolts (I) and remove assembly from carburettors. Retain gaskets (6 and 8).

3. Remove centre bolt (7) and washers, separate cover (2) plate (4) and remove elements(3).

4. Assemble in reverse order, ensuring sealing ring (4) and gaskets (6 and 8) are serviceable and correctly positioned. Install with slots at top (Fig.E.5).

FUEL TANK - Removal and Installation (Fig.E,6 & E.7)

1. Isolate battery and drain fuel tank.

   NOTE:- On Vitesse models, drain plug is under vehicle and behind left-hand side of rear wheel arch. On G.T.6. models, tank is drained by disconnecting fuel feed pipe under vehicle.

2. Remove luggage compartment floor covering and, on G.T.6. models, the left-hand side and rear trim panels.

3. Disconnect connectors at fuel contents transmitter unit.

4. On Vitesse, pull rubber fuel pipe connector (4) from tank, remove screws (1 and 2) and bolt (3), take off filler cap and manoeuvre tank from luggage compartment (Fig.E.6).

5. On G.T.6., slacken clips (I) and pull down rubber filler pipe. Remove screws (2) with strap (3), slacken clip (4)

Fig.E.1 Topping-up the carburettor damper

Fig.E.2 Removing the fuel pump filter screen

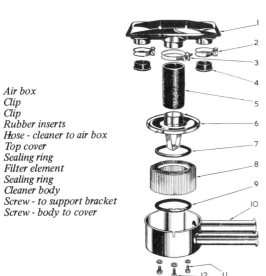

1. Air box
2. Clip
3. Clip
4. Rubber inserts
5. Hose - cleaner to air box
6. Top cover
7. Sealing ring
8. Filter element
9. Sealing ring
10. Cleaner body
11. Screw - to support bracket
12. Screw - body to cover

Fig.E.3 Details of the air cleaner assembly - Early Vitesse 6

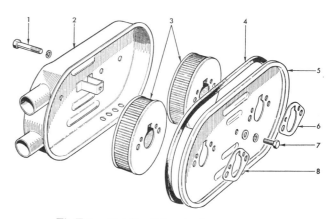

Fig.E.4 Details of the air cleaner assembly

1. Attachment bolts		5. Backplate	
2. Cover plate		6. Flange gasket	
3. Filter elements		7. Centre bolt	
4. Sealing ring		8. Flange gasket	

Fig.E.5 Installation of the air cleaner showing the relative positions of the slots.

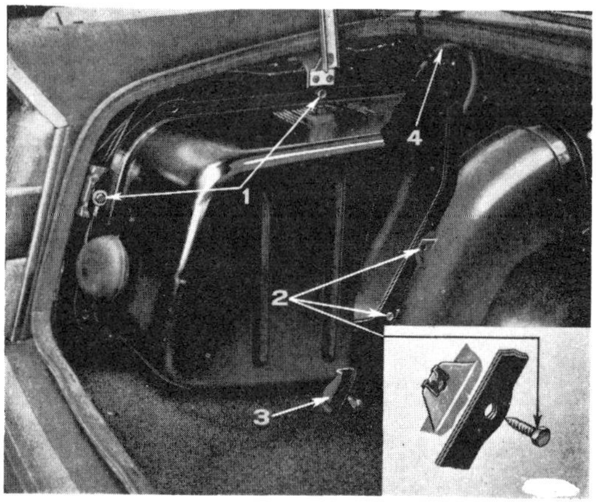

Fig.E.6 Fuel tank installation - Vitesse

1. Screw
2. Screw
3. Bolt
4. Connector

44

and pull off breather pipe; remove three bolts (6) and tank from compartment lifting front end first (Fig.E.7).

6. Reverse procedure to install tank and check for leaks after refilling.

FUEL PUMP - Removal and Installation

1. Disconnect fuel feed and outlet pipes and blank off inlet pipe to avoid loss of fuel. Remove attachment nuts, washers, pump and gasket.

2. Clean joint faces, smear new gasket with jointing compound and place gasket and pump on mounting studs. Secure with nuts and washers. Connect fuel pipes and check for correct operation and leaks.

FUEL PUMP - Dismantling and Re-assembly

1. Dismantle in sequence given in Figs. E.8 or E.9; as applicable, rotating diaphragm 90° to disengage from link lever.

   NOTE:- On some models, the valves are secured in the upper body by peening. In this case the valve retainer plate (9, Fig.E.8) is omitted.

2. Clean all parts and inspect for damage and deterioration. Renew parts as necessary.

3. Re-assemble by reversing the sequence. Ensure valves are installed pointing in correct direction on early type pump (10, Fig.E.8).

STROMBERG 150 CD CARBURETTORS (Fig.E.11)
Removal

1. Remove air cleaner (see 'AIR CLEANER').

2. Disconnect fuel pipe sleeves (30), vacuum pipe and throttle and choke controls.

3. Remove four nuts (72), washers and carburettors together with gaskets (14) and insulators (15).

Installation

NOTE:- If couplings (36 and 33) have been disturbed, leave clamping bolts (34 and 65) loose and proceed as in 3 and 4.

1. Ensure mating faces are clean, position carburettors on manifold studs with new gaskets (14) and insulators (15) and secure with nuts.

2. Reconnect fuel and vacuum pipes.

3. Turn both starter bar spindles (26) until lifting edges contact bottom of air valves and tighten bolt (34).

4. Turn back throttle stop screw (27) at both carburettors until throttle valves are fully closed and tighten bolts (65).

5. Connect throttle and choke controls.

6. Install air cleaner.

7. Carry out idling adjustments if necessary.

Dismantling

1. Release clamp bolts (65 and 34) and separate carburettors.

2. Remove dampers (12) and drain oil.

3. Scribe locating marks at edges of chamber cover (5) and body, remove screws (3) and cover with spring (6). Detach diaphragm from top cover if necessary.

4. Withdraw air valve/diaphragm assembly carefully to avoid damaging needle (11, Fig.E.12).

5. Remove four screws (10) to separate diaphragm (8) retaining ring (7) and air valve (9). Loosen screw (10) to release needle (II).

6. Unscrew bushing screw assembly (41 and 48, Fig.E.13).

7. Remove screws (42 and 43) to remove float chamber cover (44) and gasket (53).

8. Remove jet assembly (49,50,54,55,56 and 57, Fig.E.13).

9. Remove pin (45) and float assembly (46) and unscrew needle valve (51) with washer (52).

10. Remove throttle stop (21) with screw and spring from spindle (29).

11. Straighten lockplate (63) and remove coupling nut (64), unhook spring (20) remove stop lever (62) and spring from spindle.

12. Remove screws (17) and withdraw butterfly (16) from spindle and spindle from body.

13. Straighten lockplate (68), remove coupling nut (67), choke cam lever (71) with lever (23) and spring (69) attached, and remove return spring (25).

14. Remove starter bar spindle (26) from body and extract circlip (32).

15. Extract spring (38) and remove air valve lifting pin (37) and spring (39).

Inspection

1. Clean all parts and examine for wear and damage.

2. Renew "O"-rings (40), (47) and (55).

Re-assembly

1. Fit pin (37) and spring (39) into body and secure by springing clip (38) over pin.

1. Clip
2. Screw
3. Strap
4. Clip
5. Connector
6. Bolt

Fig.E.7   Fuel tank installation - GT6

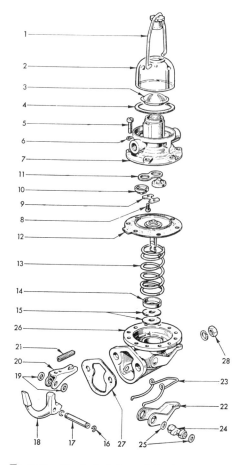

Fig.E.8   Exploded view of the fuel pump -
Early type

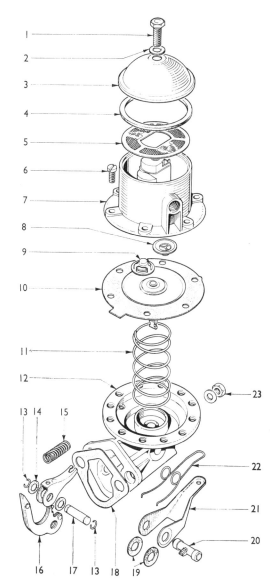

1. Retaining screw
2. Washer
3. Cover
4. Joint
5. Gauze
6. Screw
7. Body
8. Inlet valve
9. Outlet valve
10. Diaphragm assembly
11. Diaphragm spring
12. Lower body
13. Circlip
14. Distance washer
15. Return spring
16. Rocker arm
17. Rocker arm pin
18. Gasket
19. Cork seals
20. Primer lever shaft
21. Primer lever
22. Primer lever spring
23. Pump securing nut

1. Stirrup
2. Sediment bowl
3. Filter gauze
4. Cork seal
5. Screw
6. Spring washer
7. Upper body
8. Retaining plate screw
9. Retaining plate
10. Valve assemblies
11. Valve gasket
12. Diaphragm assembly
13. Diaphragm spring
14. Cup
15. Washers
16. Circlip
17. Rocker arm pin
18. Rocker arm
19. Distance washers
20. Link lever
21. Rocker arm spring
22. Primer lever
23. Primer lever spring
24. Primer lever shaft
25. Cork seals
26. Lower body
27. Pump gasket
28. Pump retainer nut

Fig.E.9   Exploded view of the fuel pump -
Late type

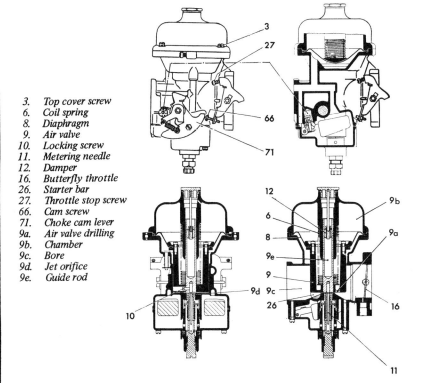

3. Top cover screw
6. Coil spring
8. Diaphragm
9. Air valve
10. Locking screw
11. Metering needle
12. Damper
16. Butterfly throttle
26. Starter bar
27. Throttle stop screw
66. Cam screw
71. Choke cam lever
9a. Air valve drilling
9b. Chamber
9c. Bore
9d. Jet orifice
9e. Guide rod

Fig.E.10 Functional diagram of the Stromberg 150 CD carburettor

Fig.E.12 Details of the air valve assembly - Stromberg (See Fig.E.11 for key).

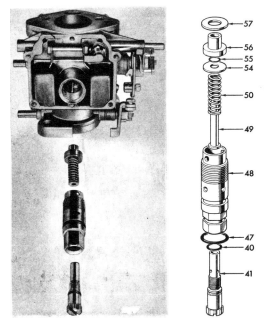

Fig.E.13 Details of the jet assembly - Stromberg (see Fig.E.11 for key)

Fig.E.14 Checking the float level - Stromberg (See Fig.E.11 for key)

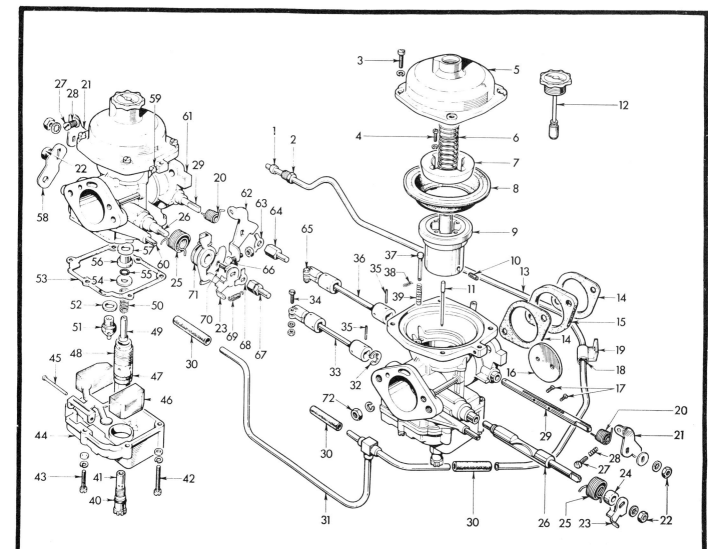

Fig.E.11 Exploded view of the Stromberg 150 CD carburettors

1. Sleeve
2. Nut
3. Top cover screw
4. Screw
5. Top cover
6. Coil spring
7. Retaining ring
8. Diaphragm
9. Air valve
10. Locking screw
11. Needle
12. Damper
13. Pipe
14. Gasket
15. Insulator
16. Butterfly throttle valve
17. Screws
18. Grommet
19. Bracket
20. Spring
21. Throttle stop lever
22. Nuts
23. Lever
24. Bush

25. Return spring
26. Starter bar spindle
27. Throttle stop screw
28. Spring
29. Throttle spindle
30. Fuel pipe connector
31. Pipe
32. Circlip
33. Coupling
34. Clamping bolt
35. Pin
36. Coupling
37. Air valve lifting pin
38. Spring clip
39. Spring
40. 'O'-ring
41. Orifice adjusting screw
42. Screw (long)
43. Screw (Short)
44. Float chamber cover
45. Fulcrum pin
46. Float assembly
47. 'O'-ring
48. Bushing screw

49. Jet
50. Spring
51. Needle valve
52. Washer
53. Gasket
54. Washer
55. 'O'-ring
56. Bushing
57. Washer
58. Connecting link
59. Screw
60. Petrol, inlet
61. Body
62. Stop lever
63. Lockplate
64. Coupling nut
65. Clamping bolt
66. Cam screw
67. Coupling nut
68. Lockplate
69. Spring
70. Cam screw
71. Choke cam lever
72. Nut

2. Fit circlip (32) in end groove and insert starter bar spindle (26) into body with flat side upwards.

3. With larger coils leading, position spring (25) on spindle boss with spring ends at each side of fuel pipe connection.

4. Assemble cam lever assembly (71) on spindle with cam next to spring, locate lever (23) on flats of spindle and engage end of spring (25) in slot on lever. Fit lockplate (68), assemble and lock coupling nut (67) and attach spring (69) to levers (23 and 71).

5. Insert spindle (29) into carburettor with countersinks, upwards, fit valve (16) into spindle slot with pipe upwards and secure with screws (17).

6. Place spring (20) on throttle spindle boss, close butterfly valve and assemble stop lever (62) on flats of spindle with spring engaged to load valve in closed position. Fit lockplate (63) and tighten and lock coupling nut (64).

7. Assemble stop lever (21) and link (58) to opposite end of spindle and secure with nut and washer.

8. Screw needle valve (57) with aluminium washer (52) firmly into body.

9. Secure float assembly (46) in position with pin (45). Invert carburettor and check that highest point of float with needle against its seating is 18.00 mm (0.71 in.) above main body face (see "A" Fig.E.14). If required, reset level by carefully bending needle abutment tag. A thin fibre washer under needle valve seat will lower fuel level.

10. Fit new "O"-ring (55) in bush (56), fit spring (50) and washer (54) on jet (49) and insert into bush. Fit aluminium washer (57) over bush and install assembly into body. With new "O"-rings (47 and 40) fitted, screw adjuster (41) into bushing screw (48) three turns, bushing screw into body one turn back from finger tight and visually centralize jet (Fig.E.13).

11. With new gasket (53) assemble float chamber (44) to body, first loosely fitted screws (42 and 43) and fully tightening after chamber has been pressed against gasket (Fig.E.15).

12. Position diaphragm (8) on shoulder of air valve (9) with inner locating tab in top face recess and screw on retaining ring (7) (Fig.E.16).

13. Insert needle (11) shoulder deep into air valve bore and secure with screw (10).

14. Carefully insert needle into jet and air valve into body and locate diaphragm outer tab in recess on body flange (see arrows in Fig.E.16).

15. Position spring (6) and cover (5) on valve stem, align scribe marks and secure cover with screws (3).

16. Replenish damper and install damper assembly (12).

Jet Centralising Procedure (Fig.E.13)

Efficient operation of the carburettor requires a freely moving air valve and a correctly centred needle in the jet valve.

Remove air cleaner and check by lifting and releasing the air valve as shown in Fig.E.17. A valve failing to fall freely indicates a sticking valve or off-centre jet. Rectify the former by removing valve and cleaning bore and valve in paraffin, and the latter by centralising the jet as follows:-

1. Lift air valve and fully tighten bushing screw (48).

2. Screw-up orifice adjuster (41) until top of orifice is just above bridge.

3. Slacken bushing screw to release orifice bush (56).

4. Allow air valve to fall and needle to enter and centralise orifice.

5. Slowly tighten bushing screw, frequently checking that needle is free in orifice by raising air valve (9) 6.3 mm (0.25 in.) and allowing to fall freely. Valve should stop firmly on bridge.

6. Proceed as in "Idling Adjustment".

Idling Adjustment (Fig.E.18)

NOTE:- Satisfactory idling depends on general engine condition as well as tappet adjustment, spark plug condition and ignition timing, and the latter points should be checked if idling is unstable.

1. Ensure screw /66) is set to give gap of 1.58 mm (0.062 in.) at choke lever cam (71) and set throttle stop screw (27) one complete turn back from contact with body flange.

2. Bring engine to normal working temperature, remove air cleaner, hold air valve down onto bridge through throttle bore, and with a coin turn jet adjustment screw until jet contacts bottom of air valve. From this position turn down adjustment screw three turns to establish a jet position from which to work.

3. Run engine until thoroughly warm and adjust stop screw (27) to give idling speed of 600/650 r.p.m.

4. Turning jet adjustment screw clockwise to weaken mixture and anti-clockwise to enrich, adjust until engine beat is smooth and regular. Check by lifting air valve a small amount 0.8 mm (0.030 in. approx.) with piston lifting pin. Properly adjusted, engine speed will remain constant or fall slightly. If engine speed rises appreciably mixture is too rich, and if engine stops it is too weak.

SOLEX CARBURETTORS (Early Vitesse Six):

The semi-downdraught Solex carburettor fitted to early models is illustrated in Fig.E.19. An accelerator pump was initially fitted but this was later deleted.

STROMBERG 150 CDSE CARBURETTORS (G.T.6 - plus)

The stromberg C.D.S.E. (Emission) carburettors installed on the G.T.6 - plus are built and installed to stringent anti-pollution requirements. Special procedures and equipment are necessary for assembly, installation and tuning which must

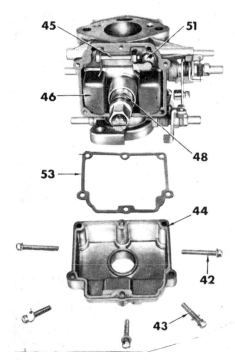

Fig.E.16 Details of the diaphragm assembly -
Stromberg (See Fig.E.11 for key)

Fig.E.15 Details of the float chamber assembly-
Stromberg (See Fig.E.11 for key)

Fig.E.17 Checking the jet for centring by
lifting the air valve - Stromberg

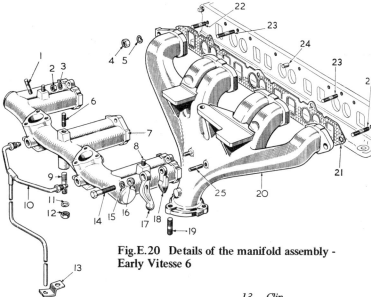

Fig.E.20 Details of the manifold assembly -
Early Vitesse 6

Fig.E.18 Choke and throttle adjustment screws -
Stromberg (See Fig.E.11 for key)

1.	Stud - carburettor	13.	Clip
2.	Nut	14.	Bolt
3.	Spring washer	15.	Spring washer
4.	Nut	16.	Coned washer
5.	Spring washer	17.	Clamp
6.	Stud	18.	Clamp pivot
7.	Inlet manifold	19.	Stud - exhaust flange
8.	Stud	20.	Exhaust manifold
9.	Stud - inlet to exhaust manifold	21.	Gasket
10.	Drain pipe	22.	Stud
11.	Spring washer	23.	Stud
12.	Nut	24.	Dowel
		25.	Stud - air cleaner bracket

1. Rear carburettor
2. Front carburettor
3. Fuel hose
4. Choke cable - inner
5. Choke cable - outer
6. Coupling assembly
7. Coupling rod
8. Plain washer
9. Nut
10. Spring coupling
11. Pinch bolt
12. Screw and spring washer
13. Top cover
14. Gasket
15. Fibre washer
16. Needle valve
17. Econostat air bleed
18. Pivot pin
19. Float assembly
20. Econostat jet
21. Carburettor body
22. Air correction jet
23. Emulsion tube
24. Idling mixture air bleed jet
25. Idling mixture fuel jet
26. Spring
27. Idling mixture adjusting screw
28. Jet block
29. Fibre washer
30. Main jet
31. Main jet carrier
32. Screw
33. Gasket
34. Starter jet
35. Fibre washer
36. Gasket
37. Insulation gasket
38. Gasket
39. Throttle disc
40. Screws
41. Throttle spindle
42. Spring
43. Throttle stop screw
44. Disc valve
45. Starter body
46. Circlip
47. Starter body cover
48. Inter-connecting cable locking
    screw
49. Circlip
50. Choke outer cable locking screw
51. Swivel
52. Circlip
53. Choke inner cable locking screw
54. Nut
55. Starter lever
56. Bolt
57. Ball
58. Spring
59. Swivel

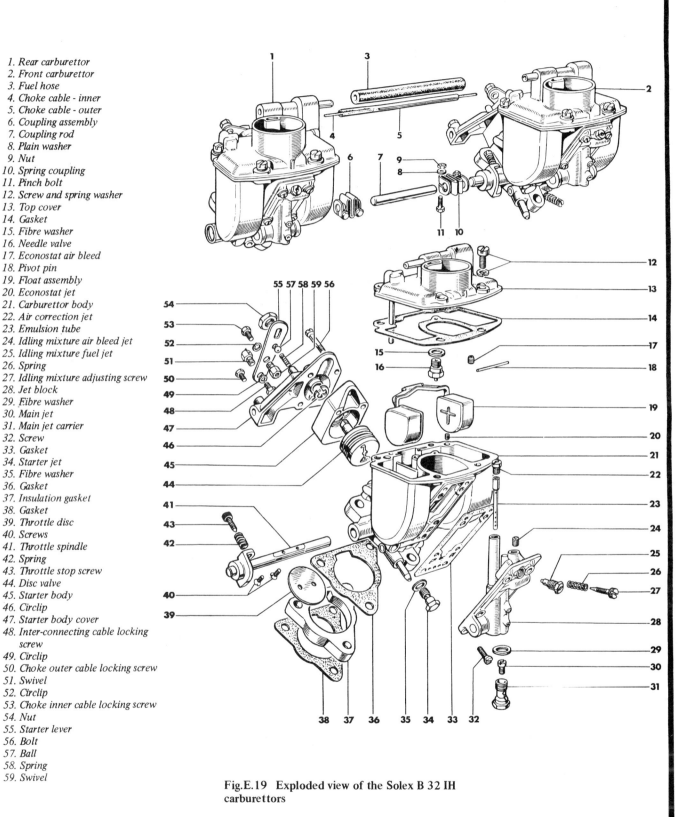

Fig.E.19 Exploded view of the Solex B 32 IH
carburettors

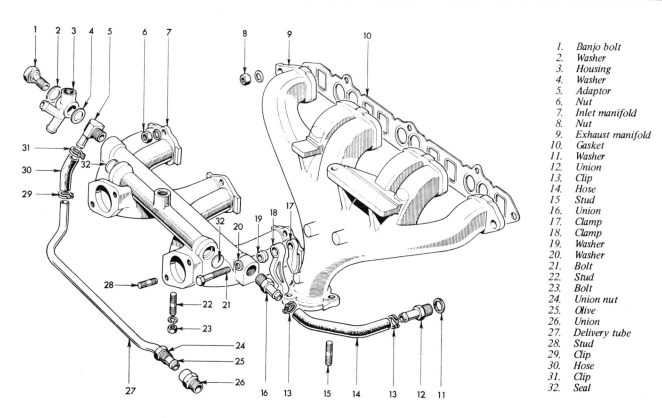

1. Banjo bolt
2. Washer
3. Housing
4. Washer
5. Adaptor
6. Nut
7. Inlet manifold
8. Nut
9. Exhaust manifold
10. Gasket
11. Washer
12. Union
13. Clip
14. Hose
15. Stud
16. Union
17. Clamp
18. Clamp
19. Washer
20. Washer
21. Bolt
22. Stud
23. Bolt
24. Union nut
25. Olive
26. Union
27. Delivery tube
28. Stud
29. Clip
30. Hose
31. Clip
32. Seal

Fig.E.21   Details of the manifold assembly

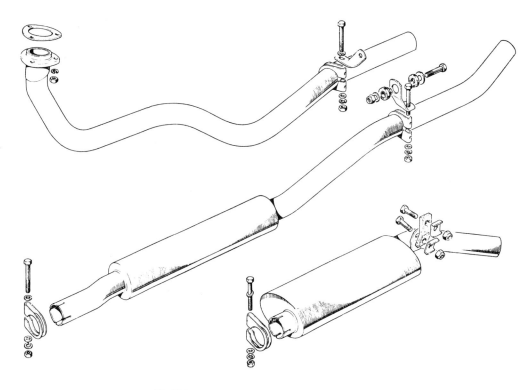

Fig.E.22   Exhaust system assembly - GT6 Mk 1

be carried out by authorised personnel. Servicing by non-authorised persons is therefore limited to maintenance of damper oil level, control cables and attachments.

On models with full emission control it is particularly important that associated routine maintenance such as on the distributor, spark plugs, valve rocker clearances, air cleaner and fuel filter should be meticulously carried out.

MANIFOLD AND EXHAUST SYSTEMS

Figs. E.20 - E.24 give details and variants of the manifolds and exhaust systems and should be used for removal and installation operations.

EMISSION CONTROL SYSTEM

Since 1968, all vehicles produced for the North American market must embody an exhaust emission control system which conforms to the Federal Regulations. In the case of the Triumph GT6 models, maximum exhaust emission limits are:-

Hydrocarbons - 350 parts per million
Carbon monoxide - 2 per cent by volume

Virtually no hydrocarbon emission is allowed from the crankcase; this necessitates the fitting of a control valve between the crankcase and the induction manifold.

Modifications to the Triumph GT6 to bring it within the requirements are:-

1. Exhaust valves.

   To maintain effective valve seating between servicing intervals, Stellite faced exhaust valves are fitted.

2. Cylinder head.

   A modified cylinder head, giving a compression ratio of 8.5 : 1, is fitted.

3. Camshaft

   To give better control of emissions during idling and low speed crusing, a new camshaft is fitted, and this has 10 - 50-50 - 10 timing.

4. Ignition distributor.

   A special distributor is fitted. In addition to the usual mechanical and vacuum advance control, it has provision for retarding the ignition at idling speeds and during acceleration by means of a double acting system.

5. Carburettors.

   Twin Stromberg C.D.S.E. (Emission) carburettors are fitted. This is shown in exploded view in Fig.E.28. For controlling emission, the following features are incorporated in this type of carburettor.

   a) Fixed, non-adjustable jet assembly, and a bias needle, so achieving consistent air/fuel ratio.

   b) A leak balancing screw to enable all carburettors to be set to a common datum, during manufacture. The screw is sealed to prevent interference, once it has been set during manufacture.

   c) A temperature compensator assembly which progressively opens at high engine temperature, so as to correct the mixture and restore even running.

   d) A throttle by-pass valve which is set to open at a predetermined manifold depression to admit air during deceleration.

   e) To discourage unauthorised interference, the cover is wire-locked and sealed.

6. Air cleaners.

   Special air cleaners are fitted. These have additional holes to match with those provided in the emission carburettor flanges.

7. Choke cables.

   A single control cable integrates the action of two separate and independently adjustable choke cables.

8. Accelerator linkage.

   This is modified so as to provide a positive idle stop. It also incorporates a 'lost motion' movement for operating a vacuum control valve when the throttles are closed.

9. A vacuum control valve is connected to, and operated by, the accelerator linkage so as to permit normal vacuum ignition advancement under part throttle opening. Releasing the accelerator pedal allows full manifold depression to operate on the distributor and so retard the ignition.

10. Crankcase Emission Control Valve.

    Pipes connect the inlet side of this valve to the engine crankcase and the outlet side to the induction manifold giving a uni-directional flow of crankcase fumes from the former to the latter. By this means, crankcase fumes are consumed by the engine, yet satisfactory performance is achieved.

11. Spark plugs.

    To improve combustion, Champion UN.12Y spark plugs are fitted.

12. Rigid metal pipes are used to connect the various units of the emission control system.

    Although very sophisticated equipment is used at the factory to set the emission control units, the commercial equipment possessed by most garages is adequate for all normal procedures. Only when a malfunction occurs (generally indicated by severe deterioration in performance or misfiring) should the system need attention. Routine maintenance as already given should be carried out at the set intervals, and will maintain the system without specialised attention.

    The procedures relating the emission control which follow are intended for the specialist or authorised Triumph Dealer, and should not be attempted by others.

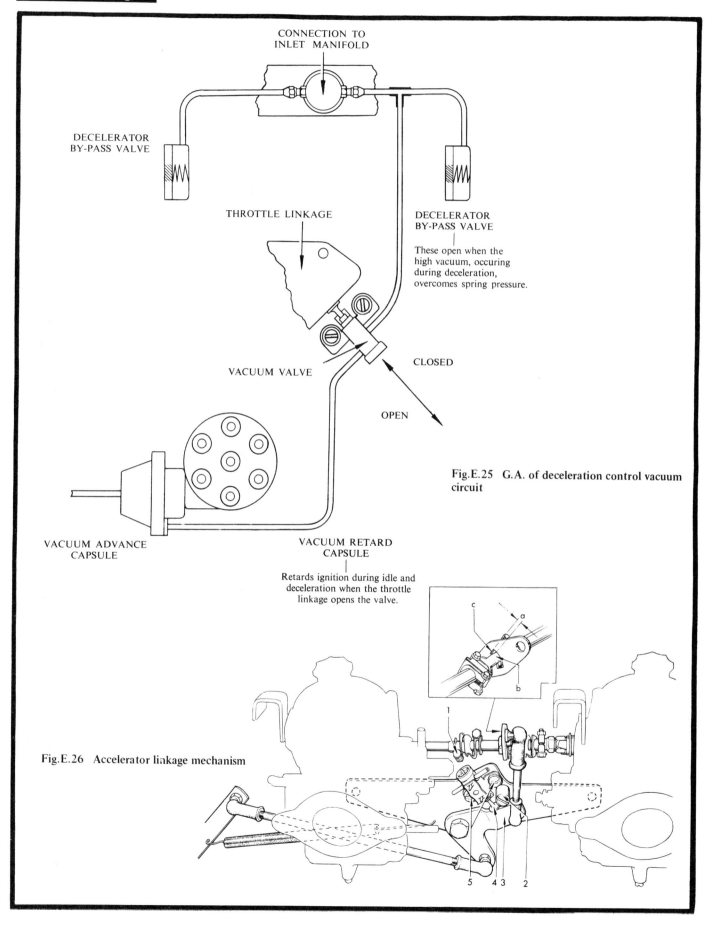

CONNECTION TO
INLET MANIFOLD

DECELERATOR
BY-PASS VALVE

THROTTLE LINKAGE

DECELERATOR
BY-PASS VALVE

These open when the
high vacuum, occuring
during deceleration,
overcomes spring pressure.

CLOSED

VACUUM VALVE

OPEN

Fig.E.25 G.A. of deceleration control vacuum
circuit

VACUUM ADVANCE
CAPSULE

VACUUM RETARD
CAPSULE

Retards ignition during idle and
deceleration when the throttle
linkage opens the valve.

c   a

b

1

Fig.E.26 Accelerator linkage mechanism

5   4 3   2

SERVICE PROCEDURE
Cylinder compression

Gas tightness of the valves and combustion chamber is very important in the emission control system. At 6,000 mile intervals, the compression per cylinder should be tested in the following manner:-

a) With the engine at operating temperature, and a fully charged battery; apply the handbrake, position the gearshift in neutral, and remove all the spark plugs.

b) Wedge the accelerator pedal in the fully depressed position to open the throttles widely.

c) Insert the compression tester into No. 1 cylinder plug hole, operate the solenoid start button and hold in position for two or three seconds, so as the revolve the engine six times. Observe the compression pressure generated.

d) Repeat the procedure on the other cylinders in turn. All cylinders should indicate a compression pressure within five pounds per square inch of one another.

e) If unsatisfactory readings are obtained, remedial action must be taken.
The foregoing service procedure coincides with that for cleaning and adjusting the spark plugs, so both can be undertaken at the same time.

Ignition distributor

A double-acting vacuum capsule, which operates in opposite directions to either advance or retard the ignition is provided for the distributors fitted to the GT6 engines.

The position of the vacuum valve which is operated by the accelerator linkage shown in Fig.E.25 determines the directional control of the vacuum retard capsule. A conventional manifold depression tapping determines the directional control of the vacuum advance capsule.

The body of the distributor has to be turned if adjustment is required, and a separate vernier adjustment is not provided. Fuels with similar octane ratings should therefore be used.

Maintenance

Every 6,000 miles. Lubricate the distributor sparingly, and adjust or renew the contact breaker points as necessary.

Every 12,000 miles. In addition to the 6,000 mile service, check the ignition timing at 800 to 850 r.p.m. (idling speed).

Accelerator linkage

Rods and levers connect the accelerator pedal to the carburettor throttles.

The features which follow are incorporated in the system.

1. Carburettor inter-connection (Fig.E. 26).

The throttle spindles of both carburettors are connected by a centre rod arrangement which has spring couplings at each end, and mid-way between an operating lever system which provides sufficient free movement of the linkage so as to allow the vacuum valve to open or close while the throttles remain closed. The function of this free movement is to permit fast idling without disturbing the closed position of the accelerator linkage.

Relay lever assembly

A bracket attached to the carburettor inner attachment studs provides a mounting for the relay lever. This bracket also accommodates the vacuum valve and throttle stop. See Fig. E.26 which shows the positions of these items.

Setting the accelerator linkage and slow-running controls

Normally, the linkage does not require adjustment, which only becomes necessary if the carburettors have been removed or the linkage has been disturbed. When necessary, proceed as follows.

a) Slacken the clamp bolts (Item 1 Fig.E.26) on both spring couplings, to isolate both throttle spindles.

b) On each carburettor, unscrew the slow-running screw so as to ensure that both throttle valves are competely closed. Then, open the throttles by an equal amount, by moving each stop screw one and a half turns. This provides a basis from which to set the final idling speed. Note: Fast-idle screw (Fig.E.27) must be clear of cam (6), and both cold start levers must be against their stops with the panel control pushed in. If necessary, adjust the controls to make this possible.

c) Run the engine until it reaches operating temperature. Measure the air intake of both carburettors; this must be in balance, and the slow-running screws must be adjusted accordingly at the correct idling speed. When balance has been achieved, stop the engine.

d) Check that the accelerator linkage is assembled as shown in Fig.E.26. Insert the shank of a 1/16" drill in the space (a) between the tongue of the lever (b) and the edge of the lever slot (c), see inset in Fig.E.26. With the drill held between these points and the relay lever (3) against the stop cam (2), tighten both spring coupling bolts (1) and remove the drill.

e) Slacken the vacuum valve securing screws (5) and move the valve body towards the relay lever until the operating plunger is fully depressed (open position). Tighten the securing screws and check the operation as follows.

f) Slowly operate the accelerator linkage until the tongue (b) contacts the edge of the lever slot (c). At this point, the valve plunger (4) should have reached the end of its stroke (fully closed) and the throttles should be about to open.

Setting the fast idling (Fig.E.27)

a) Ensure that the choke lever (6) on each carburettor bears against its stop when the choke control knob on the fascia

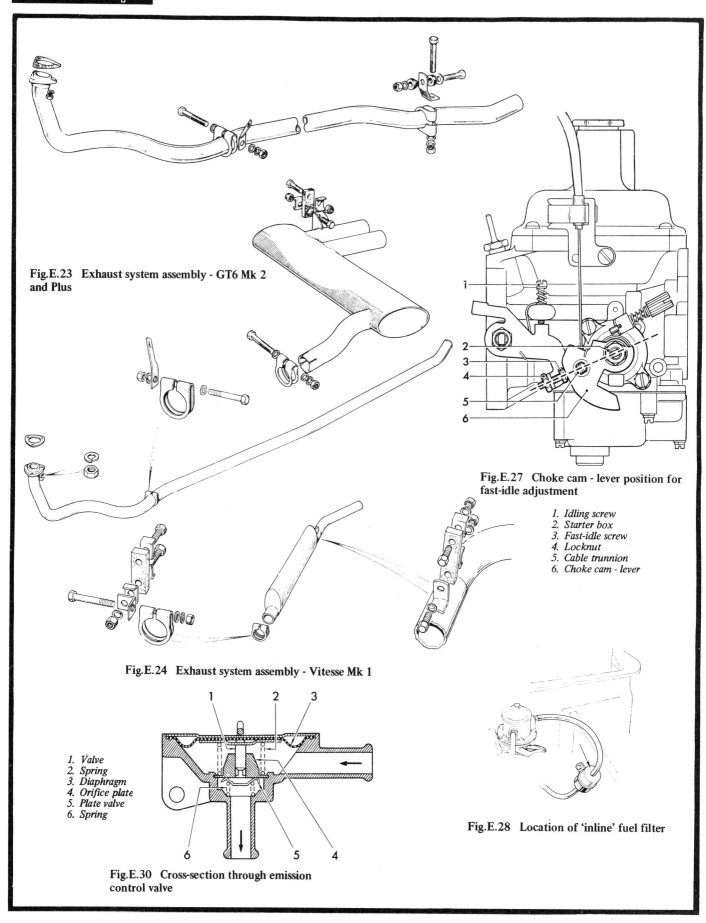

Fig.E.23   Exhaust system assembly - GT6 Mk 2
and Plus

Fig.E.27   Choke cam - lever position for
fast-idle adjustment

1. *Idling screw*
2. *Starter box*
3. *Fast-idle screw*
4. *Locknut*
5. *Cable trunnion*
6. *Choke cam - lever*

Fig.E.24   Exhaust system assembly - Vitesse Mk 1

1. *Valve*
2. *Spring*
3. *Diaphragm*
4. *Orifice plate*
5. *Plate valve*
6. *Spring*

Fig.E.28   Location of 'inline' fuel filter

Fig.E.30   Cross-section through emission
control valve

is pushed fully in. The cable must be adjusted to this condition, if necessary.

b) Pull the control on the fascia out sufficiently enough to bring the cable trunnion (5) into alignment with the centre of the fast-idle adjusting screw (3) and the centre of the starter box (2). Slacken the locknuts (4) and unscrew both fast-idle screws until each is just contacting the cam.

c) Run the engine and while it is still cool (68 to 86°F), adjust the fast-idle screws (3) in equal increments to give a tachometer reading speed of 1,100 rpm.

d) Tighten the locknuts. Recheck the fast-idle speed. If satisfied, push the control on the fascia fully home, and stop the engine.

STROMBERG C.D.S.E. (Emission) CARBURETTORS

It must be emphasised that these carburettors have been built to very fine manufacturing limits, and subsequently adjusted at the factory on very sophisticated equipment. Consequently, the extent of permissible service is restricted to the following operations.

Adjustments

Only three adjustments can be made in servicing procedures. These are:-

1. Idling speed. This is adjusted at the throttle stop screw.

2. Idle emission. This is adjusted by trimming screw, and necessitates the use of a C.O. meter or similar equipment.

3. Fast idling. This is adjusted by the fast-idle screw.

Carburettor servicing schedules

The carburettors can only be maintained at peak performance if they are serviced regularly at the 6,000 mile intervals. It is therefore essential that the operations detailed here should be undertaken at the times stated.

At the first 1,000 miles

This is the free service undertaken by the Dealer, and consists of:-

a) Topping up the dashpots with engine oil to within a quarter of an inch of the centre rod.

b) Checking, and if necessary, adjusting the slow-running by turning the slow-running adjustment screws in equal increments to maintain balance. This adjustment may also call for the adjustment of the trimming screw.

c) The idle trimming screw is fitted to give extremely fine adjustment to compensate for the difference between a new stiff engine and one that has been run-in. IT IS NOT AN ORDINARY MIXTURE ADJUSTING SCREW. Its function is to regulate a limited amount of air that can be introduced into the mixing chamber. No difference between the fully home and fully open position of this screw can

be detected by listening to the carburettor or engine; because of this, the setting must be checked by means of a C.O. meter or an air/fuel ratio instrument attached to the exhaust tail pipe. (See the table at the end of this section).

At 6,000 mile intervals

The operations listed under (a) and (b) in the foregoing paragraph should be undertaken at 6,000 mile intervals.

At 12,000 mile intervals (Fig.E.28)

The 'inline' fuel filter must be changed in the following manner. Slacken the bolt attaching the filter clip to the valance panel, and disconnect the rubber pipes to the filter. Fit a new filter, and ensure that the inlet side faces downwards towards the fuel flow.

At 24,000 mile intervals

This service necessitates the use of a Red Emission Pack 'B' which will be found to contain:-

Two float chamber gaskets (Red).
Two 'O'-rings.
Two needle valves
Two diaphragms
Four throttle spindles
Four temperature compression seals.
Two by-pass valve body gaskets.

A 'Pozidrive' screwdriver will be needed to remove the screws with special heads. Refer to Fig.E.29 and service the carburettor as follows:-

Float chamber

NOTE:- The parts of the carburettor must not be intermixed.

a) Unbolt both carburettors from the manifold and separate them. Unscrew the centre brass plug (70) and drain off the fuel. Unscrew the damper (15) from the top of the carburettor and drain the oil from the dashpot.

b) Take out the float chamber screws (68) and (69) and withdraw the float chamber (65) vertically from the body. Detach the float-chamber gaskets (62), unclip the float pivot pin (61) and take out the floats (64). Unscrew the needle valve (63) from the float-chamber cover and remove the 'O'-ring (71) from the centre plug.

c) All parts which have been removed and are not being renewed should be cleaned thoroughly. Using the new washer from the pack, securely screw the needle valve in position.

d) Inspect the float for serviceability. Rectify any damage or distortion, and then refit the float assembly. Slide in the pivot pin, and clip the assembly in position. Ensure the correct fuel level by inverting the instrument so that the tag closes the needle valve, and measure the distance from the face of the cover (with the gasket removed) to the highest point of each float. It should be 16 to 17 mm.

1. Carburettor
2. Spring - idle trimming screw
3. Idle trimming screw
4. Gasket - by pass valve
5. By-pass valve
6. Lockwasher under (7)
7. Screw - securing (5)
8. Temperature compensator unit
9. Lockwasher under (10)
10. Screw - securing (8)
11. Cover - temperature compensator
12. Screw - securing (11)
13. Seal - on compensator body
14. Seal - inside carburettor
15. Damper rod
16. Washer
17. Distance sleeve
18. Circlip
19. Cover - air valve
20. Screws - securing (19)
21. Spring - air valve return
22. Ring - diaphragm attachment
23. Screw - securing (22) (24)
24. Diaphragm
25. Air valve
26. Screw - securing (27)
27. Needle assembly
28. Spring - idle adjusting screw
29. Idling adjusting screw
30. Throttle disc
31. Screw - securing (30)
32. Seal - throttle spindle
33. Throttle spindle
34. Spring - throttle return
35. Lever - throttle
36. Screw - fast idle
37. Locknut - securing (36)
38. Lockwasher - retaining (39)
39. Nut - throttle spindle
40. Coupling - throttle spindles
41. Connecting lever assembly
42. Clamping bolt
43. Washer - under (42)
44. Nut - securing (42)
45. Nut
46. Shakeproof washer
47. Washer
48. Lever
49. Screw - cable attachment
50. Return spring
51. Screw
52. Shakeproof washer
53. Starter box cover
54. Spring
55. Spindle
56. Retainer
57. Valve plate
58. Cable abutment bracket
59. Spring clip
60. Screw - securing (58)
61. Float pivot pin
62. Gasket - float chamber
63. Needle valve
64. Float assembly
65. Float chamber cover
66. Washer - under (68/69)
67. Spring washer - under (68/69)
68. Screw - securing (65)
69. Screw - securing (65)
70. Plug
71. Rubber "O" ring for (70)

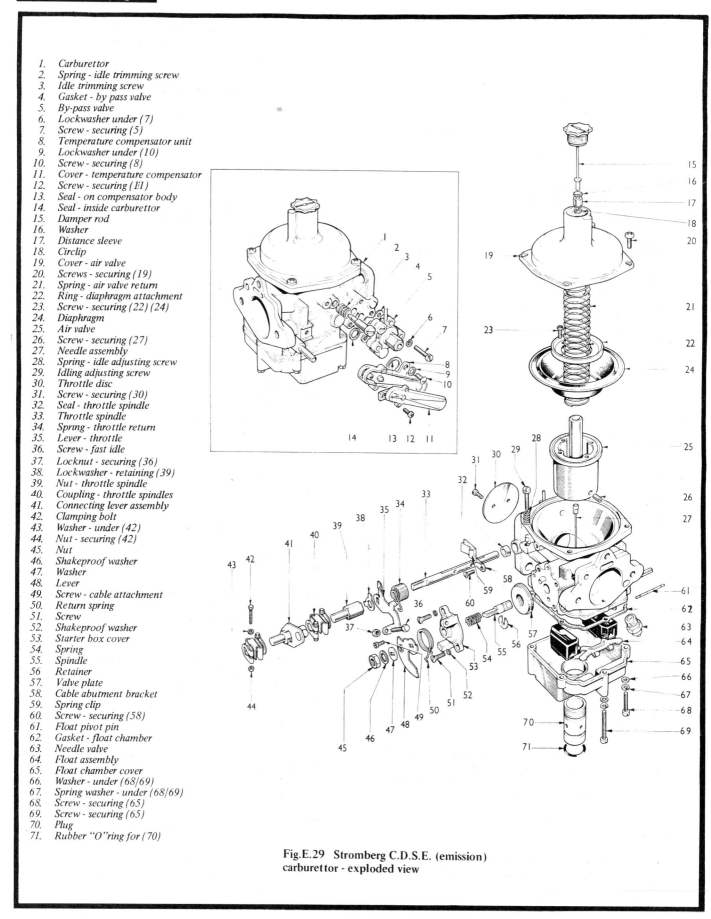

Fig.E.29 Stromberg C.D.S.E. (emission)
carburettor - exploded view

e) Position a new gasket from the pack, and refit the float chamber. Tighten the retaining screws securely from the centre outwards. Fit a new 'O'-ring to the centre plug and screw this tightly into position.

f) Position new gaskets, and refit both carburettors to the manifold. Inject engine oil into the dashpots to within a quarter of an inch of the top of the centre rod, and then refit the dampers. Connect the controls, and reset the carburettors as previously described.

Air valve assembly

a) Unscrew and remove the damper rod (15), unscrew the four cover screws (20), and carefully lift off the cover (19). Remove the air valve return spring (21), lift out the air valve (25), and drain the oil from the guide rod. Slacken the metering needle clamp screw (26) and withdraw the needle (27). Lay aside carefully so as not to damage or bend it.

b) Remove the four diaphragm retaining screws (23), ring (22) and diaphragm (24). Position a new diaphragm on the air valve, locating its tag in the recess provided. Now fit the ring, and secure firmly by tightening the four screws.

c) Check that there is spring action in the housing at the top of the metering needle shank (27), insert it into the base of the air valve lining up the flat portion with the locking screw (26). Using a narrow straight-edge (1" wide) placed against the needle shoulder, push the needle into the air valve until the straight-edge aligns the shoulder with the flat face inside the flange formed on the outer edge of the air valve. Note: This position is extremely critical. Gently tighten the locking screw so as to avoid crushing the needle biasing spring housing. When correctly fitted, the needle is biased towards the throttle and the shoulder of the needle is exactly flush with the air valve face.

d). Using great care, enter the air valve and diaphragm assembly into the main body guiding the metering needle into the jet with a finger in the air intake. Locate the outer tag of the diaphragm in a corresponding aperture on top of the body and look down the centre of the air valve to ascertain that the two depression transfer holes are towards, and in line with, the throttle spindle. The metering needle should also be biased towards the throttle.

e). Refit the air valve return spring, then holding the air valve with the finger or thumb in the air intake, slide on the cover and locate the screw holes. The damper ventilation boss must be towards the air intake. Insert the four cover screws, tighten them evenly, then check the movement of the air valve. Freedom of movement is essential so that when the air valve is released from its uppermost position, it falls with a sharp metallic click on to the bridge.

Temperature compensator unit

a). Remove the screws (10) and take off the temperature compensator unit (8).

b) Remove the two screws (12) and take off the cover (11). Check for freedom of valve movement by lifting it from its seat. The valve should return freely when released. On

no account strain the bi-metal blade or attempt to alter its tension adjustment. To allow for thermal expansion, there should be consistent radial clearance around the valve.

If offset, slacken the fixing screw and move the blade laterally to centralise the valve. Provided the valve is free, replace the cover (11), and tighten the screw (12).

c) Using the new seals from the pack, replace the inner seal (14) in the carburettor body, and the outer seal (13) on the compensator unit. Refit the unit on the carburettor and tighten the two screws (10).

Throttle spindle seals

a) Take out the three screws (7) and lift off the by-pass valve assembly (5), and gasket (4).

b) Unscrew the throttle spindle nut (39), release the throttle spring (35) and take off the spring (34).

c) Prise out the old throttle spindle seals (32) and replace them with new ones from the pack. (A small hole will be found in the face of the seal to assist removal).

d) Reassemble the spring and the lever to the throttle spindle; and securely tighten and lock the nut (39).

e) Locate a new gasket (4) and refit the by-pass valve to the carburettor body. Then tighten the three screws securely (7).

Installing the carburettors

a) Locate new flange gaskets on the manifold studs. Connect the two carburettors together, and install them on the manifold.

b) Connect all the controls, fill the dashpots with engine oil, as described previously. Reset the carburettors as described under 'Accelerator Linkage'.

Crankcase emission control valve

Refer to Fig.E.30. The valve pin and pressure plate assembly (1) which bears on the diaphragm (3) is located relative to the controlling orifice by the spring (2). The valve pin runs in the orifice plate (4) through guides which allow clearance between the pin and orifice sufficient to prevent sticking and also allow a limited flow through the valve when the engine is idling. The plate valve (5) on the outer side is controlled by the light spring (6).

Application of vacuum sucks the lightly loaded plate valve (5) off its seat so creating a depression beneath the diaphragm (3). As soon as this depression exceeds the force of the diaphragm spring, the valve (1) moves to reduce the controlling orifice until the spring and diaphragm forces balance one another. The diaphragm force is such that when operating, a reasonable depression is maintained in the crankcase. As a precaution against back-fire, the plate valve (5) acts as a non-return valve by isolating the crankcase. In addition, it also limits flow at cold starting.

The oil filler cap is sealed, and ventilation air for the crankcase is drawn through a restrictor hole on the clean air side of the air cleaner unit. This air, combined with any blow-by fumes is drawn via the emission valve into the combustion chamber.

If the blow-by gap fumes exceed the valve capacity, the excess emission reverses the cycle and escapes into the air cleaner unit from where it is drawn into the engine and consumed during combustion.

Servicing the emission control valve
Every 12,000 miles

a) Unfasten all connecting pipes.

b) Slide off the spring clip and remove the cover plate.

c) Lift out the rubber diaphragm (3) noting the correct fitted position of its top face.

d) Take out the valve plate (1) and spring (2).

e) Using clean petrol (gasolene) clean the body, pipes, and all components. Take care to ensure that the diaphragm is kept perfectly clean.

f) Check the free movement of the valve plate (1), and that it is maintained in its upward position by the spring (2).

g) Renew any items found to be defective. Reverse the dismantling process to reassemble. Ensure that the plunger locates correctly in the centre of the guides in the orifice place (4).

Ignition and carburettor settings

Idling speed (rpm).	800/850
Ignition static (approximately)	6º B.T.D.C.
Ignition at idle	4º A.T.D.C.
Idle C.O. level, warm engine	2.5% to 3.5%
Equivalent level air/ fuel ratio at idle (approximately)	13.5 to 1

Technical Data

Fuel Tank Capacity

Vitesse	8.75 Imp. gal. (40.0 litres:10.5 U.S. gal.
G.T.6.	9.75 Imp. gal. (44.3 litres:11.7 U.S. gal.

Pump

Type	A.C. mechanical diaphragm
Pressure	0.1-0.18 kg.s/cm (1.5-2.5 p.s.i.)

Carburettors (Twin)

Vitesse Six, prior to Eng. No. HB 6799	Solex B.32 PIH
Vitesse Six, from Eng. No. HB6799 to HB 27985	Solex B.32 IH
Vitesse Six, from Engine No. HB 27986	Stromberg 150 CD
Vitesse 2 litre, GT6 & Mk 2	Stromberg 150 CD
GT6 - Plus (Emisson Control Model)	Stromberg 150 CDSE

Jet needle (Stromberg)

Vitesse Six	7B
Mk 1 models	6J
Mk 2 models	6AC
G.T.6. - plus	B5AJ
Air cleaner	Paper element

Clutch

GENERAL
ROUTINE MAINTENANCE
CLUTCH UNIT - Removal and Installation
CLUTCH UNIT (VITESSE 2 LITRE/GT6) - Overhaul
CLUTCH UNIT (VITESSE SIX) - Overhaul
MASTER CYLINDER - Removal and Installation
- Overhaul
OPERATING CYLINDER - Removal and Installation
- Overhaul
BLEEDING THE SYSTEM
TECHNICAL DATA

GENERAL

A diaphragm type clutch is used on the Vitesse 2 Litre and GT6 models while the Vitesse 6 is equipped with a coil spring unit. The release mechanism is hydraulically-operated and self adjusting for wear. The clutch master cylinder with an integral hydraulic fluid reservoir is mounted on the engine compartment rear bulkhead immediately over the clutch pedal, and the operating cylinder is located at the right-hand side of the gearbox.

NOTE:- During maintenance, do not permit any dirt or other kind of fluid to enter the system. Clean around and blank all open ports and hoses. Use only fresh unaerated fluid in system.

ROUTINE MAINTENANCE
Monthly

Check fluid level in master cylinder

If necessary top-up to bring level to mark on side of reservoir. Ensure breather hole in cap is clear and investigate abnormal fluid losses.

Every 6,000 miles (10,000 km)

1. Check flexible hose for damage, deterioration and evidence of chafing. Renew if necessary.

2. Check for excessive play in pedal pivot pin or bush, and push rod link pin. Renew parts as necessary.

RELEASE BEARING ASSEMBLY - Overhaul (Fig.F.3)

1. Remove gearbox as detailed in GEARBOX section.

2. Drive pin (17) out of housing and lever (23) and remove lever assembly.

3. Remove operating cylinder attachment bolts and move push rod clear of release lever (1).

4. Disengage lever from pivot pin (2) and withdraw bearing (4) with sleeve (3).

5. Press sleeve from bearing.

6. Examine release bearing for wear and scoring and pivot pin

attachment for security. Renew parts as necessary.

7. Install by reversing removal procedure applying a smear of zinc oxide grease to pivot pin and sleeve.

CLUTCH UNIT - Removal and Installation

1. Remove gearbox as detailed in GEARBOX section.

2. Mark clutch and flywheel to maintain balance on re-assembly.

3. Progressively slacken the six setscrews and lift cover assembly and driven plate from the flywheel.

4. Inspect the flywheel friction face and skim or renew flywheel if necessary (see ENGINE section). Renew clutch plate if excessively worn.

5. With the longer hub boss towards the gearbox, centralise the clutch plate on the flywheel using a sawn-off input shaft or similar tool (Fig.F.4).

6. Locate the cover assembly on the three dowels and secure with the six setscrews tightened evenly, and in turn, to the correct torque. Remove centralising tool.

7. Install gearbox.

CLUTCH UNIT (VITESSE 2 LITRE/GT6) - Overhaul (Fig.F.5).

Due to the specialised knowledge and equipment required, dismantling by unauthorised personnel is not recommended If required, a replacement unit should be obtained.

CLUTCH (VITESSE SIX) - Overhaul (Fig.F.6)

A faulty clutch cover assembly should be renewed complete but, if dismantling should be decided upon, proceed as detailed below using Churchill Kit No. 99A or a press and wooden blocks. (Fig.F.7 and F.8).

Dismantling

1. Mark all parts to ensure re-assembly in original relative positions.

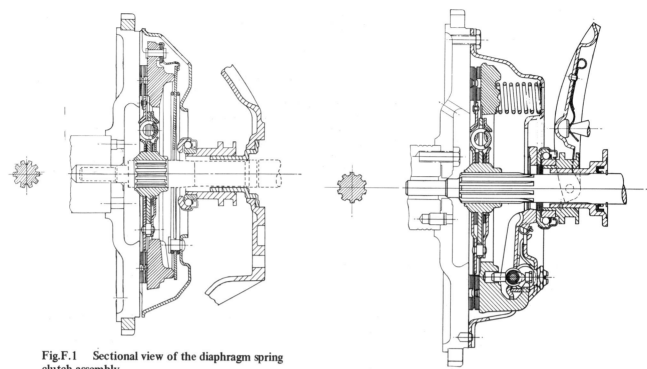

Fig.F.1   Sectional view of the diaphragm spring clutch assembly

Fig.F.2   Sectional view of the coil spring clutch assembly

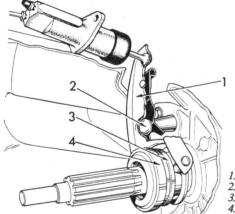

1.   Release lever
2.   Pivot pin
3.   Throwout sleeve
4.   Throwout bearing

Fig.F.3   Details of the clutch release mechanism

Fig.F.4   Centring the clutch unit

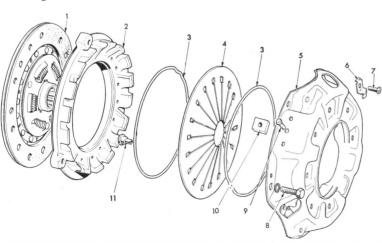

Fig.F.5   Exploded view of the diaphragm spring type clutch assembly

1.   Driven plate
2.   Pressure plate
3.   Fulcrum ring
4.   Diaphragm spring
5.   Cover pressing
6.   Retaining clip
7.   Rivet
8.   Setscrew
9.   Rivet
10.   Balance weight
11.   Rivet

Fig.F.6 Exploded view of the coil spring type
clutch assembly

1. Driven plate
2. Pressure plate
3. Toggle pin
4. Toggle
5. Strut
6. Eyebolt
7. Release lever plate
8. Plate retainer spring
9. Thrust spring
10. Anti-rattle spring
11. Clutch cover
12. Adjusting nut
13. Operating lever
14. Bearing sleeve
15. Release bearing

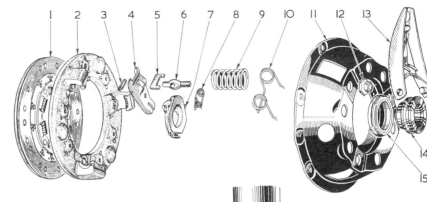

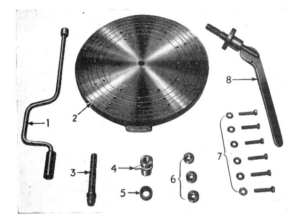

Fig.F.7 Churchill clutch unit assembly fixture,
Tool No. 99A

1. Spanner
2. Baseplate
3. Stud
4. Pointer gauge
5. Adaptor
6. Spacers
7. Attachment set screws and
   washers
8. Release handle

Fig. F.8 Compressing the clutch unit with a
press and wooden blocks.

Fig.F.9 Securing the clutch unit to the assembly
fixture baseplate

Fig.F.10 Gauge finger fitted prior to setting the
release lever height.

Fig.F.11 Checking the run-out at the release plate

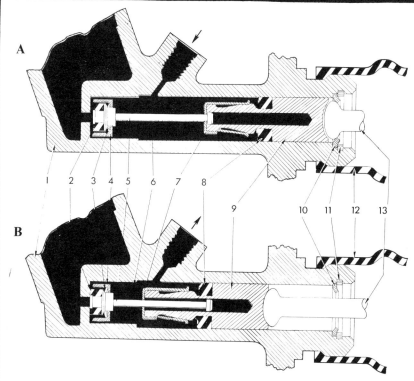

A

B

Fig.F.12   Sectional view of the clutch master cylinder

1.   Cylinder body
2.   Valve seal
3.   Valve seal spring
4.   Distance piece
5.   Valve
6.   Plunger return spring
7.   Retainer
8.   Plunger seal
9.   Plunger
10. Abutment plate
11. Circlip
12. Dust cover
13. Push rod

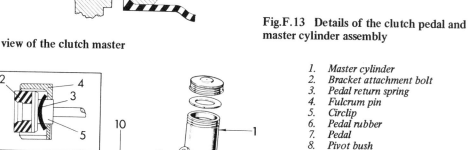

Fig.F.14   Details of the clutch master cylinder

(See Fig.F.12 for key)

Fig.F.13   Details of the clutch pedal and master cylinder assembly

1.   Master cylinder
2.   Bracket attachment bolt
3.   Pedal return spring
4.   Fulcrum pin
5.   Circlip
6.   Pedal rubber
7.   Pedal
8.   Pivot bush
9.   Bracket attachment bolt
10. Pedal bracket
11. Rubber dust excluder
12. Split pin
13. Plain washer
14. Clevis pin
15. Master cylinder bracket
16. Cylinder attachment bolt

Fig.F.15   Operating cylinder installation

1.   Dust cover
2.   Circlip
3.   Piston seal
4.   Bleed valve
5.   Cylinder body
6.   Piston return spring
7.   Piston
8.   Push rod

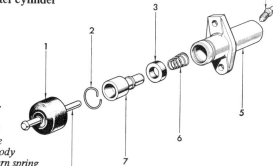

Fig.F.16   Details of the clutch operating cylinder

2. Place unit face down on toolkit baseplate with three spacers underneath at release lever positions.

3. Clamp unit to baseplate with tool operating handle and secure with six setscrews (Fig.E.10). Remove handle.

4. Press down release lever plate (7), detach retaining springs (8) and remove plate.

5. Remove nuts (12).

6. Remove baseplate setscrews evenly and in turn and remove cover (11), toggle levers (4), eyebolts (6), pins (3), struts (5) and springs (9).

7. Remove pressure plate (2).

Inspection

1. Clean all parts and inspect for damage, cracks and scores. Renew parts as necessary.

2. Examine springs and renew if deformed.

3. Set up clutch plate on lathe or surface table and with plunger of dial indicator against friction lining face, check that run-out around face does not exceed 0.23 mm (0.035 in.). Straighten plate if necessary.

4. Examine flywheel clutch face for scores and run-out (see ENGINE section).

Re-assembly

NOTE:- Assemble items in original relative positions.

1. With tool kit distance pieces under release lever positions, position pressure plate (2) on baseplate and assemble springs (9) eyebolts (6), pins (3), struts (5), toggles (4) and springs (10) and secure cover to baseplate with tool kit setscrews.

2. Fit nuts (12) to eyebolts.

3. Fit tool kit items stud (3), adaptor (5) and gauge finger (4) to baseplate (Fig.F.7).

4. Adjust nuts until gauge finger just touches end of each release lever (Fig.F.10).

5. Remove finger gauge assembly, fit tool kit operating lever and operate clutch release several times. Re-check lever height and further adjust if necessary.

6. Fit release plate (7) and secure with springs (8).

7. With dial gauge on baseplate check that release plate run-out does not exceed 0.38 mm (0.015 in.). Re-adjust levers to correct excessive run-out (Fig.F.11).

8. Release clutch with tool kit operating lever, remove setscrews and clutch unit from baseplate.

NOTE:- If press and wooden blocks are used, release plate height must be 53.54 mm (2.18 in.) measured from surface table with 8.38 mm (0.33 in.) gauge plate or spacers in place of clutch plate (see Fig.F.2).

MASTER CYLINDER - Removal and Installation (Fig.E.13).

1. Attach hose from a receptacle to slave cylinder bleed plug, loosen plug and depress clutch pedal until system is drained.

2. Disconnect hydraulic pipe from master cylinder.

3. Pull back rubber (11) and remove pin (14).

4. Remove mounting bolts (16) and cylinder.

5. Reverse procedure to install

6. Fill and bleed system

MASTER CYLINDER - Overhaul (Fig.I.4).

1. Remove cylinder

2. Remove circlip (11) to withdraw push rod (13) and stop (10).

3. Shake or gently blow out plunger and valve assemblies.

4. With small screwdriver lift tag of spring retainer (7) to permit withdrawal from plunger (9).

5. Remove spring retainer by aligning slot with valve shank head. Separate spring (6), distance cup (4), disc spring (3) and valve shank.

6. Ease seal (2) from shank and seal (8) from plunger with fingers. On Vitesse 6 remove second seal from groove in plunger.

7. Clean all parts ensuring feed and by-pass holes are clear. Renew seals. Check springs for damage, distortion or set, push rod and valve shank for straightness and cover for damage or deterioration. Renew parts as necessary.

8. Assemble in reverse order lubricating seals with hydraulic oil and installing with lips facing forward. Position disc spring (3) with lip against distance cup as shown in inset detail.

OPERATING CYLINDER - Removal and Installation (Fig.15)

1. Remove fascia support bracket and gearbox cover. Drain system and disconnect hydraulic pipe from cylinder.

2. Remove bolts (9) and cylinder.

3. Reverse procedure to install ensuring that push rod is correctly engaged in piston cup. Fill and bleed system.

OPERATING CYLINDER - Overhaul (Fig.F.16)

1. Remove cylinder

2. Remove cover (1) and circlip (2) and shake or gently blow

out piston (7) and spring (6). Ease seal (29) from piston.

3. Check spring for distortion or set and cover for damage and deterioration. Renew parts as necessary and renew seal.

4. Lubricate parts and re-assemble in reverse order ensuring that seal lip is towards hydraulic pipe end. Install cylinder.

BLEEDING THE SYSTEM

1. Clean the bleed nipple, attach length of rubber hose and immerse the free end in a jar containing hydraulic fluid.

2. Unscrew the bleed nipple half a turn, and, with the aid of a second person, depress the clutch pedal slowly. Tighten the nipple before the pedal reaches the end of its stroke and allow the pedal to return unassisted.

NOTE:- During the operation, do not allow the fluid in the master cylinder reservoir to fall below half-full to avoid the possibility of air being drawn into the system.

3. Continue bleeding until fluid entering jar is free from air bubbles. Close the nipple, remove hose and check clutch operation.

Technical Data

Clutch Unit Type	Hydraulic, self-adjusting single disc plate
Vitesse 2 Litre/GT6	Borg and Beck, diaphragm spring 21.5 cm (8.5 in.) dia.
Vitesse Six	Borg and Beck, coiled spring, 20.32 cm (8 in.) dia.
Hydraulic Fluid Specification	S.A.E. 7 OR 3

Gearbox

GENERAL
ROUTINE MAINTENANCE
GEARBOX - Removal and Installation
GEARBOX - Overhaul
OVERDRIVE
PROPELLER SHAFT
TECHNICAL DATA

GENERAL

The gearbox has four forward ratios and one reverse, gear-shifting being achieved by means of a remote gear change mechanism with the lever centrally mounted on the floor. The gearbox is similar for all models with synchromesh on all forward gears, except for the Vitesse Six on which synchromesh is confined to 2nd, 3rd and top with different 1st. and reverse gear ratios. Optional overdrive acting on 3rd and top gears is available on all models. The gearbox serial number is stamped on a flange at the right-hand side of the gearbox.

The bracketed numbers in the text refer to Figs. G.1 and G.2 except where otherwise stated. A conventional propeller shaft transmits power from the engine to the rear axle. Chassis movement is compensated by the splines and universal couplings.

ROUTINE MAINTENANCE
Every 6,000 miles (10,000 km)

With vehicle on level ground remove filler plug (2, Fig.G.3) and check that oil is level with bottom of the filler plug threads. Top-up, if necessary, with S.A.E. 90 E.P oil using a suitable pump-type oil dispenser with flexible nozzle. Allow surplus oil to drain away before refitting filler plug and wiping clean.

NOTE:- When an overdrive unit is fitted, a common oil level is obtained through a transfer hole.

GEARBOX - Removal and Installation

1. Isolate battery and remove front seats and on Vitesse, floor carpet.

2. Raise vehicle on ramp or onto axle stands.

3. Remove drain plug and drain gearbox (Fig.G.3).

4. G.T.6 only; remove bolts (A and B) to remove support bracket (C) and remove fixings (E and F) to remove cover (G) (Figs. G.4 and G.5).

5. Release gear lever knob locknut, remove knob and rubber grommet and, on GT6 floor carpet.

6. Remove twelve screws and plates (R) and cover (S) (Fig.G.6).

7. Remove bolts (N) to detach clutch operating cylinder, disconnect speedometer drive (P) propeller shaft (H) and remove mounting bracket nuts (U). Release exhaust pipe attachment (K) (Fig.G.7).
NOTE:- On Vitesse, exhaust pipe is attached to clutch housing.

8. Remove nuts (L) and gearbox extension and cover gearbox opening to exclude foreign matter (Fig.G.8).

9. Place wooden buffer block at rear of sump and jack-up until gearbox extension clears mounting bracket. Remove bolts (W) and mounting bracket (V) (Fig.G.9).

10. Remove clutch housing bolts (J) and manoeuvre gearbox from vehicle (Fig.G.8).

11. Install by reversing the removal procedure. Do not allow gearbox to hang on input shaft whilst re-installing. Renew gearbox extension gasket if damaged or distorted. With vehicle on level ground refill gearbox with oil.

GEARBOX - Overhaul

NOTE:- The overhaul procedure is described below, but, because of the gearbox complexity, the procedure should only be attempted by competent personnel. If in doubt, refer to work to an Authorised Dealer or other qualified personnel.

Dismantling (Fig.G.1)
Top Cover

1. Remove bolts (104) with washers and remove top cover (105) with gasket (106) (Fig.G.7).

2. Remove nuts (58) with washers and remove extension piece (96) with gasket.

3. Remove bolt (95) at bottom of gear lever, release cap (65) and detach gear lever assembly. (see Figs. G.10 and G.11 for attachment details).

4. Remove knob (71) with locknut and remove cap, cups (66 and 67) and outer spring (68) from gear lever. Remove snap ring (69), inner spring (70), spherical bearing (77) and finally remove reverse stop pin (73) from gear lever, and reverse stop plate (61) from top cover extension.

5. Release taper locking pin (100), withdraw remote control shaft assembly from cover extension and from selector (98) and ease out "O"-ring (99) as shown in Fig.G.12.

6. Separate front and rear control shafts by removing bolt (91) and drifting out pin (92). Remove fibre washers (63) and rubber bush (89).

7. Drive out Welch plugs as shown in Fig.G.13, ensuring selector shafts are clear of punch.

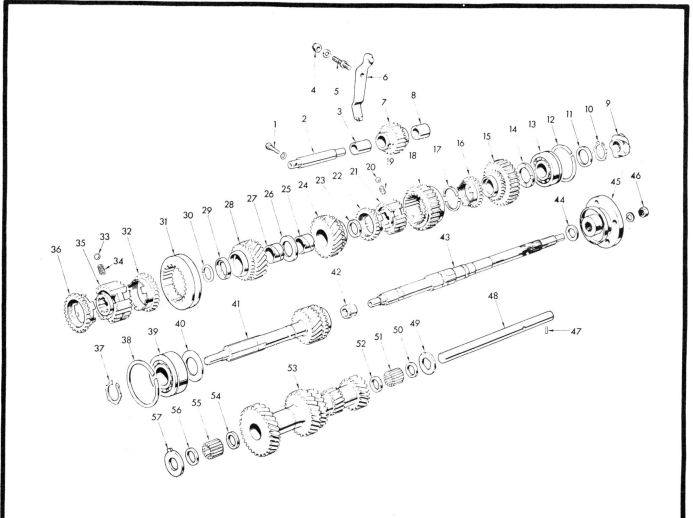

1.	Locating bolt	20.	Ball
2.	Reverse idler spindle	21.	1st/2nd synchro hub
3.	Reverse idler bush	22.	Baulk ring
4.	Nyloc nut	23.	Thrust washer
5.	Pivot pin	24.	2nd speed gear
6.	Reverse actuator	25.	2nd gear bush
7.	Reverse idler gear	26.	Thrust washer
8.	Distance tube	27.	3rd gear bush
9.	Speedo driven gear	28.	3rd speed gear
10.	Circlip	29.	Circlip washer
11.	Washer	30.	Circlip
12.	Snap ring	31.	3rd/top synchro sleeve
13.	Centre ballrace	32.	Baulk ring
14.	Thrust washer	33.	Ball
15.	1st speed gear	34.	Spring
16.	Baulk ring	35.	3rd/top synchro hub
17.	Split collars	36.	Baulk ring
18.	1st/2nd synchro sleeve	37.	Circlip
19.	Spring	38.	Snap ring

39.	Front ballrace
40.	Oil thrower
41.	Input shaft
42.	Roller bearing
43.	Mainshaft
44.	Thrust washer
45.	Coupling flange
46.	Nut
47.	Pin
48.	Countershaft spindle
49.	Rear thrust washer
50.	Retaining ring
51.	Needle rollers
52.	Retaining ring
53.	Countershaft gear cluster
54.	Retaining ring
55.	Needle rollers
56.	Retaining ring
57.	Front thrust washer

Fig.G.1   Details of gear assemblies

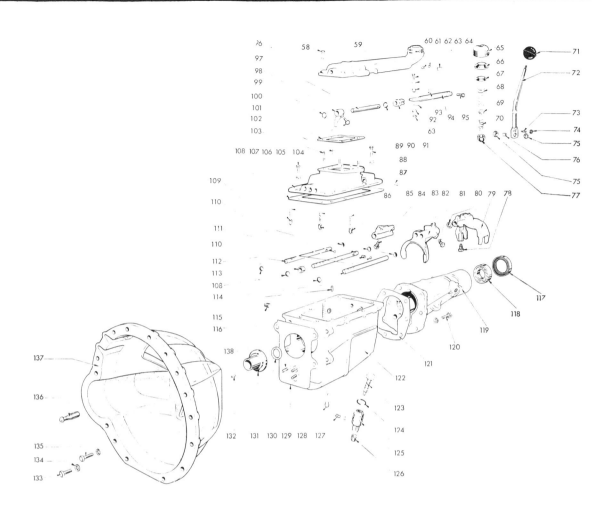

58.	Nut	79.	1st/2nd selector fork
59.	Locating pin	80.	Distance washer
60.	Screws	81.	Taper locking pin
61.	Reverse stop plate	82.	3rd/Top selector fork
62.	Pivot bolt	83.	Taper locking pin
63.	Fibre washers	84.	Reverse selector
64.	"Metalastik" bush	85.	Detent plungers
65.	Cap	86.	Springs
66.	Cup	87.	Plug
67.	Cup	88.	Bolt
68.	Spring	89.	Rubber "O"-ring
69.	Snap ring	90.	Coupling fork
70.	Spring	91.	Nyloc nut
71.	Knob	92.	Hollow pin
72.	Gear lever	93.	Nyloc nut
73.	Reverse stop bolt	94.	Gear lever shaft
74.	Locknut	95.	Screw
75.	Nylon bushes	96.	Top cover extension housing
76.	Distance tube	97.	Gear lever shaft
77.	Nylon sphere	98.	Selector
78.	Taper locking pin		

99.	Rubber "O"-ring	119.	Rear extension
100.	Taper locking pin	120.	Bolt
101.	Joint washer	121.	Joint washer
102.	Dowel	122.	Gear casing
103.	Stud	123.	Speedo driven gear
104.	Bolt	124.	Rubber "O" - ring
105.	Top cover housing	125.	Bearing
106.	Joint washer	126.	Oil seal
107.	Detent plunger	127.	Locating bolt
108.	Welch plugs	128.	Drain plug
109.	1st/2nd selector shaft	129.	Joint washer
110.	Interlock balls	130.	Oil seal
111.	Interlock plunger	131.	Oil seal housing
112.	Reverse selector shaft	132.	Pin
113.	Sleeve	133.	Bolt
114.	3rd/Top selector shaft	134.	Copper washer
115.	Dowel	135.	Bolt
116.	Filler/level plug	136.	Pivot pin
117.	Oil seal	137.	Clutch housing
118.	Rear ballrace	138.	Springs

Fig.G.2   Details of the gearbox casing and top
cover

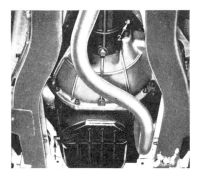

Fig.G.3   Gearbox drain plug (1) and filler/level plug (2)

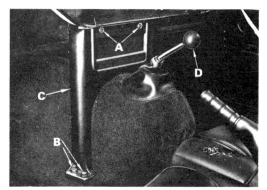

Fig.G.4   Fascia support bracket attachment - GT6

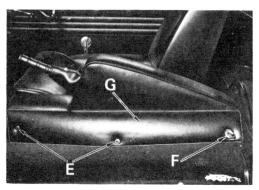

Fig.G.5   Transmission tunnel side finisher attachment - GT6

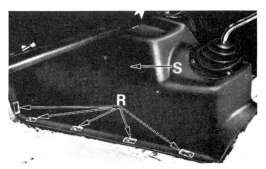

Fig.G.6   Transmission tunnel cover attachment

Fig.G.7   Right-hand view of the gearbox installation

8. Remove locking pins from selectors (78, 81 and 83), push selector shafts (109,114 and 112) from cover, removing selectors, two interlock balls (110 and 111), with plunger (85) and three selector plungers (107) with springs (86).

Clutch Housing (Fig.G.1)

1. Remove clutch release gear as detailed in CLUTCH section.

2. Remove four bolts (135) and wedgelock bolt (133) to separate clutch housing from gearbox (Fig.G.14). Remove gasket (129) and springs (138).

Rear Extension

1. Release peg bolt (127) and withdraw speedometer drive assembly. Remove gear and "O"-rings (124) (Fig.G.15).

2. Remove nut (46) and washer and withdraw driving flange (45) from mainshaft.

3. Remove bolts (120) and, with hide hammer, tap extension from mainshaft. Remove washer (44) and gasket.

4. Extract oil seal (17) and drive out ballrace (118) using tubular drift against outer race.

Main Gearbox Assembly

1. Remove countershaft securing pin (47) and withdraw shaft (48) allowing countershaft gear cluster to drop away from mainshaft gears. Follow through with 16.4 mm (0.065 in.) o/d. tube 165 mm (6.5 in.) long to retain needle bearings (51 and 55).

2. Attach Churchill tool 4235A with adaptor 4235A-2 and withdraw input shaft assembly (Fig.G.16).

3. Remove circlips (37) from shaft, circlip (38) from bearing and extract bearing (39) from shaft with Churchill press and adaptors (Fig.G.17). Remove oil deflector (40).

4. Using Churchill tool S 4221A-19, force mainshaft forward (Fig.G.18).

5. Using Churchill tool S 4221A and adaptor S4221A-19/1 remove speedometer drive gear, circlips (10) and (12), washer (11) and with bearing (13) (Fig.G.19).

6. Tilt mainshaft assembly and remove from gearbox (Fig.G.20).

7. Remove third top synchro unit and baulk ring (32). Remove thrust washer (14), first speed gear (15) and baulk ring (16).

8. With Churchill tool S144 remove circlip (30) (Fig.21).

9. Remove items (29 to 22), first/second synchro unit and split collar (17).

10. Remove reverse idler gear (7), securing bolt (1) and withdraw shaft (2). Lift gear cluster (53) from gearcase with thrust washers (49 and 57).

11. Remove nut (4), reverse gear actuator (6) and pin (5) (Fig.G.22).

12. Dismantle synchro units by removing outer sleeve (31 and 18) with units enclosed in cloth or box to avoid losing balls, springs or shims. Fig.G.23 gives exploded views of units.

Inspection

Clean all parts and inspect for damage and wear. Examine gear teeth and bearings for cracks and check that bearings rotate freely. Check countershaft bushes for wear. Renew gaskets and other parts as necessary.

Assembly
Countershaft and reverse pinion (Fig.G.24)

1. If needle bearings have been removed, position serviceable retaining rings (50, 52, 54 and 56) as shown in Fig.G.24. replace needle rollers smeared with heavy grease and retain in bore with slave tube.

2. Smear steel face of front countershaft thrust washer (57) with heavy grease as an adhesive and position in gearcase with tab in recess, bronze face towards gear and using shaft to align with hole (Fig.G.25).

3. Lower cluster into gearbox and move forward to pinch front thrust washer, apply grease to rear thrust washer (49) and insert between casing and cluster with tab in recess.

4. Thread countershaft (112) through casing aperture, thrust washers and gear cluster, ejecting slave tube, until shaft is in normal operating position.

5. Measure gear end-float with feeler gauges inserted between thrust washer and cluster (Fig.G.26). Adjust by selective assembly of thrust washers to obtain specified end-float.

NOTE:- Permissible end-float is 0.18 - 0.33 mm (0.007 - 0.013 in.) but an end-float of 0.25 mm (0.010 in.) should be aimed at. If reduction of thrust washer thickness is necessary, metal must NOT be removed from bronze face.

6. Remove countershaft inserting slave tube and allow gear cluster to lie at bottom of gearcase.

7. Screw pivot pin (5) into reverse idler gear selector lever until one thread protrudes through boss on lever, install lever in gearcase and secure with nut (4) and washer. Place idler gear in gearbox as shown in Fig.G.27.

Checking Release Loading of Synchro Units

1. Assemble spring (34), balls (33) and shims if fitted to hub of 3rd/Top synchro hub and position assembly inside sleeve (31) (Fig.G.23).

2. Similarly assemble hub and sleeve of 1st/2nd synchro unit.

3. Check release loads of both synchro units as shown in Fig.G.28 with spring balance attached to loading hook. Release load (both units) - 8.62-9.53 kg (10 - 21 lbs).

Fig.G.8   Left-hand view of the gearbox installation

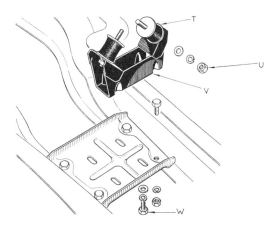

Fig.G.9   Details of the gearbox mounting bracket

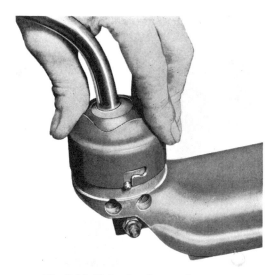

Fig.G.10 Releasing the gear lever cap

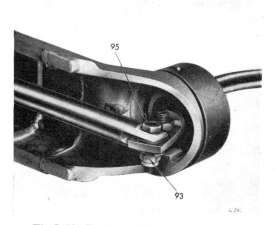

Fig.G.11 Gear lever linkage attachment

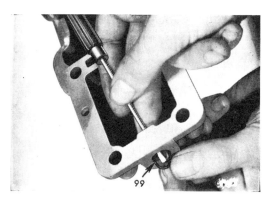

Fig.G.12 Extracting the "O" ring from the extension housing

Fig.G.13 Driving out the Welch plugs at the selector shafts

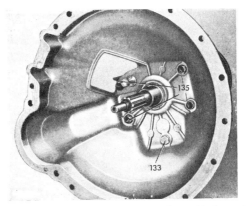

Fig.G.14 Clutch housing to gearbox attachment

Fig.G.15 Removing the speedometer drive assembly

Fig.G.16 Extracting the input shaft assembly

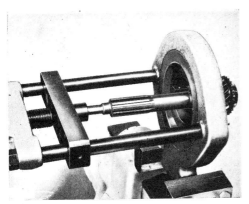

Fig.G.17 Removing the ballrace from the input shaft

Fig.G.18 Mainshaft abutment plate in position

Fig.G.19 Removing the ballrace from the mainshaft

Fig.G.20 Removing the mainshaft assembly

Fig.G.21 Removing the circlip from the mainshaft with Churchill Tool No. S.144

Fig.G.22 Reverse actuator assembly

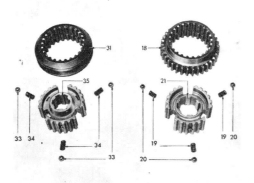

Fig.G.23 Details of the synchro units; 3rd/top - left 1st/2nd - right.

(See Fig.G.1 for key)

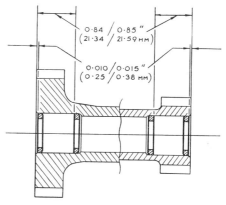

Fig.G.24 Locations of the counter shaft needle bearing retaining rings

Adjust number of shims under synchro springs to correct loading if necessary.

End-Float of 2nd and 3rd Mainshaft Gears on Bushes (Fig.G.29)

1. Measure end-float of each gear on its bush. This should be 0.5-0.15 mm (0.002-0.006 in.). Fit new bush to increase float or shorten bush to decrease float.

   CAUTION: Reduced bush length will increase bush end-float on shaft.

Overall End-Float of Bushes (Mainshaft) (Fig.G.30)

1. Assemble thrust washer (23), bush (25), washer (26), bush (27) and thrust washer (29) to mainshaft and secure with discarded half circlip (30).

2. Measure total end-float which should be 0.10 - 0.25 mm (0.004 - 0.010 in.). Adjust by selective use of thrust washers (see TECHNICAL DATA).

Estimating Circlip Washer Thickness Required

1. Assemble split collars (17), first speed gear (15), thrust washers (14), bearing inner race (or distance tube of appropriate length), washer (11) and circlip (10) to mainshaft.

2. Check gap as shown in Fig.G.31 and adjust to give 0.00-0.05 mm (0.000 - 0.002 in.) by selective use of washer (11) (see TECHNICAL DATA).

Mainshaft Assembly

1. Refer to Figs. G.32 to G.36 and assemble following items to mainshaft:

   (a) 1st/2nd synchro unit
   (b) Baulk ring (22) and thrust washer (23)
   (c) 2nd gear (24), bush (25) and washer (26)
   (d) 3rd gear (28) and bush (27)
   (e) Washer (29)

2. Fit circlip (30) with Churchill tool S145 (Fig.G.37).

3. Refer to Figs. G.38 to G.40 and assemble following items.

   (a) 3rd/top synchro unit
   (b) Split collars (17)
   (c) 1st gear baulk ring (16) and 1st gear (15)

4. Position mainshaft assembly in gearbox, fit Churchill abutment tool S4221A-19/2 (Fig.G.18), secure tool in vice with gearbox in vertical position and fit thrust washer (14) (Fig.G.41).

5. With circlip (12) in position, fit ballrace over mainshaft which must be correctly located in abutment plate and drive ballrace home with Churchill tool S314/1 with adaptor S4221A-19/3 (Fig.G.42).

6. Fit washer (11), circlip (10) and press speedometer drive gear onto shaft.

Input Shaft

1. Insert baulk ring (36) into 3rd/top synchro unit (Fig.G.43).

2. Smear oil deflector (40) with grease, place on input shaft and press on bearing (39) using Churchill press and adaptor. 21A-19 (Fig.G.44).

3. Secure bearing with circlip (37) and fit circlip (38) on bearing.

4. Locate roller bearing (42) in shaft bore.

5. Install input shaft into casing and engage with mainshaft.

Countershaft and Reverse Idler Shaft

1. Align countershaft gear cluster and thrust washers together with slave tube, insert shaft (48) and push out slave tube (Fig.G.44).

2. Insert reverse idler shaft (2) into gearbox and through idler gear and fit distance tube (8). Secure with bolt (1) and washer (Fig.G.45).

Rear Extension

1. Drive bearing (118) into housing at rear of extension piece, then oil seal (117) with lip facing forward.

2. Lubricate and assemble speedometer drive gear assembly with new "O" rings (124) and install in rear extension. Secure with locking bolt (127) and washer (Fig.G.5).

3. Fit washer (44) over mainshaft, smear gasket (121) with grease and place against rear face of gearbox.

4. Place extension over mainshaft and with tubular drift against bearing outer race, drive bearing onto mainshaft. Secure rear extension tightening bolts evenly and in turn.

5. Fit driving flange (45) and secure with spring washer and nut (44).

Clutch Housing

1. Insert springs (138) in front of gearbox. Renew oil seal (130).

2. Smear gasket (60) with grease and secure housing to gearbox with four bolts (59) and Wedgelock bolt (57), with new copper plated washer (58).

3. Install clutch release gear.

Top Cover

1. Insert springs 86 and plungers (85 and 107) in top cover.

2. Slide 3rd/top selector shaft (114) into front end of top

Fig.G.25 Front thrust washer located in the casing

Fig.G.26 Measuring the countershaft end-float

Fig.G.27 Installation of the reverse idler gear

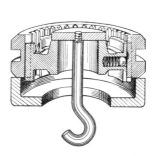

Fig.G.28 Checking the release load of the synchro unit

Fig.G.29 Measuring the gear end-float on the mainshaft bush

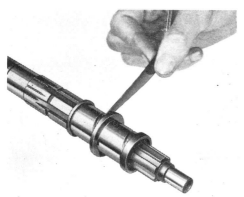

Fig.G.30 Measuring the bush end-float on the mainshaft

Fig.G.31 Determining the thickness of circlip washer required

Fig.G.32 1st/2nd synchro unit in position on the mainshaft

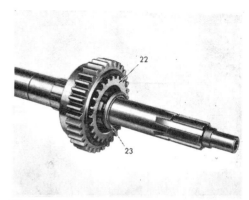

Fig.G.33 2nd gear baulk ring and thrust washer in position

Fig.G.34 2nd gear with bush and thrust washer in position

Fig.G.35 3rd gear in position with bush

Fig.G.36 Circlip washer installed on the mainshaft

Fig.G.37 Fitting the mainshaft circlip with special tool, No. S.145

Fig.G.38 3rd gear baulk ring in position

Fig.G.39 3rd/top synchro unit fitted on the mainshaft

Fig.G.40 1st gear with baulk ring on the mainshaft

Fig.G.41 1st gear thrust washer installed on the mainshaft

Fig.G.42 Installing the centre ball race on the mainshaft

Fig.G.43 Installation of the top gear baulk ring

Fig.G.44 Inserting the countershaft into the gearbox.

Fig.G.45 Installation of the reverse idler assembly

cover, depress plunger to permit passage of shaft, thread on selector fork and continue insertion until plunger engages middle indent of shaft. This is neutral position

3. Insert reverse selector shaft (112) in same way to engage selector (84) and to reach neutral position.

4. Enter 1st/2nd selector shaft into top cover with interlock plunger (111) in position, slide shaft into cover then through third/top fork and 1st/2nd selector fork together with sleeve (113) and washer (80).

5. Before shaft reaches neutral position, insert both interlock balls (50 and 26) into the cross bore between shaft bores as shown in Fig.G.46, then push shaft to neutral position. Interlock balls and plunger are then retained by the shafts.

6. Secure selector forks and reverse selector with new lock- ing pins (83, 81 and 78).

7. Apply jointing compound around edges of Welch plugs (108) and tap them in the ends of the shaft bores.

8. Ensure selectors and gears are in neutral position, smear gasket (106) with grease, position cover on gearbox and secure with bolts and spring washers tightening evenly and, in turn, placing longer bolts at rear.

9. Assemble fork (90) to shaft (97) with new pin (92), renew bush (64) and secure shaft to fork with bolt (62), and new fibre washers (63).

10. Fit new "O" rings (89 and 99) into top cover extension and thread shaft (97) into cover extension and through selector (98). Secure selector with new pin (100).

11. Assemble reverse stop pin (73), spherical bearing (77), spring (70) and snap ring (69) to gear lever (Fig.G.47).

12 Fit reverse stop plate (61) to cover with screws (60).

13. Position gear lever assembly into cover with two new stepped washers (75), fit bush (76) and bolt lever to shaft (94).

14. Assemble spring (68), cups (66 and 67) and secure with cover (65).

15. Adjust reverse stop pin (61) to give clearance in neutral position of 1st/2nd gate as shown in Fig.G.48.

16. Assemble extension cover to top cover with new gasket (101).

OVERDRIVE

The overdrive is an additional gear unit, mounted on the rear face of the gearbox in place of the normal extension, to provide a higher overall gear ratio on third and top gears (Fig.G.49).

The overdrive is operated by an electric solenoid, controlled by a switch mounted on the steering column. When overdrive is selected, the solenoid actuates the operating valve, redirecting the flow of fluid under pressure and causing engagement of the epicyclic overdrive gears. Hydraulic pressure is developed by a plunger pump, cam-operated from the input shaft. An inhibitor switch, fitted in the electrical circuit, prevents engagement of over-drive in reverse, 1st or 2nd gears.

NOTE:- As specialised knowledge and equipment are required to overhaul the overdrive unit, any repair work should be entrusted to an Authorised Dealer or other qualified personnel.

Lubrication

The gearbox and overdrive unit are interconnected and thus have a common oil level, which is maintained by topping-up the gearbox. When draining, however, the separate drain plugs for the gearbox and overdrive unit must be removed. Removal of the overdrive drain plug will provide access to a gauze filter which should also be removed and cleaned, before refilling the unit with new oil.

Under normal circumstances, the special oil used for the initial fill of the gearbox and overdrive unit should NOT be changed but merely topped-up with an approved oil. Where a new unit is fitted, or parts of the existing unit removed, the unit should be refilled with new special oil, available from Triumph dealers. If this oil is not available, an approved oil may be used as an alternative.

NOTE:- Always use clean oil and take great care to avoid entry of dirt or lint from the wiping cloth into the unit whenever any part of the casing is opened.

After refilling the unit, run the car for a short distance and recheck the oil level. It will probably be necessary to top-up the level to make up for the oil which has been distributed around the hydraulic system.

Adjustment of the Solenoid Operating Lever

When correctly set, with solenoid engaged, a hole in the operating lever should align with a hole in the overdrive casing. This indicates the operating valve is fully open. To check setting, remove operating lever cover, energise solenoid and insert 4.76 mm (3/16 in.) dia. pin through both holes (Fig.G.50).

If holes are mal-aligned proceed as follows:

1. Move lever until setting pin (2) enters both holes.

2. With solenoid energised, screw adjusting nut (3) until it just contacts lever.

3. Remove pin, de-energise and re-energise solenoid and re- check hole alignment.

4. With solenoid de-energised, align holes and insert pin.

5. Hold solenoid plunger against blanking plug and check dimension "A" is 2.54 - 3.05 mm (0.10 - 0.12 ins) (Fig. G.51). If necessary, vary thickness of washer under head of blanking plug (On later units the plug is adjustable).

6. Remove pin and refit cover.

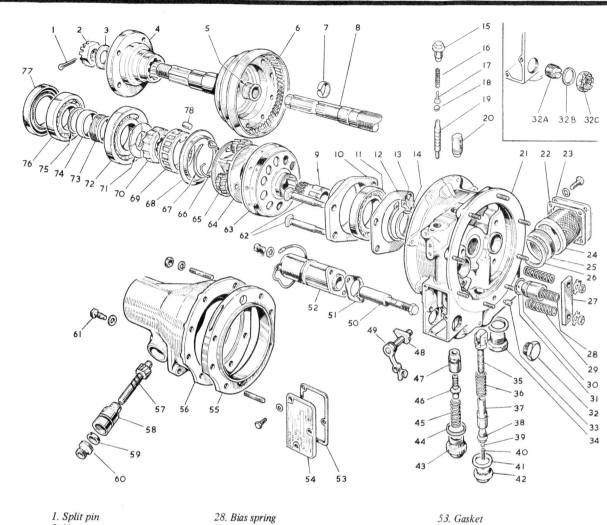

1. Split pin
2. Nut
3. Washer
4. Coupling flange
5. Needle bearing
6. Annulus
7. Spring
8. Main shaft
9. Sungear
10. Thrust ring
11. Thrust bearing
12. Retaining plate
13. Circlip
14. Circlip
15. Plug
16. Spring
17. Plunger
18. Ball
19. Operating valve
20. Lubrication bush
21. Front casing
22. Gasket
23. Cover plate
24. Filter
25. Magnetic rings
26. Rubber/Steel washer
27. Bridge piece

28. Bias spring
29. Clutch return spring
30. Piston
31. Piston 'O' ring
32. Plug
32A. Adjuster screw ⎱ These items replace
32B. Locknut ⎰ item 32 on later
32C. Fibre washer ⎰ units
33. Pump locating screw
34. Plug
35. Pump plunger
36. Return spring
37. Pump body
38. Non-return valve body
39. Ball
40. Spring
41. Washer
42. Plug
44. Washer
45. Spring
46. Relief valve plunger
47. Relief valve body
48. Cam
49. Operating lever
50. Solenoid plunger
51. Gasket
52. Solenoid

53. Gasket
54. Cover plate
55. Brake ring
56. Rear casing
57. Speedometer pinion
58. Speedometer pinion bush
59. Seal
60. Screwed end
61. Locating screw
62. Bolts
63. Cone clutch
64. Planet carrier assembly
65. Planet gear
66. Spring
67. Circlip
68. Oil thrower
69. Cage
70. Inner member
71. Thrust washer
72. Front bearing
73. Speedometer drive gear
74. Distance piece
75. Spacer
76. Rear bearing
77. Oil seal
78. Roller

Fig.G.49 Exploded view of overdrive

Fig.G.46 Installing the interlock balls in the top cover

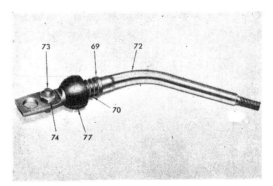

Fig.G.47 Gear lever assembly

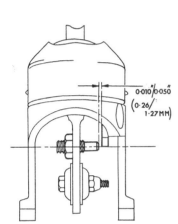

0·010/0·050″
(0·26/1·27MM)

Fig.G.48 Adjustment of the reverse stop plate and bolt clearance

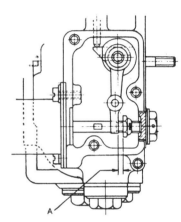

Fig.G.50 Setting the solenoid operating lever position on the overdrive unit.

1. *Operating lever*
2. *Setting pin*
3. *Adjusting nut*
4. *Solenoid plunger*

Fig.G.51 Checking dimension for the solenoid plunger

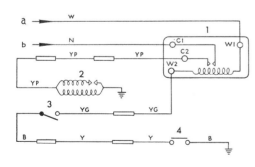

Fig.G.52 Overdrive electrical circuit

1. *Solenoid relay*
2. *Overdrive operating solenoid*
3. *Overdrive switch*
4. *Gearbox isolator switch*

a. *To No. 2 terminal on the ignition switch*
b. *To No. 1 terminal on the ignition switch*

Fig.G.53 Checking the alignment of the planet carrier and uni-directional clutch

Fig.G.54 Mainshaft and adaptor plate used with the overdrive unit

7. Spring clip
79. Woodruff key
80. Spring ring
81. Cam

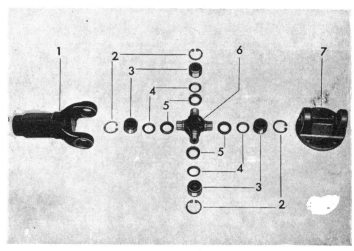

Fig.G.56 Exploded details of universal coupling

1. Sliding yoke
2. Circlips
3. Bearing cups
4. Seals
5. Retainers
6. Spider
7. Flange

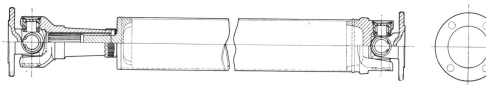

Fig.G.55 Cross-section through propeller shaft

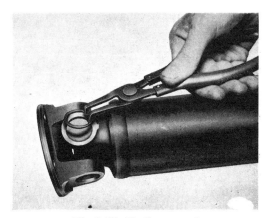

Fig.G.57 Circlip removal

Fig.G.58 Releasing cup from yoke 1

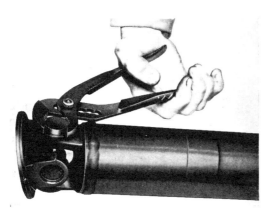

Fig.G.59 Withdrawing the cup

Fig.G.60 Releasing cup from yoke 11

Fig.G.61 Pressing in cup

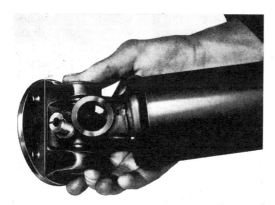

Fig.G.62 Assembling spider

Fig.G.63 Assembled universal joint and servicing plug

Checking the Electrical Circuit (Fig.G.52)

If any operation failure of the overdrive unit occurs, first check the wiring and connections of the overdrive circuit, as in many cases failures are due to corroded terminals or faulty wiring.

If after checking all the electrical connections, the overdrive still fails to operate proceed as follows:

1. Switch on ignition and engage top gear. Set overdrive switch on steering column to overdrive position. Check that battery voltage is present at terminals C1 and W2.

2. Short out terminals C1 and C2 on relay unit. If overdrive solenoid operates, then relay unit, column switch and isolator switch are suspect. Remove shorting link from relay unit.

3. Earth terminal W1 on relay unit. If solenoid now operates. column switch and isolator switch are suspect. If solenoid does not operate, replace relay unit.

4. Earth the yellow/green cable on the column switch. If solenoid now operates, replace isolator switch. If solenoid does not operate, replace the column switch.

Removal and Installation

The overdrive is removed in unit with the gearbox and, apart from the disconnection of the solenoid and isolation switch electrical leads, the removal procedure is the same as described previously for the gearbox.

Separation from Gearbox

Remove attachment nuts and spring washers and carefully withdraw overdrive unit from gearbox.

Assembly to Gearbox

1. Align splines of planet carrier and uni-directional clutch with a long screwdriver; confirm by inserting dummy mainshaft (Churchill tool L201) (Fig.G.53).

2. Turn gearbox mainshaft until overdrive pump operating cam peak (81) is upper-most. Ensure spring clip (7) on mainshaft is located in groove and does not protrude above splines (Fig.G.54).

NOTE:- Do not rotate mainshaft or overdrive coupling until assembly is complete.

3. Remove dummy mainshaft and fit unit to gearbox, tightening nuts evenly and in turn.

PROPELLER SHAFT

Fig.G.55 shows a cross-sectional view through this power link which is attached to the gearbox rear and front of the rear axle. A splined sliding joint is installed at the forward end together with a universal coupling. A similar coupling is also located at the rear and these units. prevent the shaft from damage

distortion and breakage when the vehicle is in motion.

The sliding joint must not be dismantled and, in order to maintain the fine degree of balance throughout the transmission system, should radial wear develop in the universal couplings replace the entire assembly with an exchange unit.

If exchange units are not available, replace the universal couplings as follows:-

Shaft removal

Support and secure the vehicle on stands or ramp. Uncouple gearbox cover and fascia support bracket as previously described. Unscrew and remove Nyloc nuts clamping shaft flanges to rear axle and gearbox units. Slide out bolts and manipulate propeller shaft rearwards from car.

Shaft dismantling

1. Mark flanges of shaft and universal couplings to ensure correct reassembly.

2. At forked end of shaft unclip circlip (Fig.G.57) and lightly tap lug until the bearing cup protrudes (Fig.G.58). Swivel cup out of the yoke as shown in Fig.G.59: Repeat this procedure on the opposite bearing assembly and uncouple the companion flange.

3. Remove the remaining circlips. Support exposed spider trunnions on a wooden block and tap flange lugs or yoke. to remove cups (Fig.G.60). Repeat procedure for other universal joint.

Shaft re-assembly

1. Apply jointing compound to the new spider journal shoulders. Locate oil seal retainers over trunnions with tubular drift; position oil seals to retainers.

2. Lining-up marks on respective flanges made during dismantling, pass spider trunnions through bearing bores in companion flange. Assemble bearing cups and circlips (Fig.G.61) and check for correct seating.

NOTE:- Spider must be assembled with lubrication boss towards propeller shaft (Fig.G.63).

3. Manipulate the other trunnions through prop shaft bearing bores in forked end (Fig.G.62). Assemble cups and circlips.

4. Repeat the procedure for the second universal coupling and assemble shaft to vehicle in reverse order of removal.

Technical Data

Type	Four forward speeds and one reverse with synchromesh on 2nd 3rd and top gears for Vitesse 6 and on all forward gears on other models.
Ratios: Top	1.00 : 1
3rd	1.25 : 1
2nd	1.78 : 1
1st	2.65 : 1 (Vitesse 6 - 2.93 : 1)
Reverse	3.10 : 1 (Vitesse 6 - 2.93 : 1)
Overdrive	0.80 : 1

Oil Capacity

Gearbox	1.5 imp. pints (0.85 litres (1.8 U.S. pints)
Gearbox and Overdrive	2.38 imp pints (1.35 Litres (2.85 U. S. pints)
Lubricant Specification	SAE 90EP

Dimensions and Tolerances.

Input shaft spigot bush I/D	12.81-12.79 mm (0.5055-0.4998 in.)
Mainshaft	
- Spigot dia.	12.7-12.687 mm (0.5005-4.995 in.)
- 2nd/3rd gear bush journal dia.	22.195-22.182 mm (0.8738-0.8733 in.)
- Centre bearing journal dia.	25.41-25.4 mm (1.0004-1.0000 in.)
- Rear bearing journal dia.	19.067-19.055 mm (0.7504-0.7501 in.)

Mainshaft gear and bushes

2nd and 3rd gear - I/D	27.80-27.77 mm (1.0945-1.0935 in.)
2nd and 3rd speed bush - I/D	22.25-22.25 mm (0.876-0.875 in.)
O/D	27.76-27.71 mm (1.0928-1.0908 in.)
3rd speed bush - length	25.45-25.40 mm (1.002-1.00 in.)
2nd speed bush - length	25.45-25.40 mm (1.002-1.00 in.)
2nd/3rd gear thrust washer	3.91-3.86 mm (0.154-0.152 in.)
2nd gear thrust washer	3.15-3.10 mm (0.124-0.122 in.)

Centre ballrace circlip washer

Pt. No. 143289	2.36-2.31 mm (0.093-0.091 in.)
143290	2.44-2.39 mm (0.096-0.094 in.)
143291	2.51-2.46 mm (0.099-0.097 in.)
143292	2.59-2.54 mm (0.102-0.100 in.)
2nd/3rd gear circlip	1.83-1.75 mm (0.072-0.069 in.)

Maximum overall end-float	0.25-0.10 mm (0.010-0.004 in.)
Reverse gear bush O/D	19.85-19.83 mm (0.7815-0.7805 in.)
Reverse gear bush I/D	16.33-16.23 mm (0.643-0.639 in.)
Reverse gear spindle main dia	16.65-16.64 mm (0.6555-0.6550 in.)
Reverse gear end dia.	14.27-14.26 mm (0.5618-0.5613 in.)

Countershaft assembly

Countershaft O/D	16.65-16.64 mm (0.6555-0.6550 in.)
Countershaft bushes - length	35.18-34.67 mm (1.385-1.365 in.)
-I/D	16.71-16.70 mm (0.6580-0.6573 in.)
Front thrust washer	3.18-3.12 mm (0.125-0.123 in.)
Rear thrust washer	1.73-1.68 mm (0.068-0.066 in.)
Overall end-float	0.33-0.18 mm (0.013-0.007 in.)
Ballraces - Front and rear mainshaft	Hoffman MS 10K
- Rear extension	Hoffman LS 8
Needle bearing	Torrington B 810

Propeller Shaft

GT6	Normal Fitment	O/Drive Condition
Length(closed)	948.3 mm (38.75 in.)	896.1 mm (35.28 in.)
(fitted)	1004.8 mm (39.56 in.)	916.7 mm (36.09 in.)
Extension	40.13/42.67 mm (1.58/1.68 in.)	31.75 mm (1.25 in.)

Vitesse

Length (closed)	1210.3 mm (47.65 in.)	1122.7 mm (44.20 in.)
(fitted)	1188.5 mm (46.49 in)	1105.6 mm (43.53 in.)
Extension		31.75 mm (1.25 in.)
Mounting flange holes P.C.D.		76.02/76.18 mm 2.997/3.003 in.)
Angular movement		15o
Maximum run-out (at ends)		0.203 mm (0.008 in.)
(at centre)		0.305 mm (0.012 in.)
Maximum out of balance (at each end)		36.06 grm.cm (0.5 oz in.)

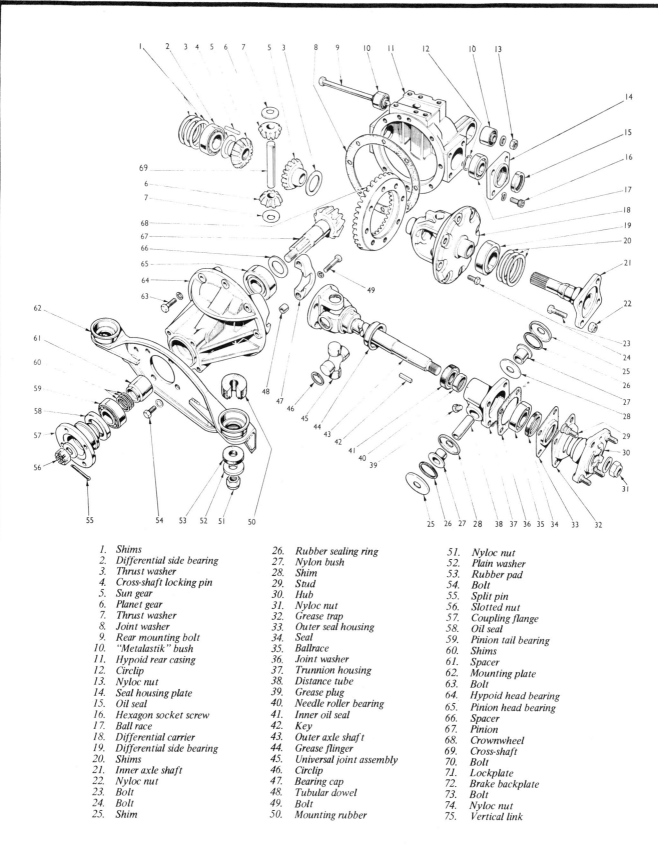

1. Shims
2. Differential side bearing
3. Thrust washer
4. Cross-shaft locking pin
5. Sun gear
6. Planet gear
7. Thrust washer
8. Joint washer
9. Rear mounting bolt
10. "Metalastik" bush
11. Hypoid rear casing
12. Circlip
13. Nyloc nut
14. Seal housing plate
15. Oil seal
16. Hexagon socket screw
17. Ball race
18. Differential carrier
19. Differential side bearing
20. Shims
21. Inner axle shaft
22. Nyloc nut
23. Bolt
24. Bolt
25. Shim

26. Rubber sealing ring
27. Nylon bush
28. Shim
29. Stud
30. Hub
31. Nyloc nut
32. Grease trap
33. Outer seal housing
34. Seal
35. Ballrace
36. Joint washer
37. Trunnion housing
38. Distance tube
39. Grease plug
40. Needle roller bearing
41. Inner oil seal
42. Key
43. Outer axle shaft
44. Grease flinger
45. Universal joint assembly
46. Circlip
47. Bearing cap
48. Tubular dowel
49. Bolt
50. Mounting rubber

51. Nyloc nut
52. Plain washer
53. Rubber pad
54. Bolt
55. Split pin
56. Slotted nut
57. Coupling flange
58. Oil seal
59. Pinion tail bearing
60. Shims
61. Spacer
62. Mounting plate
63. Bolt
64. Hypoid head bearing
65. Pinion head bearing
66. Spacer
67. Pinion
68. Crownwheel
69. Cross-shaft
70. Bolt
71. Lockplate
72. Brake backplate
73. Bolt
74. Nyloc nut
75. Vertical link

Fig. H.1   Exploded view of the rear axle
assembly

Rear Axle & Final Drive

GENERAL
ROUTINE MAINTENANCE
AXLE SHAFT AND HUB ASSEMBLY -
Removal and Installation
OUTER AXLE SHAFT - Overhaul
OUTER AXLE SHAFT COUPLINGS - Inspection
- Spider and Cup Assemblies Renewal
INNER AXLE SHAFT ASSEMBLY -
Dismantling and Assembly
PINION OIL SEAL - Replacement
FINAL DRIVE UNIT - Removal and Installation

AXLE SHAFT AND HUB ASSEMBLY (Mk.2 models) -
Removal and Installation
ROTOFLEX COUPLING (Mk.2 models) - Replacement
REAR HUB (Mk.2 models) - Dismantling
- Re -assembly
INTERMEDIATE SHAFT COUPLING (Mk.2 models) -
Inspection
FINAL DRIVE UNIT (Mk.2 models) -
Removal and Installation
FINAL DRIVE UNIT - Overhaul
TECHNICAL DATA

GENERAL

The hypoid level gear final drive unit is centrally mounted to the chassis through rubber insulators at four points. On Vitesse Six and Mk.1 models, right and left-hand short inner axle shafts are universally jointed to outer axle shafts which are keyed to the wheel hubs and supported in trunnion housings attached to the bottom of the rear suspension vertical links: On Mk.2 models, the inner shaft is universally jointed to an intermediate shaft with a Rotaflex coupling connection to the outer shaft which is splined to the wheel hub. Procedures applicable only to Mk.2 models are separately described.

ROUTINE MAINTENANCE
Every 6,000 miles (10,000 km).

Top-up approved oil at filler/level plug (Fig.H.2). Allow surplus oil to drain before replacing plug. Clean oil from exterior *

AXLE SHAFT AND HUB ASSEMBLY -
Removal and Installation (Figs. H3,H4 and H5)
Removal

1. Raise rear of vehicle with jack and support on chassis stands.

2. Remove road wheel.

3. Disconnect brake hose (A) at bracket (B).

4. Disconnect handbrake cable from lever (D) and unhook spring.

5. Remove four attachment bolts (F) and nuts (G) from axle shaft coupling.

6. With jack locating at bottom of vertical links to relieve damper load, remove nut (H) with washer and pull damper clear of attachment pin and remove bolt (E) to disconnect radius rod.

7. Remove jack from beneath vertical links, support brake unit by hand, remove nut (J) and bolt to disconnect road spring from vertical links.

8. Remove shaft and hub assembly.

Installation

1. Place assembly in position and fit bolt to vertical link and road spring eye. Do not fully tighten nut (J).

2. Carefully jack vertical link and secure bottom of damper and radius rod to link.

3. Secure axle shaft coupling with four bolts and remove jack.

4. Load vehicle to "static laden" condition and fully tighten nut (J).

5. Reconnect handbrake cable and spring and flexible brake hose.

6. Replenish and bleed brake system and fit road wheel.

OUTER AXLE SHAFT - Overhaul (Fig.H.6
Dismantling

1. Remove brake drums

2. Remove hub nut (31) and plain washer and withdraw hub with Churchill tool S109C. Retain key (Fig.H.7).

3. Remove trunnion bolt (73) vertical links (75) shims (25 and 28), seals (26), steel bush (38) and nylon inserts (27) from trunnion.

4. Straighten tabs of locking plate (71), remove bolts (70), grease trap (32), backplate (72), seal housing (33) and gasket (36). Separate oil seal gasket (36). Separate oil seal (34) from housing.

5. Using Churchill tool S4221A with adaptor S4221A/14, remove trunnion (37) together with ballrace (35) and grease flinger (44).

6. Withdraw inner oil seal (41) and needle roller bearing (40) from trunnion.

Inspection

1. Clean all parts and inspect for wear or damage. Check needle and ballbearings for cracks and rough rotation. Renew if in doubt. Examine seals for deformation. Renew

Fig.H.2   Final drive unit filler/level plug.

Fig.H.3   Vertical link and brake pipe attachments.

Fig.H.4   Handbrake, radius rod and damper attachments

Fig.H.5   Axle shaft driving flange attachments

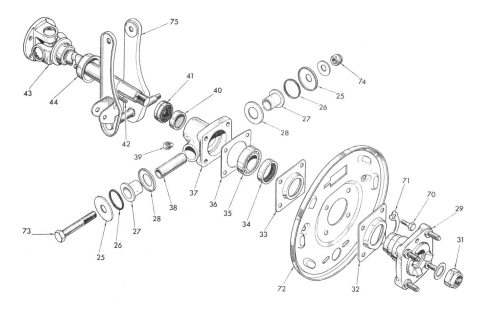

Fig.H.6   Exploded view of the outer axle shaft and hub assembly

(See Fig.H.1 for key)

Fig.H.7 Removing the rear hub

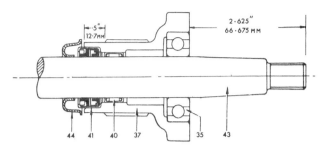

Fig.H.8 Fitting dimensions for the rear hub assembly

(See Fig.H.1 for key)

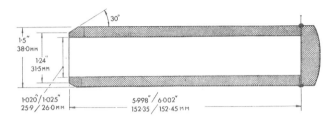

Fig.H.9 Dimensions of drift for fitting the flinger on the shaft

Fig.H.10 Installing needle roller bearing in the hub trunnion

Fig.H.11 Pressing the axle shaft through the trunnion assembly

Fig.H.12 Driving the ballrace onto the shaft

Fig.H.13 Axle shaft coupling attachments

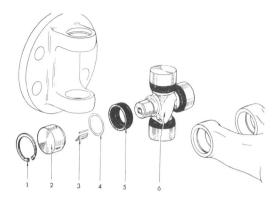

Fig.H.14   Details of the universal coupling

1. Circlip
2. Bearing cup
3. Needle rollers
4. Washer
5. Seal
6. Spider

Fig.H.15   Extracting the circlips from the universal coupling

Fig.H.16   Tapping coupling yoke to displace bearing cup

Fig.H.17   Extracting the needle roller cup.

Fig.H.18   Assembling the cup and needle rollers to the yoke

Fig.H.19   Details of the inner axle shaft

(See Fig.H.1 for key)

gasket, sealing rings and other parts as necessary.

Re-assembly

NOTE:- Fig.H.8 shows position of needle roller bearing in trunnion and trunnion main bearing on shaft.

1. Press needle roller bearing (40) into trunnion to depth of 12.7 mm (0.50 in.) with Churchill tool S300A. Press on lettered end of bearing (Fig.H.10).

2. Drive oil seal (41) into trunnion with lips trailing.

3. With tool shown at Fig.H.9, drive grease flinger (44) onto shaft.

4. Pack needle roller bearing with grease, carefully thread axle shaft through oil seal and bearing and press into position (Fig.H.11).

5. Pack ballrace with grease and drive onto shaft using Churchill tool S304. Secure and protect shaft in vice (Fig.H.12). Ensure trunnion and ballrace are positioned as shown in Fig.H.8

6. Press seal (34) into housing (33) with lip trailing.

7. Assemble vertical links to trunnion.

8. Coat new gasket with grease, place against trunnion face and assemble seal housing, backplate (72) (with wheel cylinder at bottom in relation to vertical links) and grease trap (32) (with duct at bottom). Fit bolts (70) and secure with lockplates (71).

9. Fit and key hub (30) and secure with washer and new Nyloc nut.

10. Assemble brake drum.

11. Assemble nylon inserts (27), sleeve (38), shims (28 and 25) and sealing rings (26).

OUTER AXLE SHAFT COUPLINGS - Inspection

1. Raise rear of vehicle with jack and support on chassis stands. Remove road wheels.

2. Raise vertical link on one side with trolley jack until in normal operating position.

3. Remove coupling attachment bolts (Fig.H.13).

4. Complete removal of cup assembly using grips (Fig.H.17).

5. Remove opposite cup, separate flange yoke from spider and repeat procedure for outer yoke cups.

6. Clean bores of yokes.

7. Carefully fit seal (5) and washers (4) onto cups.

8. Position spider in outer yoke. Push cup assemblies squarely into yoke making sure needle rollers fit around yoke (Fig.H.18).

9. Repeat with flange yoke and secure cups with circlips.

10. Carefully lever flanges apart allowing vertical link to slide on trolley jack.

11. Hold shaft firmly and move flange yoke axially along spider journals. If end-float exists, spider and cup assemblies must be renewed.

12. Repeat inspection procedure on opposite hand coupling.

NOTE: Needle rollers, cup, spiders and circlip are supplied only as a complete replacement kit. Wear in yoke bore necessitates yoke renewal and the outer yoke is renewable only as part of shaft assembly.

OUTER AXLE SHAFT COUPLINGS -
Spider and Cup Assemblies Renewal (Fig.H.14)

1. Remove outer axle shaft

2. Remove roller cup circlips (Fig.H.15)

3. Support yoke and tap with hide hammer to eject cup (Fig.H.16).

4. Complete removal of cup assembly using grips (Fig.H.17).

5. Remove opposite cup, separate flange yoke from spider and repeat procedure for outer yoke cups.

6. Clean bores of yokes.

7. Carefully fit seals (5) and washers (4) onto cups.

8. Position spider in outer yoke. Push cap assemblies squarely into yoke, making sure needle rollers fit around yoke (Fig.H.18).

9. Repeat with flange yoke and secure cups with circlips.

NOTE:- Circlips are available in the following sizes to cater for varying spider lengths:

Part number	Width
128651	1.47-1.50 mm (0.058-0.059 in.)
128652	1.50-1.52 mm (0.059-0.060 in.)
128653	1.52-1.55 mm (0.060-0.061 in.)
128654	1.55-1.57 mm (0.061-0.062 in.)

INNER AXLE SHAFT ASSEMBLY -
Dismantling and Assembly (Fig.H.19)
Removal

1. Remove hub and outer shaft assembly.

2. Drain hypoid gear housing.

3. With hexagon key 6.76 mm (3/16 in.) remove socket screws from seal housing plate (14) (Fig.H.20).

4. Remove shaft assembly.

Fig.H.20 Removing the hexagon socket screws
from the seal housing plate

Fig.H.21 Pressing inner axle shaft out of the
bearing race

Fig.H.22 Driving the inner axle shaft oil seal
into its housing

Fig.H.23 Pressing inner axle shaft through
the bearing and housing

Fig.H.24 Installing the pinion shaft oil seal

Fig.H.25 View of the inner axle shaft and prop
shaft couplings

Fig.H.26 Rear spring attachment

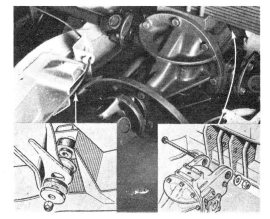

Fig.H.27 Final drive unit attachments

Fig.H.28 Removing final drive unit from its casing

Fig.H.29 Removing hypoid unit using the spreading tool

Fig.H.30 Releasing crown wheel attachment bolts

Fig.H.31 Checking run-out on the differential carrier flange

Fig.H.32 Removing the differential side bearings

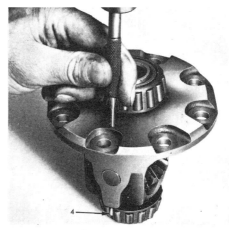

Fig.H.33 Driving out the cross-shaft locking pin

Fig.H.34 Removing the pinion flange nut

Fig.H.35 Pressing the pinion out of the head bearing

Fig.H.36 Driving outer races from the pinion casing

Fig.H.37 Assembling the head bearing to the pinion

Dismantling

1. Remove circlip (12).

2. Withdraw bearing (17) from shaft with Churchill tool and adaptor set S4331A - 7B. (Fig.H.21).

3. Separate seal housing plate (14) and drive out oil seal (15).

Re-assembly

1. Drive seal with lip leading into housing plate (Fig.H.23).

2. With seal lip trailing slide housing carefully over serrations onto shaft.

3. Press shaft into housing and bearing (Fig.H.23).

4. Fit circlip (12) to shaft groove.

Installation

1. Install inner axle shaft in hypoid housing and secure with screws (16).

2. Refill hypoid housing with oil.

3. Install outer shaft and hub assembly

PINION OIL SEAL - Replacement (Fig.H.1)

1. Drain final drive unit, remove exhaust tail pipe and disconnect propeller shaft.

2. Remove nut (56) and driving flange (57).

3. Lever out seal (58).

4. Drive seal into nose casing (Fig.H.24).

5. Assemble driving flange to nose casing, connect propeller shaft and refit tail exhaust pipe.

6. Refill hypoid housing with oil.

FINAL DRIVE UNIT - Removal and Installation

1. Raise rear of vehicle with jack and support on chassis stands. Remove road wheels and drain unit.

2. Place jacks at bottom of vertical links to relieve damper load.

3. Disconnect bottom of damper and pull clear of mounting pins.

4. Remove exhaust silencer and tail pipe.

5. Disconnect inner shaft couplings and propeller shaft couplings (Fig.H.27).

6. Remove rear seat assembly and access panel over spring plate. Remove holding nuts, plate and three rear studs

from axle casing (Fig.H.26).

7. Remove bolts (9) from rear attachment, take weight of unit and remove nuts (51), washers (52) and rubber pads (53) from nose mounting plate (62)(Fig.H.27).

8. Lower unit forward and down to clear vehicle.

9. Reverse procedure to install ensuring that rubber pads (53) are correctly located in nose mounting plate.

AXLE SHAFT AND HUB ASSEMBLY (Mk.2 models) - Removal and Installation

NOTE:- A road spring extension bar to the dimensions given in Fig.H.54 will be required for this operation.

Removal

1. Raise rear of vehicle with jack and support on chassis stands.

2. Remove road wheel and jack up vertical link (Fig.H.55).

3. Disconnect brake pipe and hose from bracket (Fig.H.56) and cable and spring from operating lever.

4. Remove from bolts (20) at axle shaft coupling (Fig.H.57).

5. Secure extension bar to road spring as shown in Fig.H.54. with jack under bar raise spring to relieve damper load and support bar with axle stand. Ensure bar is securely supported.

6. Disconnect radius arm at axle end and swing clear of shaft.

7. On Vitesse Mk.2 slacken nut at bottom of damper link, remove nut at top of link and tap link taper clear of damper arm.

8. On GT6 Mk.2 slacken upper damper nut, remove bottom damper nut and move damper clear to axle.

9. Disconnect lower wishbone at chassis and remove road spring eyebolt.

10. Withdraw hub and shaft assembly.

Installation

1. Position axle shaft and hub assembly under vehicle and attach lower wishbone to chassis frame leaving nut finger-tight.

2. If road spring extension bar has been removed, attach and support as in Fig.H.58.

3. Jack up vertical link until road spring eyebolt can be inserted and fully tighten nut.

4. Remove extension bar and connect intermediate to inner shaft (Fig.H.57).

5. Attach damper link or damper, as applicable, together with radius arm to vertical link.

Fig.H.38 Measuring the pinion height

Fig.H.39 Identification markings on the crown wheel and pinion

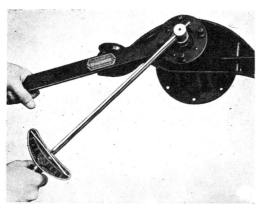

Fig.H.40 Torqueing the pinion flange nut

Fig.H.41 Measuring the pinion bearing pre-load

Fig.H.42 Checking run-out on the pinion flange

Fig.H.43 Components of the differential assembly

(See Fig.H.1 for key)

6. Tighten lower wishbone attachment nut.

7. Connect handbrake cable and spring to brake lever and brake pipe and hose to support bracket.

8. Adjust and bleed brakes, fit road wheel and road test vehicle.

ROTOFLEX COUPLING - Replacement (Fig.53)

1. Remove axle shaft and hub assembly;

2. Fit Churchill compression tool S328 to coupling and remove bolts (17 and 28) to detach coupling from shafts.

3. Remove brake drum and hub nut (40) with washer.

4. Using Churchill tool S109B with thread protector S109C, press outer shaft (18) from hub assembly. Retain shims (36) and spacer (37) on neck of shaft.

5. Press stoneguard and spacer from outer shaft with Churchill tool S4221 and adaptors S4221A-17 (Fig.H.59).

6. Withdraw Rotoflex coupling.

7. Feed outer drive shaft into new Rotoflex coupling and attach coupling to spider with new bolts (28).

8. Using a tubular drift, replace stoneguard and spacer on outer shaft,

9. Replace collar and shim on outer shaft, force spliced end into hub assembly until hub nut with washer can be started and tighten nut.

10. Secure intermediate shaft to Rotoflex coupling with new bolts (28) and remove steel band from coupling.

11. Refit brake drum.

12. Install axle shaft and hub assembly.

REAR HUB (Mk.2 models) - Dismantling

1. Remove hub assembly.

2. Fit Churchill tool S323/1 and tool S342; secure suitable bolt and push hub clear of vertical link (Fig.H.61).

3. Lever out inner seal (29) (Fig.H.62).

4. Remove inner bearing cup with Churchill tool S123A or soft metal drift (Fig.H.63).

5. Secure Churchill tool S323 with adaptors S323-1 to outer bearing (34) and withdraw bearing (Fig.H.62).

6. Remove seal (35) and drift away outer bearing cup.

REAR HUB (Mk.2 models) - Re-assembly (Fig.H.53)

1. Place Churchill gauge S325-1 over hub extension, place gauge plate S325-3 on end of extension, measure and note clearance between gauges (Fig.H.63).

2. Assemble inner and outer bearing into vertical link in a dry condition and fit Churchill tool S325-2 through bolt bearings.

3. Fit gauge S325-1 with slot uppermost, assemble and lightly tighten gauge plate S325-3 to bed-down bearings but permitting rotation . Use feeler gauge size obtained in procedure "1", selected spacer and two shims if required to tightly fill slot (Fig.H.64). This ensures correct hub float of 0.013-0.064 mm (0.0005-0.0025 ins). on assembly.

NOTE:- Spacers of five thicknesses are available and shim thickness is 0.076 mm (0.003 ins.) (see TECHNICAL DATA).

4. Remove gauges and both tapered bearings leaving cups in position.

5. Apply Shell Retina "X" grease, or approved alternative to outer tapered bearing and assemble on cup in vertical link. Position oil seal (35) and, using Churchill tool S322 and 550, drive seal and bearing into housing (Fig.H.65).

6. Position vertical link over hub and drive onto hub with tool S324 against bearing cone (Fig.H.66).

7. Grease tapered bearing and cone and tap into position until vertical link extremities have up-and-down movement of 1.6 mm (0.63 in.) (Fig.H.67).

NOTE:- Bearing will be drawn home at final assembly.

8. Assemble inner seal (29) in similar manner to outer seal.

9. Fit spacer (36) previously selected and shim, if applicable, to outer axle shaft. Assemble with grease while threading shaft splined section into hub. Draw shaft through hub with slave nut initially without assembling washer, remove slave nut and with washer in position finally tighten Nyloc nut - turning vertical link at same time to bed-down bearing.

10. Install hub assembly.

INTERMEDIATE SHAFT COUPLING - Inspection

1. Remove rear road wheel, jack vertical link and support road spring extension bar (Fig.H.58).

2. Remove flange bolts (Fig.H.57). Lever flanges apart.

3. Hold shaft firmly and turn flange yoke axially in both directions (Fig.H.68). If end-float exists, remove outer drive shaft and renew spider cup assemblies as previously described.

4. Connect flanges, remove supports and replace road wheel.

FINAL DRIVE UNIT (Mk.2 models) - Removal and Installation

1. Jack up rear of vehicle and support on chassis stands. Remove road wheels and drain unit.

2. Disconnect inner axle shaft coupling and rear end of propeller shaft.

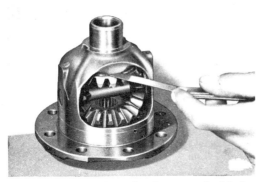

Fig.H.44 Measuring the planet gear backlash

Fig.H.45 Assembling side bearings to the differential carrier

Fig.H.46 Measuring total side-float of the differential unit

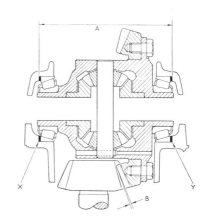

Fig.H.47 Determining required shim pack thickness for the differential side gears

Fig.H.48 Measuring crown wheel "in" and "out" of mesh

Fig.H.49 Assembling the bearing caps

3. Remove exhaust silencer and tail pipe.

4. Disconnect radius arm from chassis and release handbrake clevis-pin and spring from brake backplate.

5. Attach and support road spring extension bars (Fig.H.58).

6. Remove damper links (Vitesse) or dampers (GT6).

7. Remove spring eyebolts.

8. Proceed as detailed in procedures 6 to 9 for Mk. 1 models.

FINAL DRIVE UNIT - Overhaul (Fig.H.1)

1. Clean unit with paraffin and overhaul on clean surface.

NOTE:- Identify parts to avoid mixing and keep shim packs intact to assist assembly.

Dismantling

1. Remove inner axle shafts (Fig.H.20).

2. Remove bolts (63) with spring washers and rotate pinion until two chamfered edges on differential carrier (18) permit withdrawal from rear casing (Fig.H.28).

3. Remove bearing caps (47) and attach Churchill spreading tool S101 to nose piece casing as shown in Fig.H.29. Open out tool by turning extension screw until hand-tight, then spread casing by giving a further HALF TURN ONLY with spanner.

CAUTION:- Do not spread more than this amount of housing will be irreparably damaged. .

4. Remove differential carrier, identify bearings, caps and shim packs with their respective positions.

5. Remove crownwheel (Fig.H.30).

6. Re-assemble differential carrier in casing and secure with bearings and shims. Release spreading tool.

7. Mount dial indicator gauge on housing with plunger against carrier face, rotate carrier and check run-out (Fig.H.31). Run out must not exceed 0.076 mm (0.003 in.)

NOTE:- Excessive run-out indicates distorted cage or defective bearings.

8. Spread casing to remove carrier, release and remove spreading tool.

9. Withdraw bearings (19) with Churchill tool S4221A-8C (Fig.H.32).

10. Drive out locking pin (4) as shown in Fig.H.33 and cross-shaft (69), rotate to remove differential gears (5 and 6) and thrust washers (3 and 7).

Pinion Removal

1. Secure flange (57) against rotation and remove nut (56) and washer (Fig.H.34).

2. Drive pinion from casing with soft hammer to avoid damage to threads. Remove and retain shim pack complete and remove spacer (61).

3. Extract pinion head bearing with Churchill tool S4221A-4A as shown in Fig.H.35 and remove selective spacer (66).

4. Drive head and tail bearing outer races from casing (Fig. H.36).

5. Remove four bolts (54) and front mounting plate.

Inspection

1. Remove all traces of jointing material from joint faces. Clean all parts in trichlorethylene or paraffin and dry with air. Remove any burrs from bores, housing and joint faces. Examine all parts for cracks or damage. Check for excessive wear against tolerances given in TECHNICAL DATA. Renew parts as necessary. Bearings must be renewed complete and crownwheels and pinions are identified matched pairs, replaceable only by similarly identified components (Fig.H.39). Renew joint gasket and oil seals and use Hermetite or similar compound on gasket joint.

Re-assembly
Pinion

NOTE:- Lightly oil bearings before assembly.

1. Using Churchill tool S124 assemble pinion bearing outer races in housing (64).

2. Assemble head bearing (65) to pinion without selective spacer (66) (Fig.H.37).

3. Install pinion in housing, assemble tail bearing flange (57), plain washer and nut (56) and tighten nut to specified torque. Do not assemble spacer (61), shims (60) and oil seal (58) at this stage.

NOTE:- Spin pinion during tightening process to "bed" bearing rollers.

4. Check pinion height with Churchill tool S108 as shown in Fig.H.38. Use ground button to fully depress gauge plunger and zero gauge before placing tool in casing with plunger on pinion head. When gauge is pressed downwards, the dial indicates shim thickness required between normal pinion and head bearing.

NOTE:- Pinions of normal height are marked "N" on top face. Pinions varying from normal in height are marked with a plus or minus figure which indicates an amount to be added to, or subtracted from, gauge reading with gauge reading of 0.013 in. and pinion marked as in Fig.H.39, shim thickness required is 0.013 + 0.001 in. = 0.014 in.).

Fig.H.50 Measuring the crownwheel backlash

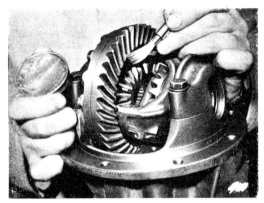

Fig.H.51 Applying marking compound to the crown wheel teeth

ADDENDUM—Pitch line to tooth tip
DEDENDUM—Pitch line to tooth root

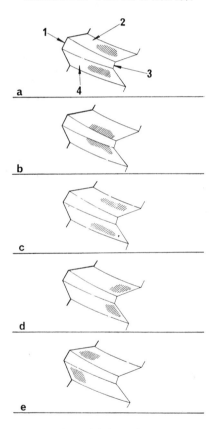

1 Heel (thick end)
2 Coastside (concave)
3 Toe (thin end)
4 Drive side (convex)

Fig.H.52 Contact markings on the crown wheel teeth

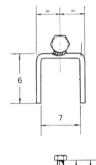

Fig.H.54 Rear road spring extension bar

1. 915 mm (36 in.)
2. Weld area as shown
3. Drill two holes 9.5 mm (0.375 in.) dia.
4. 25 mm (1 in.)
5. 146 mm (5.75 in.)
6. 70 mm (2.75 in.)
7. 57 mm (2.25 in.)
8. 9.5 mm (0.375 in.) nut and bolt
9. 63 mm (2.5 in.)
10. 89 mm (3.5 in.)
11. Make from 6.3 mm (0.25 in.) mild steel
12. Make from 25 mm (1 in.) hexagon bar mild steel

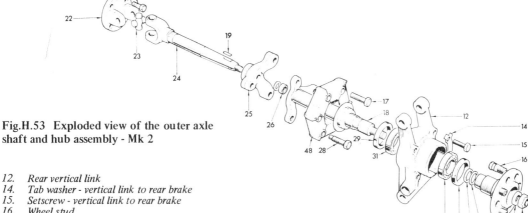

Fig.H.53 Exploded view of the outer axle shaft and hub assembly - Mk 2

12. Rear vertical link
14. Tab washer - vertical link to rear brake
15. Setscrew - vertical link to rear brake
16. Wheel stud
17. Bolt - outer drive shaft to Rotoflex coupling
18. Outer drive shaft assembly
19. Key - intermediate shaft
20. Bolt - shaft joint to inner axle shaft
21. Nyloc nut - inner axle shaft
22. Flange yoke - coupling
23. Yoke
24. Intermediate drive shaft
25. Driven shaft
26. Nyloc nut - driven flange to shaft
28. Bolt - driven flange to Rotoflex coupling
29. Inner oil seal
31. Inner bearing
34. Outer bearing
35. Outer oil seal
36. Spacer - outer drive shaft
37. Shim - outer drive shaft
38. Rear hub and stud assembly
39. Washer
40. Nyloc nut
48. Rotoflex coupling
49. Lower wishbone assembly
60. Brake drum
61. Brake backplate

Fig.H.55 Jacking up the vertical link - Mk 2

Fig.H.56 Handbrake cable and brake pipe attachment - Mk 2

Fig.H.57 Axle shaft drive flange attachments - Mk 2

Fig.H.59 Pressing stone guard and spacer from shaft - Mk 2

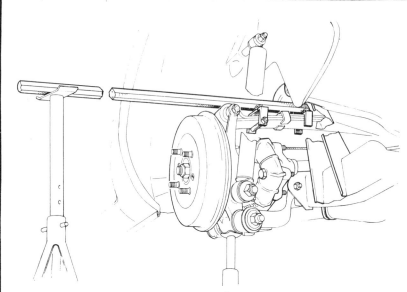

Fig.H.58 Spring extension bar in position - Mk 2

Fig.H.61 Pressing hub out of the vertical link - Mk 2

Fig.H.62 Assembling Special Fitting Tool No. S 323, to the outer bearing - Mk 2

(See Fig.H.53 for key)

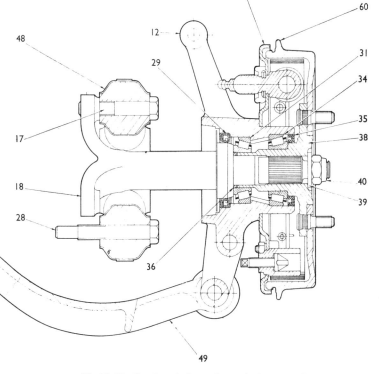

Fig.H.60 Sectional view of rear hub assembly Mk 2

5. Remove flange, bearings and pinion from casing, leaving outer races in position. Remove head bearing inner race from pinion, fit shims or spacer (66) and re-assemble head bearing.

6. Assemble spacer (61) and shim pack (60) to pinion shaft. install shaft in casing and fit bearing (59), flange (57) and washer and tighten nut (56) to specified torque (Fig. H.41).

7. With pre-load gauge Churchill tool S98A attached to driving flange, move weight along calibrated arm until pinion begins to turn (Fig.H.41). Gauge reading should be 0.014-0.0185 kg/m (12 - 14 lb/ in.). To increase loading, subtract shims from shim pack (60) and to decrease loading add shims.

8. Remove flange and fit oil seal (58) then assemble flange and washer and secure with nut (56) and split pin.

9. Attach dial gauge as shown in Fig.H.43 and check that flange run-out does not exceed 0.05 mm (0.002 in.)

Differential Unit - Assembly (Fig.H.43)

1. Assemble thrust washers to both sun gears and insert into differential cage.

2. Attach thrust washers to planet wheels with grease, insert wheels from opposite sides to mesh with the sun gears.

3. Rotate sun gears together until planet gear and cage bores are aligned and insert cross-shaft.

4. Check planet gear backlash by measuring sun gear end-float (Fig.H.44).

5. Adjust for minimum backlash consistent with freedom of rotation by altering thickness of thrust washer fitted.

6. Align cross-shaft, fit locking pin and retain by peening the edge of drilling in cage

Differential - Total End - Float

1. Fit differential bearing (2 and 19) to carrier journals and assemble in casing without shims (1 and 20).

2. Mount dial gauge as shown in Fig.H.46 with plunger against crown-wheel mounting flange.

3. Pressing both bearing outer races towards each other, lever differential away from indicator and zero gauge.

4. Lever differential towards indicator and note reading.

This gives float "A" (Fig.H.47)

Crown Wheel - "In and Out" of Mesh

1. Ensure mating faces of differential carrier and crown wheel are clean and free from burrs. Secure crownwheel to carrier using new bolts (24) tightening evenly and in turn to specified torque.

NOTE:- Apply two drops of Loctite Studlock to each bolt before fitment.

2. Install differential assembly in casing without bearing caps and mount indicator with plunger against head of crown-wheel attachment bolt (Fig.H.48).

3. Move differential assembly away from indicator to full mesh position and zero gauge.

4. Move assembly towards indicator and note dial reading. This gives float "B" (Fig.H.47).

5. Remove differential unit from housing retaining outer bearing race at its respective side.

Differential Bearing - pre-load (Fig.H.47)

The shim thickness required to give correct bearing pre-load is calculated as follows substituting actual float values for the hypothetical figures given:

EXAMPLE

Dimension A (Total end-float)	0.060 in.
Bearing pre-load	+ 0.003 in.
Total shim thickness required	0.063 in.
Dimension "B" (In and Out of Mesh)	0.025 in.
Specified backlash (0.004-0.006 in.)	- 0.005 in.
Shim thickness required at "Y"	0.020 in.
Total shim thickness required	0.063 in.
Shim thickness required at "Y"	- 0.020 in.
Shim thickness required at "X"	0.043 in.

Fit the appropriate shim packs and bearings to the differential cage trunnions.

Assembly of Differential Unit to Casing

1. Use spreading tool to assembly unit complete with shims into casing. Remove tool.

2. Fit bearing caps with new spring washers (Fig.H.49).

Note identification markings.

Crownwheel backlash

1. Mount dial indicator with plunger on one of the crown-wheel teeth (Fig.H.50).

2. Hold pinion firmly, rock crownwheel to fullest extent and note total indicator reading. Measure at several points and check that backlash is within 0.01-0.15 mm (0.004-0.006 in.)

3. If backlash is excessive, transfer shims to equivalent value by which backlash is to be reduced from "X" to "Y". To increase backlash, transfer from "Y" to "X".

Fig.H.63 Measuring hub bearing end-float - Mk2

Fig.H.64 Determining thickness of spacer and shims required - Mk 2

Fig.H.65 Installing outer bearing and grease seal in vertical link - Mk 2

Fig.H.66 Assembling vertical link to the hub - Mk 2

Fig.H.67 Installing the inner bearing - Mk 2

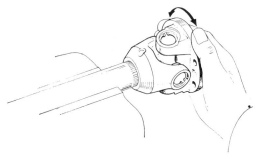

Fig.H.68 Checking for end-float at the spider journals - Mk 2

Tooth Contact

With the backlash correctly set, coat eight to ten teeth on the crown wheel with Engineers blue (Fig.H.51). Turn the pinion until all the marked teeth have been in contact with the pinion teeth. Check tooth pattern on both sides of the gears (Fig.H.52).

a. Correct marking: If the pinion bearing pre-load and crownwheel backlash have been set correctly, the margins above the area of contact should be the same. The marking should be lozenge-shaped and nearer to the toe than the heel.

b. High Contact: In this case the area of contact is above the centre-line of the tooth, due to the pinion being too far away from the crownwheel. To rectify, increase the shim thickness between the tail bearing cone and the pinion bearing spacer must also be increased by the same amount to maintain correct bearing pre-load.

c. Low Contact: In this case the area of contact is below the centre-line of the tooth, indicating that the pinion too/far in mesh. To rectify, decrease the shim thickness under the pinion head bearing outer ring. The pinion bearing pre-load must be decreased a corresponding amount to maintain correct bearing pre-load.

d. NOTE: The above correction tends to move the tooth contact area towards the heel on "DRIVE" and the toe on "COAST". It may, therefore, be necessary to re-adjust the crownwheel "IN and "OUT" of mesh and backlash.

d. Toe Contact: When the area of contact is running off the toe of the tooth, this indicates insufficient backlash. Move the crownwheel away from the pinion by transferring shims from the crownwheel side of the differential carrier to the opposite side.

e. Heel Contact: When the area of contact is concentrated at the large end of the tooth, this is an indication of excessive backlash. Move the crownwheel further into mesh with the pinion transferring shims from the opposite side of the differential carrier to the crownwheel side.

NOTE:- Backlash: Always move the crownwheel when adjusting to obtain the correct backlash as this has a more direct effect than moving the pinion. Crownwheel Movement: Moving the crownwheel out of mesh has the effect of moving the contact area up the tooth flank and towards the heel of the tooth.

Pinion Movement: Moving the pinion out of mesh has the effect of moving the contact area up the tooth and towards the heel on "DRIVE" and the toe on "COAST".

Final Assembly

1. Manoeuvre differential unit into rear casing using new gasket (8) and join casing sections tightening bolts evenly and in turn.

2. Assemble inner axle shafts and install final drive unit.

Technical Data

Crown Wheel

Maximum run-out	0.076 mm (0.003 in.)
Permissible backlash	0.10-0.15 mm (0.004-0.006 in.)

Pinion

Journal diameter-Head Bearing	28.59-28.63 mm (1.1256-1.1261 in.)
	25.415-25.428 mm (1.0006-1.0011 in.) *
- Tail Bearing	25.410-25.423 mm (1.0004-1.0009 in.)
	19.06-19.073 mm (0.7504 0.7509 in.)*
Bearing pre-load	0.014-0.19 kg/m (12-16 lb/ in.)
Bearing spacer length	36.83-36.96 mm (1.450-1.455 in.)
(Alternative)	39.22-39.34 mm (1.544-1.549 in.)

Hypoid Housing

Internal diameters

Pinion head bearing housing	68.224-68.25 mm (2.6860-2.6870 in.)
Pinion tail bearing housing	57.112-57.137 mm (2.2485 2.2495 in.)
	53.937-53.962 mm (2.1235-2.1245 in.) *
Differential bearing housing	61.996-62.022 mm (2.4418-2.4428 in.)

Differential Carrier

Bore for cross-shaft	15.86-15.89 mm (0.6245-0.6255 in.)
	12.68-12.70 mm (0.4993-0.5000 in.)*
Bore for sun gear spigot	31.78-31.83 mm (1.251-1.253 in.)
	28.60-28.65 mm (1.126-1.128 in.) *
Side bearing spigot dia.	31.78 mm (1.251 in.)

Differential Gears

Sun gear - spigot dia.	31.798mm (1.2485 in.)
	28.537-28.557 mm (1.1235-1.1243 in.)*
Planet gear bore dia.	15.815 mm (0.625 in.)
	12.7-12.738 mm (0.5000-0.5015 in.) *
Cross-shaft dia.	15.842-15.855 mm (0.6237-0.6242 in.)
	12.60-12.61 mm (0.4990-0.4995 in.) *

Inner Axle shaft

Bearing journal dia.	25.001-25.024 mm (0.9847-0.9852 in.)
	22.215-22.228 mm (0.8754-0.8759 in.)

Rear Hub

Needler roller bearing housing dia.	31.775-31.750 mm (1.2508-1.2498 in.)
Main bearing housing dia.	57.132-57.147 mm (2.2493 2.2499 in.)

Differential Bearing Shims

Part No.		Thickness
123813	0.216-0.241 mm	0.0085-0.0095 in.
4	0.300-0.330 mm	0.012-0.013 in.
5	0.350-0.381 mm	0.014-0.015 in.
6	0.406-0.432 mm	0.016-0.017 in.
7	0.483-0.533 mm	0.019-0.021 in.

Planet Gear Thrust Washers

138440	0.560-0.511 mm	0.025-0.028 in.
134076	0.562-0.613 mm	0.030-0.032 in.
136441	0.664-0.714 mm	0.034-0.036 in.
138442	0.765-0.816 mm	0.038-0.040 in.

Planet Gear Thrust Washers*

145282	0.838-0.889 mm	0.033-0.035 in.
104572	0.839-0.939 mm	0.035-0.037 in.
145262	0.939-0.990 mm	0.037-0.039 in.
108935	0.990-1.041 mm	0.039-0.041 in.
142167	1.041-1.092 mm	0.041-0.043 in.
108963	1.092-1.143 mm	0.043-0.045 in.
142168	1.143-1.193 mm	0.045-0.047 in.
108937	1.193-1.244 mm	0.047-0.049 in.
108938	1.295-1.320 mm	0.051-0.055 in.
108939	1.397-1.447 mm	0.055-0.057 in.

Pinion Head Bearing Shims

140793	0.076 mm	0.003 in.
140792	0.127 mm	0.005 in.
140791	0.25 mm	0.010 in.
140790	0.76 mm	0.030 in.

Pinion Head Bearing Spacers

145918	1.905 mm	0.075 in.
9	1.943 mm	0.0765 in.
20	1.481 mm	0.078 in.
1	2.019 mm	0.0795 in.
2	2.057 mm	0.081 in.
3	2.096 mm	0.0825 in.
4	2.134 mm	0.084 in.
5	2.172 mm	0.0855 in.
6	2.210 mm	0.087 in.
7	2.248 mm	0.0888 in.
145928	2.287 mm	0.90 in.
9	2.325 mm	0.0915 in.
30	2.363 mm	0.093 in.
1	2.401 mm	0.0945 in.
2	2.439 mm	0.096 in.

Hub Bearing Spacers **

152483	3.531 mm	0.139 in.
4	3.581 mm	0.141 in.
5	3.632 mm	0.143 in.
6	3.759 mm	0.148 in.
7	3.937 mm	0.155 in.

Hub Bearing Shim **

142340	0.076 mm	0.003 in.

*Vitesse Six models

** Mk.2 models

Oil Capacity	1.0 Imp pint (1.2 U.S. pint 0.57 litres)
Oil specification	SAE 90EP

Rear Suspension

GENERAL
REAR TRANSVERSE SPRING - Removal and Installation
DAMPER - Removal and Installation
DAMPER LINK (Vitesse Mk 2) - Removal and Installation
RADIUS ARM - Removal and Installation
REAR WHEEL - Alignment
TRUNNION HOUSING - Overhaul
LOWER WISHBONE (Mk 2 models) - Overhaul
TECHNICAL DATA

GENERAL

The swing axle type rear suspension has a transverse leaf spring centrally clamped to the final drive unit casing. The spring is joined with vertical link plates to hub assemblies with hub trunnions on Mk 1 models and lower wishbone assemblies on Mk 2 models. Telescopic dampers connected to the chassis control suspension damping, except on Vitesse Mk 2 models which have lever arm dampers. Rear mounted radius arms connected to the hub assemblies control rear wheel alignment.

REAR TRANSVERSE SPRING - Removal and Installation
Removal

1. Raise rear of vehicle with jack and place onto axle stands. Remove rear road wheels.

2. Disconnect each brake hose at chassis bracket, and disconnect handbrake cable and spring at backplate.

3. With jack under vertical link relieve damper load.

4. Disconnect inner axle shaft couplings.

5. Slacken nut (8), remove nut (13) with washer and pull each damper off lower attachment (Fig.I.3). On Mk 2 models, remove bolts (63) (Fig.I.9) to disconnect damper on GT6 or bolts (13) (Fig.I.10) to disconnect damper link on Vitesse.

6. Supporting vertical links (10), remove spring eye bolt (46) from each side (Fig.I.4). Fit and support road spring extension bar to remove spring eyebolt (see REAR AXLE section).

7. Remove rear passenger seat and spring centre attachment access cover. Remove nuts (4) with washers, plate (3) and extract three rear studs (42) (Fig.I.5).

8. Remove road spring extension bar on Mk 2 models.

9. Withdraw spring from under vehicle (Fig.I.6).

Installation

1. With spring "FRONT" marking in correct direction, pass spring over axle casing until centre bolt engages in locating hole. Turn shorter threaded lengths of studs (42) into axle casing, install spring plate and secure with nuts (4).

2. Apply "Prestik" sealer or similar at edge of access cover, secure cover, and coat joint with "Seelastik" or similar. Install passenger seat.

3. On Mk 2 models fit and support road spring extensions bars.

4. Assemble vertical links to spring eyes but do not fully tighten eyebolt nuts.

5. Jack up vertical links to relieve damper load, attach bottom of dampers, or damper link on Vitesse Mk 2, and connect axle shaft couplings.

6. Connect handbrake cables and pull-off springs. Connect brake hoses and fill and bleed brake system.

7. On Mk 2 models, remove road spring extension bars.

8. Position trolley jack under axle casing, remove chassis stands, support vertical links at working height, load vehicle and lower trolley jack until axle shafts are at static laden position (see TECHNICAL DATA section). Fully tighten eyebolt nuts.

9. Install road wheels and remove jack.

DAMPER - Removal and Installation
Removal

1. Raise rear of vehicle with jack and place onto axle stands. Remove rear road wheels.

2. With jack under vertical link, relieve damper load.

3. Remove bolt (44) and nut (13) (Fig.I.3), or nuts (62 and 63) (Fig.I.9) for GT6 Mk 2, and remove dampers. On Vitesse Mk 2, remove socket screws (6) and nut (13) to remove damper and link (Fig.I.10).

4. Examine rubber bushes at telescopic damper attachment points for damage or deterioration and renew if necessary.

Installation

1. Remove air from telescopic damper by operating over full stroke whilst in vertical position.

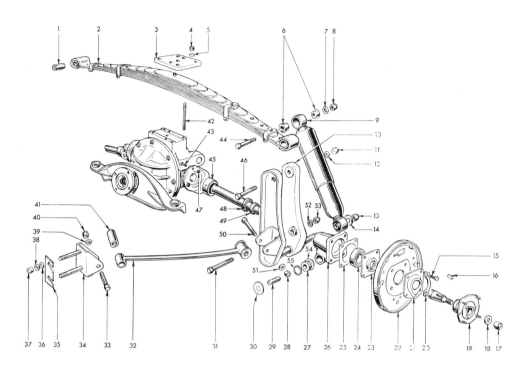

1.	Spring eye bush	
2.	Road spring	
3.	Spring clamp plate	
4.	Nut	
5.	Washer	
6.	Rubber bush	
7.	Washer	
8.	Nut	
9.	Damper	
10.	Vertical link	
11.	Nut	
12.	Washer	
13.	Nut	
14.	Washer	
15.	Bolt	
16.	Key	
17.	Nut	
18.	Washer	
19.	Hub	
20.	Locktab	
21.	Grease retainer	
22.	Brake backplate	
23.	Seal housing	

24.	Bearing
25.	Gasket
26.	Trunnion housing
27.	Nylon bush
28.	Nut
29.	Steel bush
30.	Dust seal
31.	Bolt
32.	Radius arm
33.	Bolt
34.	Radius arm bracket
35.	Shim
36.	Washer
37.	Nut
38.	Washer
39.	Washer
40.	Nut
41.	Rubber bush
42.	Stud
43.	Bolt
44.	Bolt
45.	Axle shaft coupling

46.	Bolt
47.	Nut
48.	Flinger
49.	Seal
50.	Bolt
51.	Washer
52.	Washer
53.	Nut
54.	Dust seal
55.	Rubber ring
56.	Brake pipe union nut
57.	Flexible brake hose
58.	Nut
59.	Locknut
60.	Square nut
61.	Clevis pin
62.	Clevis
63.	Handbrake pull-off spring
64.	Handbrake secondary cable
65.	Adjustable spring anchor
66.	Adjusting nut
67.	Locknut

Fig.I.1 Exploded view of the rear suspension

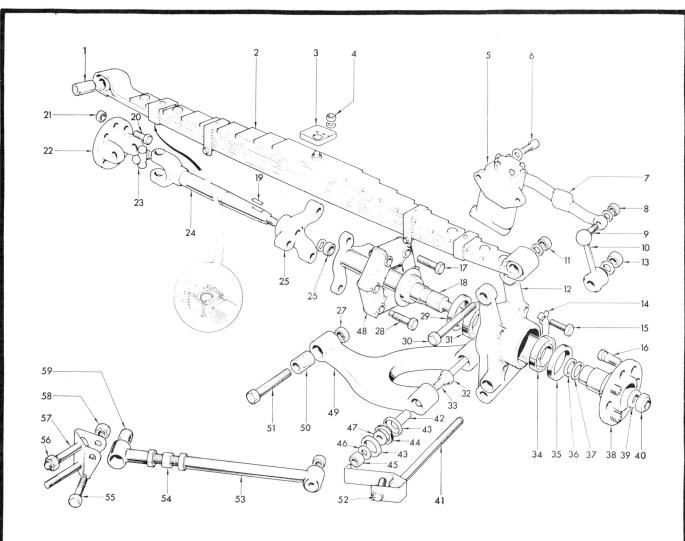

1.	Rubber bush - spring eye	
2.	Rear transverse road spring	
3.	Spring plate	
4.	Nyloc nut - spring plate to axle housing	
5.	Rear damper - lever arm type	
6.	Screw - damper to mounting bracket	
7.	Damper arm	
8.	Nyloc nut - damper arm to damper link	
9.	Ball end taper	
10.	Link assembly	
11.	Nyloc nut - rear road spring ends to vertical link	
12.	Rear vertical link	
13.	Nyloc nut - damper link to vertical link	
14.	Tab washer - vertical link to rear brake	
15.	Setscrew - vertical link to rear brake	
16.	Wheel stud	
17.	Bolt outer drive shaft - rotoflex coupling	
18.	Outer drive shaft assembly	
19.	Key - intermediate shaft	
20.	Bolt - shaft joint to inner axle shaft	

21.	Nyloc nut - inner axle shaft
22.	Flange yoke - coupling
23.	Yoke
24.	Intermediate drive shaft
25.	Driven flange
26.	Nyloc nut - driven flange to shaft
27.	Nyloc nut - lower wishbone to chassis
28.	Bolt - driven flange to rotoflex coupling
29.	Inner oil seal
30.	Bolt - rear spring ends to vertical link
31.	Inner bearing
32.	Outer bush } wishbone to vertical link
33.	Bolt
34.	Outer bearing
35.	Outer oil seal
36.	Spacer } outer drive shaft
37.	Shim
38.	Rear hub and stud assembly
39.	Washer
40..	Nyloc nut - rear hub to outer drive shaft

41.	Bracket - assembly mounting radius arm to vertical link
42.	Distance piece }
43.	Water shield } wishbone to vertical link
44.	Dirt seal
45.	Nyloc nut }
46.	Washer } wishbone to vertical link
47.	Outer bush }
48.	Rotoflex coupling
49.	Lower wishbone assembly
50.	Lower wishbone - inner bush
51.	Bolt - wishbone to chassis
52.	Bolt - radius arm to vertical link
53.	Radius arm
54.	Radius arm adjuster
55.	Bolt - radius arm to bracket
56.	Nyloc nut - radius arm to bracket
57.	Bolt - radius arm support bracket
58.	Nut - radius arm to bracket
59.	Rubber bush - radius arm

Fig.I.2 Exploded view of the rear suspension - Mk 2

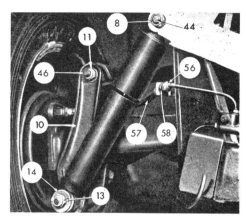

Fig.I.3 Vertical link, brake pipe and damper attachments

(See Fig.I.1 for key)

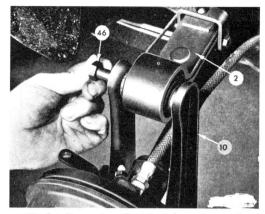

Fig.I.4 Removing pivot bolt from the vertical link and spring eye.

Fig.I.5 Rear spring clamp plate attachments

Fig.I.6 Withdrawing the rear spring.

Fig.I.7 Radius arm attachments

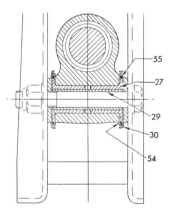

Fig.I.8 Sectional view of the trunnion assembly

(See Fig.I.1 for key)

2. Install damper and obtain "static load" condition before tightening attachment nuts.

3. Refit road wheels.

DAMPER LINK (Vitesse Mk 2) - Removal and Installation (Fig.I.10)

1. Raise rear of vehicle and place onto axle stands. Remove rear road wheel.

2. With jack under vertical link remove damper load.

3. Remove nuts (8 and 13). Remove link from damper arm with extractor.

4. Install by reversing removal procedure.

RADIUS ARM - Removal and Installation

1. Carry out damper removal procedure until jack is positioned under vertical links.

2. Adjust jack height until attachment bolts can readily be removed and radius arm withdrawn (Fig.I.7) (see Fig.I.11 for Mk 2 models).

3. Examine rubber bushes for damage or deterioration. If necessary remove with press, clean bores and press in new bushes.

NOTE: If chassis mounting brackets are removed on Mk 1 models, ensure the same number of shims (35) are replaced behind bracket.

4. Reverse procedure to install radius arms.

REAR WHEEL - Alignment

Check and, if necessary, adjust rear wheel alignment by removing shims (35) to increase toe-in and adding shims to decrease toe-in, on Mk 1 models. Radius arms on Mk 2 models are adjustable.

NOTE:- Toe-in should be checked with jigs or preferably with optical equipment which enables front and rear wheels to be aligned together. This equipment projects a light beam at right-angles to the axle onto a screen where dimensions and angles can be directly read off. An approximate check may be made as follows.

1. Ensure tyres are evenly inflated and vehicle is on level ground.

2. Mark inside of each wheel rim in front of, and level with axle and measure distance between wheels: - distance "A".

3. Move vehicle until rim marking is behind, and level with, axle and again measure distance between wheels: - Distance "B".

4. The difference when "A" is subtracted from "B" is approximate toe-in which should be 0-1.6 mm (0-0.0625 in.) with vehicle in static laden condition.

TRUNNION HOUSING - Overhaul (Fig.I.1)

1. Raise vehicle onto chassis stands, remove rear road wheels and relieve damper load.

2. Disconnect brake hose at chassis bracket, handbrake cable and return spring from backplate axle shaft coupling and radius arm from vertical link.

3. Remove damper and jack from under vertical link.

4. Support brake drum, remove bolt (46) from road spring eye and brake/shaft assembly. Clean exterior of assembly and place on clean bench.

5. Detach links (10) from trunnion housing and remove dust seal (30), steel bush (29), flanged nylon bushes (27), "O"-rings (55) and inner dust seals (54).

6. Clean and examine all parts for damage, deterioration or wear. Renew parts as necessary.

7. Apply grease (Shell Retinax "A" or similar) to bushes and assemble parts as shown in Fig.I.8.

8. Position brake/shaft assembly under vehicle and attach vertical link to road spring eye bush. Do not fully tighten bolt (44).

9. Place jack beneath vertical link and connect damper, radius arm and axle shaft coupling.

10. Position trolley jack under axle casing, remove chassis stands, support vertical links at working height, load vehicle and lower trolley jack until axle shafts are at static laden position. Fully tighten nut (11).

11. Connect brake hose and handbrake. Replenish and bleed brakes.

12. Fit road wheels and remove jack.

LOWER WISHBONE (Mk 2 models) - Overhaul (Fig.I.2)

1. Raise rear of vehicle onto chassis stands, remove road wheel and relieve damper load.

2. Remove attachment bolts (51 and 33) and remove wishbone.

3. Remove outer water shield (43), dirt seal (44), bush (47) inner water shield and distance piece (42) from outer wishbone and press out inner bush (50).

4. Examine bushes and seals for damage and deterioration and renew if necessary.

5. Apply grease, (Mobilgrease MP or similar) to wishbone outer bushes and assemble parts as shown in Fig.I.12.

6. Press inner bush (50) into position.

7. Assemble wishbone to vertical link and secure with bolt (33) leaving nut (27) semi-tight.

8. Secure inner end of wishbone to chassis mounting with bolts (51).

Fig.I.9 Damper attachment - GT6 Mk 2

Fig.I.10   Damper attachment - Vitesse Mk 2

Fig.I.11   Radius arm assembly - Mk 2 models

(See Fig.I.2 for key)

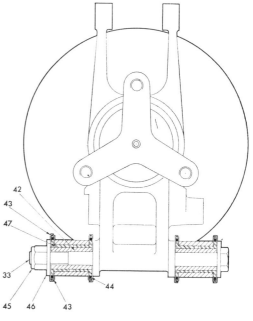

Fig.I.12   Sectional view of the lower wishbone bushes

(See Fig.I.2 for key)

9.   Fully tighten nut (27).

10. Fit road wheels and remove jacks.

Technical Data

Road spring - Type	Transverse leaf
Camber angle (Static laden)	
- Vitesse 6, Vitesse 1 litre to HC1419DL and Vitesse Mk 2	2o negative
- Vitesse 2 litre from HC1420DL	3½o negative
- GT6	2½o negative
- GT6 Mk 2	2o negative
Toe-in (Static laden)	
- Vitesse 6 and Vitesse litre to HC1419DL	0-1.5 mm (0-0.063 in.)
- Vitesse 2 litre from HC1420DL	1.5-3.0 mm (0.063-0.125 in.)
- Vitesse Mk 2	0-0.79 mm (0-0.031 in.)
- GT6 Mk 1	0-1.5 mm (0-0.063 in.)
- GT6 Mk 2	1.5-3.0 mm (0.063-0.125 in.)
Damper	- Telescopic hydraulic
- Vitesse Mk 2	- Lever arm hydraulic
Static laden.	

The condition when a weight of 68 kg (150 lb)
is placed on each seat.

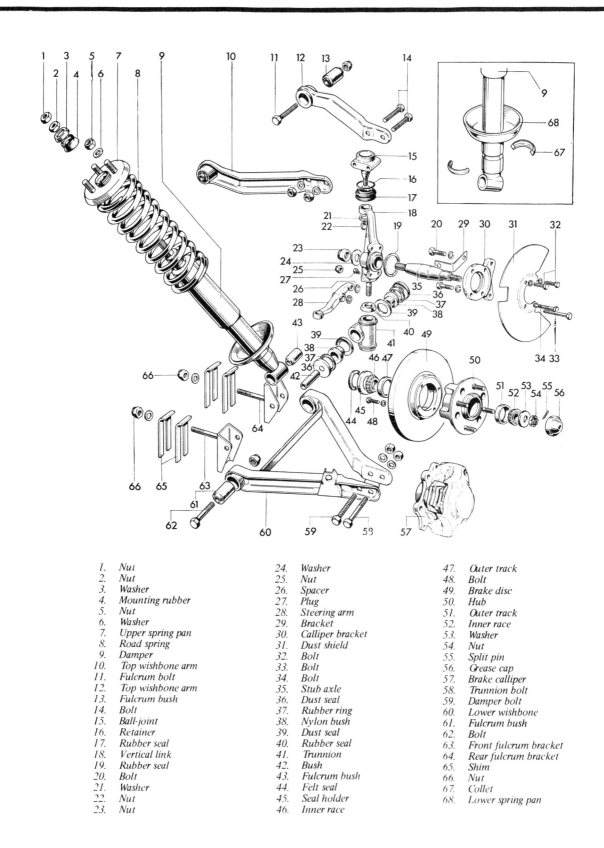

**Fig.J.1 Exploded view of the front suspension
assembly - L.H. shown**

1.	Nut	24.	Washer	47.	Outer track
2.	Nut	25.	Nut	48.	Bolt
3.	Washer	26.	Spacer	49.	Brake disc
4.	Mounting rubber	27.	Plug	50.	Hub
5.	Nut	28.	Steering arm	51.	Outer track
6.	Washer	29.	Bracket	52.	Inner race
7.	Upper spring pan	30.	Calliper bracket	53.	Washer
8.	Road spring	31.	Dust shield	54.	Nut
9.	Damper	32.	Bolt	55.	Split pin
10.	Top wishbone arm	33.	Bolt	56.	Grease cap
11.	Fulcrum bolt	34.	Bolt	57.	Brake calliper
12.	Top wishbone arm	35.	Stub axle	58.	Trunnion bolt
13.	Fulcrum bush	36.	Dust seal	59.	Damper bolt
14.	Bolt	37.	Rubber ring	60.	Lower wishbone
15.	Ball-joint	38.	Nylon bush	61.	Fulcrum bush
16.	Retainer	39.	Dust seal	62.	Bolt
17.	Rubber seal	40.	Rubber seal	63.	Front fulcrum bracket
18.	Vertical link	41.	Trunnion	64.	Rear fulcrum bracket
19.	Rubber seal	42.	Bush	65.	Shim
20.	Bolt	43.	Fulcrum bush	66.	Nut
21.	Washer	44.	Felt seal	67.	Collet
22.	Nut	45.	Seal holder	68.	Lower spring pan
23.	Nut	46.	Inner race		

Front Suspension

GENERAL

The independent front suspension is of the double wishbone type with coil springs and telescopic dampers. The unequal length wishbones are anchored through rubber-bushed fulcrum pivots at their inner ends a cast vertical link is swivel-mounted to their outer ends. The stub axle is a separate item attached to the vertical link and the wheel hub assembly is carried on tapered roller bearings. The suspension coil springs are mounted co-axially on the telescopic hydraulic dampers, the units acting on the lower wishbones. A transverse anti-roll bar also acts on the lower wishbones.

The bracketed numbers in the text refer to Fig.J.1, except where otherwise stated.

ROUTINE MAINTENANCE
Weekly

Check tyres and adjust to correct pressures as necessary.

Every 6,000 miles (10,000 km)

Check tightness of wheel nuts and examine tyres for wear.

Every 12,000 miles (20,000 km)

Raise front of vehicle and check road wheels for freedom of rotation and front hub bearing end-float. Adjust end-float as necessary.

At overhaul periods strip, clean, re-lubricate and adjust front hubs as described later in this section.

WHEELS AND TYRES
Wheel balancing

Imbalance of the road wheels may cause wheel tramp, vibration in the steering or abnormal tyre wear.

To obtain maximum ride comfort and tyre lift, the balance of the road wheels should be checked periodically. Whenever any of the wheels are interchanged on the car, they should be re-balanced if previously balanced on the car. Since specialised knowledge and equipment are required to perform this operation, the work should be entrusted ot an Authorised Dealer or tyre specialist.

Tyre pressures

The tyre pressures should be checked and adjusted to the recommended pressure at least once a month. The recommended inflation pressures for the original equipment tyres are listed in TECHNICAL DATA at the end of this section. Check pressures when the tyres are cold as tyre pressure may increase by as much as 0.4 kg/m^2 (6 psi) when hot. Incorrect inflation pressure will result in abnormal wear, (Fig.J.2) and premature failure. There is an average loss of 13% tread mileage for every 10% reduction in inflation pressure below the recommended figure.

Tyre wear

Abnormal tyre wear can be caused by improper inflation pressures, wheel imbalance, misaligned front suspension or mechanical irregularities. When rapid or uneven tyre wear becomes apparent, the fault should be sought and rectified.

Fins and feathers on the tread surface are an indication of severe wheel misalignment. The condition take the form of a sharp "fin" on the edge of each pattern rib and the position of this indicates direction of misalignment . Fins on the outboard edges are caused by excessive toe-out, whereas fins on the inboard edges of the pattern ribs are caused by excessive toe-in. Finning on the nearside front tyre only may be due to severe road camber conditions and cannot be eliminated by mechanical adjustment. In this event, frequent interchanging of the affected wheel is the only way to evenout tyre wear.

Some mechanical defects which could be a cause of abnormal tyre wear are:- loose wheel bearings, uneven brake adjustment, oval brake drum. distorted brake disc, excessive looseness of damage in the suspension, loose steering connections or bent steering arms.

Radial and Cross-Ply Tyres

It is dangerous to use a vehicle which is fitted with an unsuitable combination of tyres. Radial-ply and cross-ply tyres should not be used on the same axle. Radial-ply tyres should not be fitted to the front wheels when cross-ply tyres are fitted at the rear wheels. Radial-ply tyres may be fitted to the rear wheels when cross-ply tyres are fitted to the front wheels, but this is not recommended. It is far safer to fit radial-ply or cross-ply tyres in complete sets.

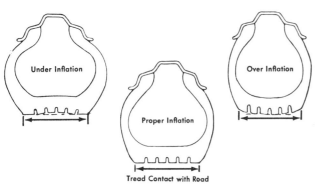

Fig.J.2 Effects of inflation pressures

Fig.J.3 Brake calliper attachments

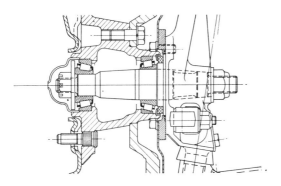

Fig.J.4 Sectional view of the front wheel hub assembly

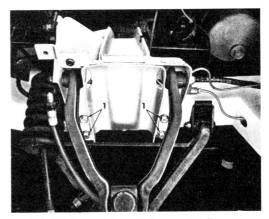

Fig.J.5 Brake pipe and hose connection

Fig.J.6 Lower suspension arm and steering arm attachments

(See Fig.J.1 for key)

Fig.J.7 Suspension sub-frame attachments

SUSPENSION ALIGNMENT

The castor, camber, king pin inclination (K.P.I) and turning angles of the front suspension are inherent in the design of the suspension and are not adjustable. However, they should be checked at regular intervals, particularly if the suspension has been subjected to heavy impact, as excessive wear or accidental damage may disturb one or more of the settings necessitating rectification. Specialised knowledge and equipment are necessary to check these dimensions satisfactorily and this operation should therefore be entrusted to an Authorised Dealer.

The above also applies in respect of the front wheel toe-in which must be correctly set to ensure parallel tracking when the vehicle is moving . A method of setting the toe-in is given in the STEERING section, but this should only be regarded as a temporary measure after the replacement of suspension or steering components. The toe-in should be re-checked as soon as possible afterwards with proper equipment.

FRONT HUB - Removal (Fig.J.4)

1. Raise front of vehicle, place on chassis stands and remove road wheels.

2. Remove two bolts (20) to uncouple disc brake calliper (Fig.J.3).

3. Support removed calliper with wire hook and place wedge between brake pads to retain pistons.

4. Remove grease cap (56) by screwing No. 10UNF bolt into cap centre, nut (54) and washer (53) and withdraw hub assembly from stub axle.

Dismantling

1. Remove inner bearing race (46) from shaft, seal retainer (54) and seal (53) from stub axle.

2. With soft metal drifts drive outer bearing inner race (56) and both outer races (47 and 51) from the hub.

3. If required, remove disc (49) from hub.

Assembly

NOTE:- Assemble bearing without grease initially to obtain correct adjustment. Re-assemble brake disc, if applicable.

1. Lightly oil stub axle and hub bearing housing.

2. Lubricate seal (44), squeeze out surplus oil and fit onto stub axle followed by seal retainer (45).

3. Press inner bearing inner race (46) onto axle and outer race (47), together with outer bearings (51 and 52), into hub.

4. Fit hub assembly onto axle with washer (53) and, while rotating hub by hand, tighten nut until all slack is removed. Slacken nut to next split-pin hole and mark position on nut and washer.

5. Remove hub assembly pack bearings with grease, re-assemble

to axle shaft and secure with split-pin in marked hole. Fit cap (56).

6. Assemble brake calliper, attach road wheels and remove chassis stands.

End-Float Adjustment
(Road wheel and brake calliper removed)

1. Apply torque of not more than 0.7 kg/m (5 lb/ft) to hub nut whilst rotating by hand in same direction.

2. Slacken nut to nearest split-pin hole and secure.

FRONT SUSPENSION UNIT - Removal and Installation

1. Raise front of vehicle and place on chassis stands just rear of front cross-member.

2. If drivers side unit is being removed, withdraw steering column from coupling (see STEERING section).

3. Disconnect brake pipe and hose at bracket and drain system (Fig.J.5).

4. Remove engine bay valance.

5. Disconnect anti-roll bar from lower wishbone

6. Remove nut and washer and detach steering tie-rod from steering arm (28) with Churchill tool No. S.160.

7. Remove two nuts (66) from lower wishbone fulcrum brackets (63 and 64) and note number of shims (65) at each bracket.

8. Remove four bolts (1), washers and tapping plates and one bolt (1) with packing piece, if fitted (Figs. J7 and J8).

9. Remove suspension unit complete.

10. Reverse procedure to install ensuring shims (65) are in original position. Re-fill and bleed hydraulic system. Fit road wheels and check suspension geometry.

Dismantling

NOTE:- The front suspension unit may be dismantled either on the vehicle as detailed or with unit removed as previously described. Follow applicable instructions.

1. Remove spring damper strut as described in separate instruction.

2. Detach brake calliper.

3. Separate steering tie-rod from steering arm with Churchill tool S 160.

4. Remove front hub as earlier described.

5. Remove bolts (32,33 and 34) and remove calliper mounting bracket (30), dust shield (31), and steering arm (28).

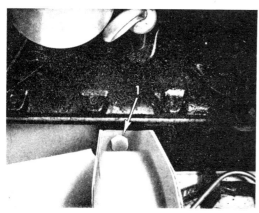

Fig.J.8 Sub-frame inner attachment bolt

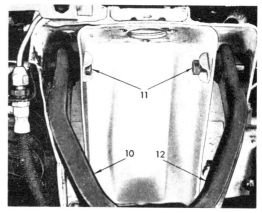

Fig.J.9 Upper wishbone inner fulcrum bolts.

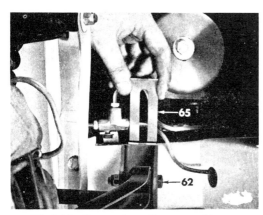

Fig.J.10 Suspension adjustment shims at lower wishbone fulcrum brackets

Fig.J.11 Detaching the upper wishbone ball joint from the vertical link.

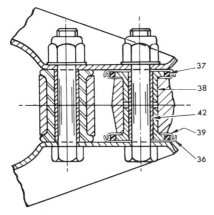

Fig.J.12 Sectional view of the lower wishbone trunnion bushes

(See Fig.J.1 for key)

Fig.J.13 Fitting the lower trunnion seal to the vertical link

6. Disconnect anti-roll bar at lower wishbone (Fig.J.9).

7. Remove bolts (II) from upper wishbone attachments and nuts (66) from lower wishbone brackets (63 or 64). Note number and location of shims (65). Remove bolts (62) to remove bottom brackets (J10).

8. Remove vertical link and wishbone assembly.

9. Remove nut (22) and washer and with Churchill tool S166A separate ball joint (15) from vertical link (Fig.J.12).

10. Remove bolts (14) to detach upper wishbone arms from ball joint.

11. Remove bolt (58) and remove lower wishbone assembly from lower trunnion (Fig.J.6).

12. Remove steel bush (42), flanged bushes (38), rubber rings (39) and dust seals (36 and 39) from trunnion (Fig.J.12)

13. Remove nut (23), washer and press stub axle from vertical link.

Inspection

1. Examine rubber bushes (13 and 61) at inner end of wishbone arms for deterioration cracks. If necessary remove old bushes and insert new items with press and pilot tool until bush protrudes equally at each side.

2. Inspect all seals and nylon bushes and renew if damaged or deteriorated.

3. Examine all parts for wear and damage and renew as necessary.

Re-assembly

1. Insert stub axle in vertical link with split-pin hole horizontal and secure with nut (23) and washer.

2. Fit flanged bushes (38) with dust seal (39) under flange into trunnion, insert steel bush (42), stretch rubber dust excluders (37) over bush flanges (Fig.J.12).

3. With serviceable rubber seal (40) fitted as shown in Fig. J.13, screw vertical link into trunnion as far as possible then unscrew until 180° rotation in each direction is available.

NOTE:- The left-hand vertical link and trunnion has left-hand mating threads and right-hand assembly has right-hand threads, and has reduced diameter at trunnion lower end for identification.

4. Fit washers (36) and assemble lower wishbone arms to trunnion (Fig.J.12).

5. Assemble fulcrum brackets to lower wishbone arms with bolts (62).

6. Assemble ball joint unit (15) between upper wishbone arms and secure with bolts (14), washers and nuts.

7. With rubber gaiter (17), over shank, assemble ball joint to vertical link and secure with nut (22) and washer.

8. Assemble steering arm (28), dust shield (30), calliper

bracket (30) and rubber seal (19) to vertical link. Secure with bolts (32,33 and 34) and assemble bracket (29).

9. Assemble and adjust hub assembly.

10. Attach upper and lower wishbones to sub-frame and chassis with original shim packs (65) behind lower fulcrum brackets (63). Do not fully tighten bolts (14 and 62).

11. Install road spring assembly.

12. Attach steering tie-rod to steering arm.

13. Refit calliper unit replacing any shims between calliper and bracket.

14. Lubricate lower trunnion with oil gun.

15. Refit road wheels and lower vehicle to ground, load to "static laden" condition and fully tighten bolts (14 and 62).

16. Check castor, camber and front wheel alignment.

SPRING DAMPER STRUT - Removal and Installation
Removal

1. Raise front of vehicle, support on chassis stands and open bonnet.

2. Remove road wheel.

3. Disconnect anti-roll bar from wishbone and slacken damper bolt (59).

4. Remove three nuts (5) and washers from upper spring pan attachments (Fig.J.14).

5. Remove bolt (59), support brake assembly and remove spring damper strut (Fig.J.15).

6. Reverse procedure to install unit.

SPRING DAMPER STRUT - Overhaul
Dismantling

1. Remove damper strut from vehicle.

2. Compress sufficient coils of road spring to relieve load from upper spring pan (7), using Churchill tool S4221A with adaptor S4221A-5 as shown in Fig.J.16.

3. Remove nuts (1 and 2), washer (3) and rubber bush (4) and gradually release load on spring.

4. Remove upper spring pan (7) and road spring. On Woodhead Monroe type remove lower spring pan (68) and collets (67).

Inspection

1. Examine rubber bushes for damage or deterioration. Renew if necessary.

2. Inspect lower Metalastic bush for distortion or deterioration cracks in rubber. If necessary press out old bush and insert new item with press and pilot tool.

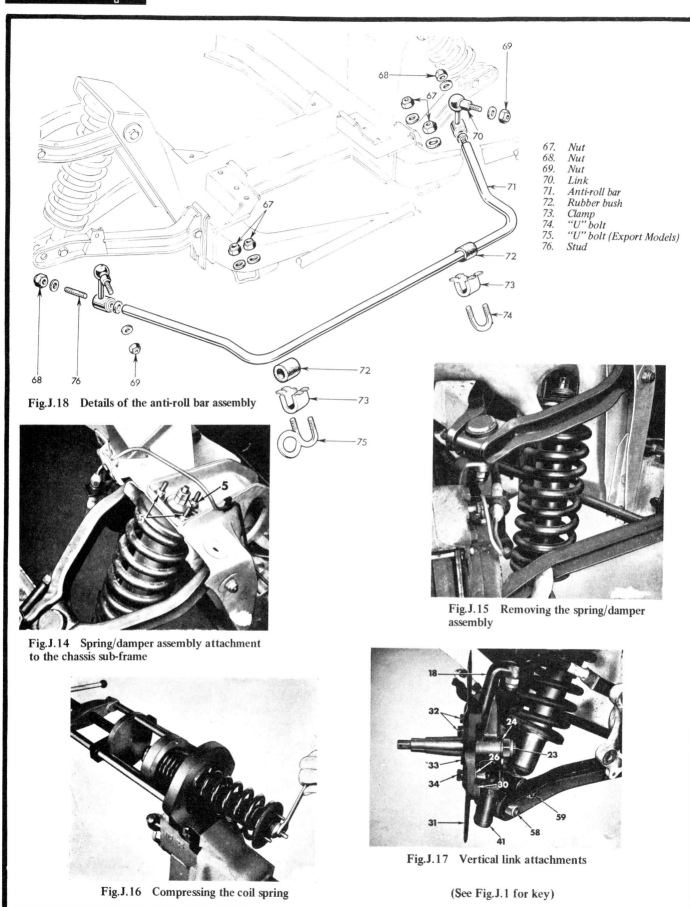

67. Nut
68. Nut
69. Nut
70. Link
71. Anti-roll bar
72. Rubber bush
73. Clamp
74. "U" bolt
75. "U" bolt (Export Models)
76. Stud

Fig.J.18   Details of the anti-roll bar assembly

Fig.J.14   Spring/damper assembly attachment to the chassis sub-frame

Fig.J.15   Removing the spring/damper assembly

Fig.J.16   Compressing the coil spring

Fig.J.17   Vertical link attachments

(See Fig.J.1 for key)

3. Check coil spring for free length (see TECHNICAL DATA) and for deformation or cracks. Renew if necessary.

4. With damper in vertical position, slowly extend and compress about ten times when resistance should be appreciable and constant. Renew if resistance is excessive, light, or irregular, or if damage, leakage or distortion is present.

Assembly

1. If applicable, fit collets (67) and lower spring pan (68).

2. Extend damper and insert in spring and upper spring pan (7).

3. Compress road spring sufficiently to fit rubber (4) washer (3) and nuts (2 and 1) (Fig.J.16). Release spring.

4. Install spring damper strut.

VERTICAL LINK - Removal and Installation
(Fig.J.17)
Removal

1. Raise front of vehicle support on chassis stands, open bonnet and remove road wheels.

2. Remove hub assembly.

3. Remove bolts (32, 33 and 34), spacers (26) (if fitted), dust shield (31), calliper bracket (30) and rubber seal (19). Pull off steering arm (28).

NOTE:- Tie up brake calliper to avoid strain on brake hose.

4. Remove nut (22) and washer and detach ball joint from vertical link (Fig.J.11).

5. Unscrew vertical link from trunnion (41) and remove seal (40).

NOTE:- Left-hand vertical link has left-hand thread and right-hand link has left-hand thread.

6. Remove nut (23) and washer and press stub axle from vertical link.

Installation

1. Insert stub axle in vertical link with split-pin hole horizontal and secure with nut (23) and washer.

2. With serviceable rubber seal (40) fitted as shown in Fig.J.13, screw vertical link into trunnion as far as possible then unscrew until 180º rotation in each direction is available.

3. With rubber gaiter (17) over shank, assemble link to ball joint (15) and secure with nut (22) and washer.

4. Assemble steering arm (28) to vertical link. Assemble rubber seal (19), calliper bracket (30) and dust shield (31) to vertical link with bolts (32, 33 and 34).

5. Install hub assembly and lubricate bottom trunnion with oil gun.

6. Fit road wheel and lower vehicle from stands.

ANTI-ROLL BAR - Removal and Installtion
(Fig.J.18)
Removal

1. Remove nuts (69) and washers.

2. Remove nuts (67) and washers and detach "U"-bolts (74) and clamps (73) from each side of chassis. Withdraw anti-roll bar (71).

3. If required, remove nuts (68) with washers and detach links (70).

Installation

1. Renew rubber sleeves (72) if damaged or deteriorated.

2. Secure anti-roll bar to chassis brackets with clamps and "U"-bolts leaving nuts finger-tight only.

3. Assemble links (70) onto adjustable ends and engage in lower wishbone brackets. Do not fully tighten nuts (68 and 69).

4. With vehicle in "static laden" condition tighten all nuts.

Technical Data

Type	Independent coil spring with telescopic damper
Spring	
Free length (approx)	
- Vitesse	317.3 mm (12.49 in.)
- GT6	316.5 mm (12.46 in.)
Fitted length	
- Vitesse	207.8 ± 2.3 mm (8.18 ± .09 in.)
- GT6	204.7 ± 2.3 mm (8.06 ± .09 in.)
Fitted load	
- Vitesse	426.5 kg (940 lbs)
- GT6	399 kg (880 lbs)
Toe-in (Static laden)	1.6 mm (0-0.063 in.)
Camber angle (Static laden)	2º positive
Wheel-Type	
Steel disc	(Wire type optional on GT6)

Tyres and Pressures (2 up)	Front	Rear
- Vitesse Six 5.60-13	1.55 kg/cm²	1.69 kg/cm²)
	22 psi	24 psi
- Vitesse 2 litre (Goodyear G8) 5.605-13	1.55 kg/cm²	1.69 kg/cm²
	22 psi	24 psi
- Vitesse Mk 2 (Goodyear G800) 155 SR-13	1.69 kg/cm²	1.83 kg/cm²
	24 psi	26 psi
- GT6 (Dunlop SP68) 155 SR -13	1.69 kg/cm²	1.97 kg/cm²
	24 psi	28 psi

Static laden condition
This condition is obtained when 68 kg (150 lb) weight is placed on each seat.

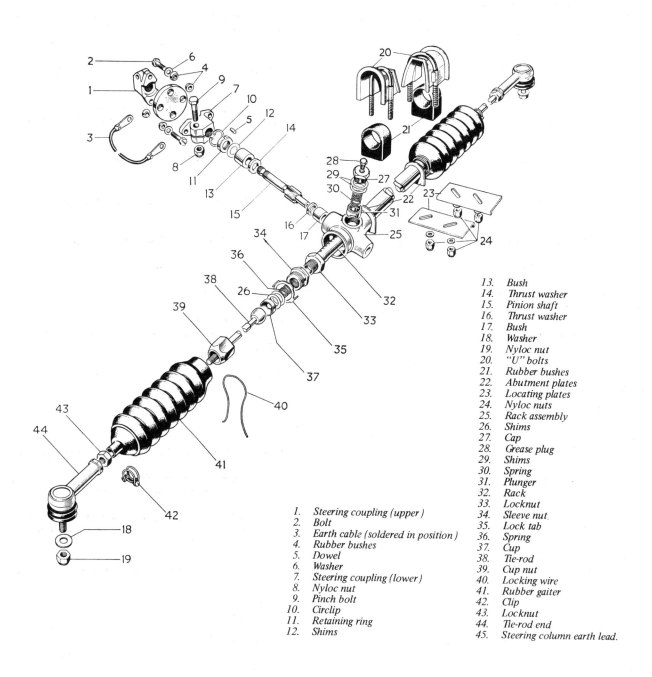

13. Bush
14. Thrust washer
15. Pinion shaft
16. Thrust washer
17. Bush
18. Washer
19. Nyloc nut
20. "U" bolts
21. Rubber bushes
22. Abutment plates
23. Locating plates
24. Nyloc nuts
25. Rack assembly
26. Shims
27. Cap
28. Grease plug
29. Shims
30. Spring
31. Plunger
32. Rack
33. Locknut
34. Sleeve nut
35. Lock tab
36. Spring
37. Cup
38. Tie-rod
39. Cup nut
40. Locking wire
41. Rubber gaiter
42. Clip
43. Locknut
44. Tie-rod end
45. Steering column earth lead.

1. Steering coupling (upper)
2. Bolt
3. Earth cable (soldered in position)
4. Rubber bushes
5. Dowel
6. Washer
7. Steering coupling (lower)
8. Nyloc nut
9. Pinch bolt
10. Circlip
11. Retaining ring
12. Shims

Fig.K.1   Exploded view of the steering unit

Steering

GENERAL
ROUTINE MAINTENANCE
TOE-IN
TIE-ROD OUTER END - Replacement
STEERING RACK - Removal
- Installation
- Dismantling
- Inspection
- Assembly
STEERING COLUMN - Removal
- Dismantling
- Re-assembly and Installation
TECHNICAL DATA

GENERAL

The steering gear is of the rack-and pinion type, rubber mounted on two front suspension crossmember brackets with the pinion shaft connected to the steering column and wheel through a flexible coupling. The rack ends are connected to the steering arm at each wheel by a tie-rod. The tie-rods are fitted with ball joints at each end and are adjustable. The steering column is designed to telescope on impact as a safety feature and this also provides a limited column length adjustment.

ROUTINE MAINTENANCE
Every 6,000 miles (10,000 km)

Raise front wheels clear of ground, remove plug (2) (arrowed on Fig.K.3), fit screwed grease nipple and with an oil gun pump hypoid oil until oil exudes from lower swivel. Remove nipple and refit plug. Repeat on other side (Fig.K.3).

Every 12,000 miles (20,000 km)

1. Remove plug on steering unit (arrowed on Fig.K.4), fit screwed grease nipple and apply five strokes with grease gun. Remove nipple and replace plug.

2. Check tightness of steering unit attachments and retaining bolts.

TOE-IN

The following methods of setting the toe-in should be used only as a temporary measure after replacement of steering or suspension components. It is highly recommended that the toe-in be rechecked as soon as possible using proper equipment so that the toe-out on turns can also be checked.

Roll the car straight forward on level ground and stop it without using the brakes. Take a reading "A" of the distance between the inside edges of the front wheel rims at a point level with, and in front of the wheel axis. Mark the measurement points with chalk. Roll the car forwards until the chalk marks are level with, but behind, the wheel axis and take a second reading "B". The toe-in is the difference by which "B" is greater than "A" This should be 0-1.6 mm (0-0.063 in.)

If adjustment is necessary, first check distance between the centre lines of the tie-rod inner and outer ball joints in both tie-rods (Dimension 1, Fig.K.5). This should be the same for both tie-rods. If otherwise, both tie-rods should be set initially to 22.15 cms (8.72 in.) and toe-in rechecked.

To adjust the tie-rod length, release locking nut at the tie-rod outer end and clip securing the rack bellows to the tie-rod. Twist the tie-rod in the appropriate direction, using a pair of plier grips if necessary, until the correct setting is obtained (Fig. K.6).

NOTE:- Adjustment made to correct the toe-in setting should be made equally to both tie-rods, except in the case above to obtain the initial setting.

When the correct toe-in setting is obtained, tighten the tie-rod end locknut and the bellows clip.

TIE-ROD OUTER END - Replacement

Wear in the tie-rod outer ends cannot be removed by adjustment and thus renewal of the complete tie-rod end is necessary. The tie-rod outer ends should be renewed in pairs.

1. Apply handbrake, jack up front end of vehicle and support on stands.

2. Remove road wheels.

3. Scribe a line on one flat of locknut (43) at tie-rod outer end (44) and corresponding line on tie-rod. Slacken locknut (Fig.K.6).

4. Remove ball stud retaining nut (19) and disconnect tie-rod end from steering arm using Churchill tool S160.

5. Unscrew tie-rod outer end from tie-rod, noting number of turns required to release it.

6. Screw on new tie-rod end the same number of turns as was required to remove old end. Tie-rod end should now be located in original position on tie-rod, thus ensuring that distance between centre-lines on inner and outer ball joints on tie-rod is the same as previously.

7. Connect tie-rod end to steering arm and secure with retaining nut.

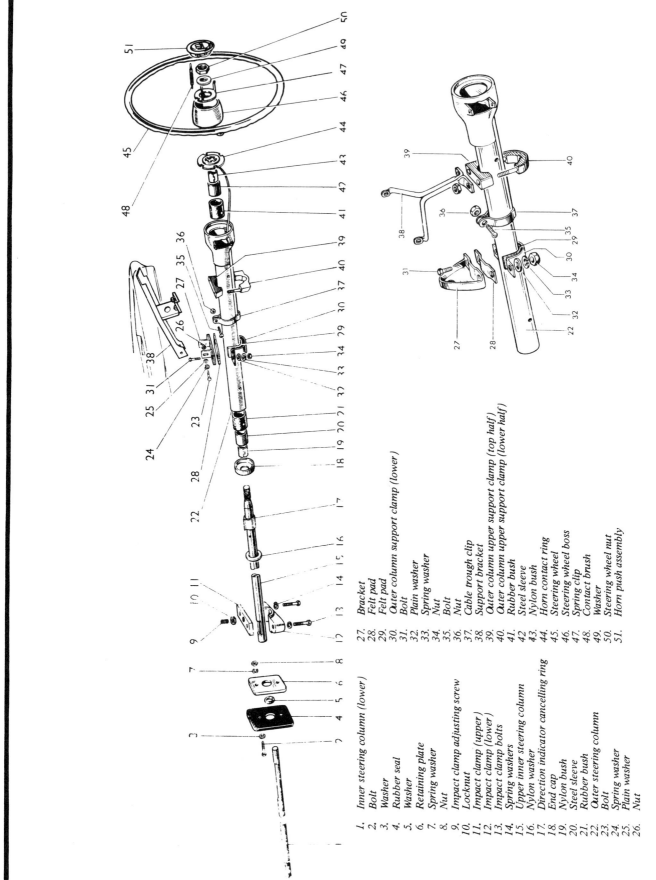

Fig.K.2 Details of steering column assembly

1. Inner steering column (lower)
2. Bolt
3. Washer
4. Rubber seal
5. Washer
6. Retaining plate
7. Spring washer
8. Nut
9. Impact clamp adjusting screw
10. Locknut
11. Impact clamp (upper)
12. Impact clamp (lower)
13. Impact clamp bolts
14. Spring washers
15. Upper inner steering column
16. Nylon washer
17. Direction indicator cancelling ring
18. End cap
19. Nylon bush
20. Steel sleeve
21. Rubber bush
22. Outer steering column
23. Bolt
24. Spring washer
25. Plain washer
26. Nut

27. Bracket
28. Felt pad
29. Felt pad
30. Outer column support clamp (lower)
31. Bolt
32. Plain washer
33. Spring washer
34. Nut
35. Bolt
36. Nut
37. Cable trough clip
38. Support bracket
39. Outer column upper support clamp (top half)
40. Outer column upper support clamp (lower half)
41. Rubber bush
42. Steel sleeve
43. Nylon bush
44. Horn contact ring
45. Steering wheel
46. Steering wheel boss
47. Spring clip
48. Contact brush
49. Washer
50. Steering wheel nut
51. Horn push assembly

Fig.K.3   Lower swivel lubrication point

Fig.K.4   Steering unit lubrication point

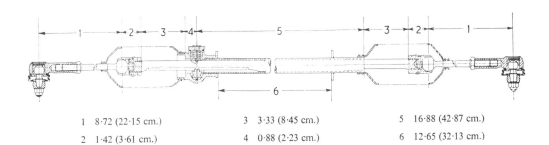

1	8·72 (22·15 cm.)	3	3·33 (8·45 cm.)	5	16·88 (42·87 cm.)
2	1·42 (3·61 cm.)	4	0·88 (2·23 cm.)	6	12·65 (32·13 cm.)

Fig.K.5   Setting dimension for the steering unit

1. *221.5 mm (8.72 in.)*
2. *36.1 mm (1.42 in.)*
3. *84.5 mm (3.33 in.)*
4. *22.3 mm (0.88 in.)*
5. *428.7 mm (16.88 in.)*
6. *321.3 mm (12.65 in.)*

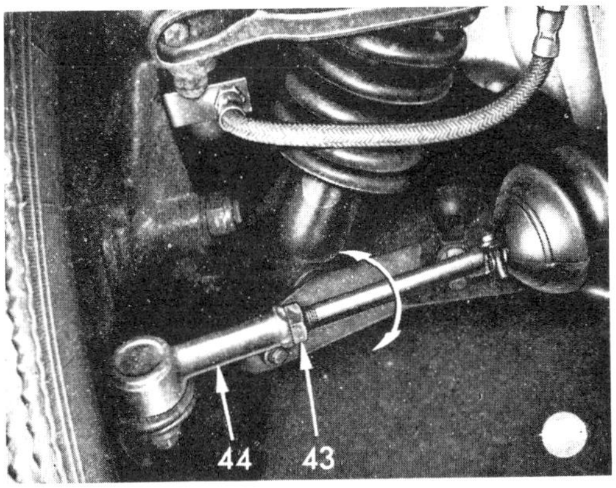

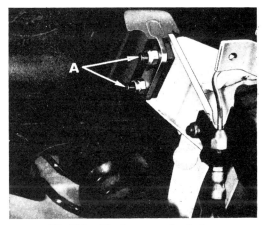

Fig.K.6   Removal of the tie-rod end

Fig.K.7   Steering coupling attachments

Fig.K.8   Engine mounting bolts

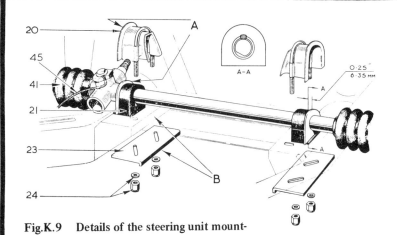

Fig.K.9 Details of the steering unit mountings

Fig.K.10 Measuring the pinion end-float

A. Distance between flanges must be 3.17 mm (0.125 in.)
B. Flange of item (23) must contact innermost flange
of frame

(See Fig.K.1 for key)

Fig.K.11 Determining the shim thickness required under the cap nut

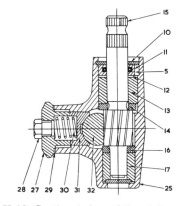

Fig.K.12 Sectional view of the pinion assembly

(See Fig.K.1 for key)

Fig.K.13 Measuring the turning torque at the pinion

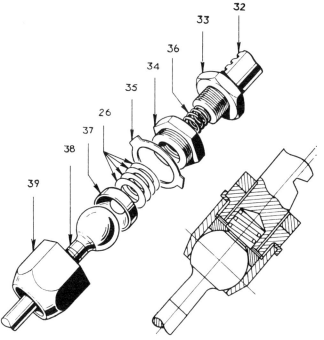

Fig.K.14 Details of the tie-rod inner ball joint

(See Fig.K.1 for key)

8. Tighten tie-rod end locknut. Scribed lines made previously should be aligned.

9. Repeat for tie-rod end on the other side of vehicle.

10. Mount road wheels and check toe-in as described above, adjusting as necessary.

STEERING RACK - (Fig.K.1)
Removal

1. Raise and support front of vehicle on chassis stands. Remove road wheels.

2. Remove pinch bolt (9) and disconnect earth strap from bolt (28) (Fig.K.7)

3. Disconnect tie-rod end from steering arm using Churchill tool S160.

4. Remove left hand engine bay valance.

5. Remove nuts (24) and locating plates (23).

6. Attach, hoist and sling, take weight of engine and remove bolts (A) (Fig.K.8).

7. Raise engine carefully approximately 40 mm (1.5 in.) and remove "U"-bolts (20) and rubber bushes (21).

8. Move rack forward to disengage from coupling and remove from vehicle through valance aperture on driver's side.

Installation

1 Ensure steering rack is assembled to dimensions given in Fig.K.5.

2. Centralise rack on pinion by counting number of revolutions from lock-to-lock and turning pinion back half of this number.

3. Position steering wheel with spokes horizontal and beneath wheel boss centre.

4. With engine slightly raised, insert steering rack through valance aperture, position rack onto crossmember brackets and engage pinion shaft in coupling.

5. Loosely assemble "U"-bolt assemblies (20) and locating plates (23). Attach earthing cable to one "U"-bolt. Lower engine and fit mounting bolts.

6. Use Churchill tool S341 or similar to push "U"-bolt assemblies outwards until 3.17 mm (0.125 in.) clearance remains between "U"-bolt bracket flange "A" and tube flange plate "A". Slide plates (23) inboard until edge "B" is against frame flange "B". Elongate slots further if necessary. Tighten "U"-bolt nuts and remove spreading tool (Fig.K.9).

7. Fit and secure pinchbolt (9) and connect earth strap to bolt (28) (Fig.K.7).

8. Connect tie-rod ends to steering arms.

9. Mount road wheels and lower vehicle.

10. Check wheel alignment.

Dismantling (Fig.K.1)

1. Release clips (42) and (40), move gaiters outwards, slacken locknuts (33) and remove both tie-rod assemblies from the rack. Remove springs (36).

2. Release tab washers (35) and remove sleeve nut (34), tabwasher, shims (26) and thrust cup (37). Detach both tie-rod ends (44).

3. Remove locknut (43), gaiters, clips and cup nut (39) from each tie-rod. Remove locknut (33).

4. Remove cap nut (27), shims, spring and pressure pad (31) from housing.

5. Extract circlip (10) and withdraw pinion assembly with dowel (5). Remove items (11), (12), (13), and (14). Remove "O"-ring from (11).

6. Remove rack from the tube and thrust washers (16 and 17) from housing.

Inspection

1. Clean and check all parts for wear, damage and deterioration. Renew parts as necessary.

2. Renew "O"-ring.

3. If worn, drift out the bush in the end of rack tube and press in a new item.

Assembly

1. Insert the rack into tube and place bush (17) and thrust washer (16) into pinion housing.

2. Adjust pinion end-float as follows:

a) Assemble thrust washer (14), bush (13) and retainer (11) to pinion. Insert assembly into housing and secure with circlip (10).

b) Mount dial gauge as shown in Fig.K.10. Push pinion down and zero the gauge. Lift rack until retaining ring contacts circlip and note total end-float. Remove assembly and fit new "O"-ring in retainer (11).

c) Shim to give minimum end-float consistent with free rotation. Maximum end-float should be 0.254 mm (0.010 in.)

(Shims are available in 0.10 mm (0.004 in.) and 0.25 mm (0.010 in.) thickness.

d) Re-insert assembly and secure with dowel (5) and circlip (10).

3. Adjust pinion pressure pad end-float as follows.

Fig.K.15 Details of steering column clamps

(See Fig.K.2 for key)

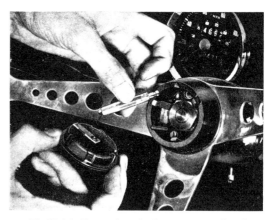

Fig.K.16 Removing the horn contact brush

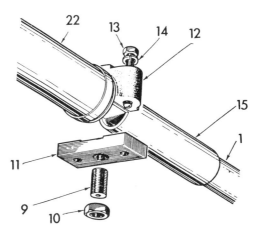

Fig.K.17 Details of the steering column impact clamp

(See Fig.K.2 for key)

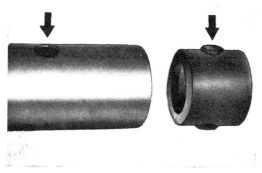

Fig.K.18 Locating protrusions on the rubber bush and holes in the outer column

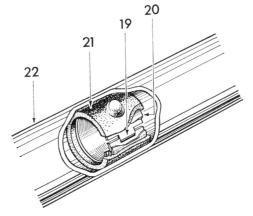

Fig.K.19 Details of the steering column bush assembly

(See Fig.K.2 for key)

a) Fit pressure pad and cap nut (27). Tighten cap nut to just eliminate all end-float and measure clearance under cap nut head (Fig.K.11). Remove pressure pad.

b) Make shim pack equal to clearance plus 0.1 mm (0.004 in.) nominal end-float.

c) Pack unit with grease and assemble pad, spring, shim pack and cap nut with grease plug (Fig.K.12).

d) When correctly adjusted, a 0.91 kg (2 lb) on an 20.3 cm (8 in.) arm should turn the pinion shaft three quarters of a turn either side of mid-position, and must not exceed 1.36 kg (3 lb) for the remainder of rack travel. (Fig.K.13). Adjust shimming if necessary.

4. Assemble and adjust inner ball joints as follows (Fig.K.14).

a) Position cup nut over tie-rod ball end, fit thrust cup (37) and attach sleeve nut (34) with tab washer.

b) With the fully tightened cup nut held in vice, pull and push the tie-rod to estimate end-float. Make up shim pack in excess of estimated end-float and insert in assembly and measure gap under sleeve nut flange. Reduce shim pack by gap dimension plus 0.05 mm (0.002 in.) to give specified 0.05 mm (0.002 in.) end-float. Check assembly by applying load of 0.68 kg (1.51 lbs) at outer end of tie-rod (38) when tie-rod should articulate freely. Lock with tab washer. (Shims are obtainable in 0.05 mm (0.002 in.) and 0.25 mm (0.010 in.) thickness).

5. Assemble locknut (33) and spring (36) to each end of rack and screw on tie-rod assemblies. Adjust to dimension in Fig.K.5 and secure with locknuts.

6. Fit gaiters (41), pack with grease (½ oz. Retinax "A" from dry), and secure with clip (42) and wire (40).

7. Assemble tie-rod ends (44) to tie-rods with locknuts (43). Adjust ends to dimensions in Fig.K.5 and secure with locknuts (43).

STEERING COLUMN (Fig.K.2)
Removal

1. Isolate battery and disconnect electrical leads under fascia.

2. Remove bottom halves of clamps (30 and 40).

3. Remove pinch bolt (9) from bottom coupling (7) (Fig.K.7).

4. Withdraw steering column from vehicle.

Dismantling

1. Remove bolt (35) and remove cable trough clip (37).

2. Lever horn button assembly (51) from steering wheel boss and remove horn contact (Fig.K.16).

3. Remove switch covers and detach switches.

4. Remove impact clamp sections (11 and 12) (Fig.K.17).

5. Withdraw lower column (1) and washer (16). Remove

upper inner column with steering wheel attached from outer column (22).

6. Grip column (15) in vice with jaws protected, remove nut (50), washer and clip (47), and with Churchill tool S3600 remove steering wheel.

7. Remove end cap (18) and push out rubber bushes (21 and 41) with a bar after depressing protrusions as shown in Fig.K.18. Remove steel sleeve (42 and 20) and nylon inserts (19 and 4) from rubber bushes (Fig.K.19).

8. Inspect all parts for damage and wear and renew as necessary. Renew rubber bushes if deteriorated.

Re-assembly and Installation

1. Assemble steel sleeves and nylon inserts into bushes (21 and 41) and insert in column until locating protrusions engage in holes in column (Fig.K.19). Metal reinforcement rings at end of bush must be towards lower end of column. Fit end cap (18).

2. Assemble horn contact ring (44) then steering wheel to column with direction indicator cancelling lugs in line with steering wheel spokes. Fit clip (47) secure wheel with nut (50), and lock nut by peening.

NOTE:- If new direction indicator switch is being fitted, the cancellation clip and screw must also be renewed.

3. Thread inner column into outer column.

4. Insert direction indicator and lighting switches through holes at top of column, and fit switches and covers.

5. Fit horn contact plunger (48) in boss and fit horn button assembly (51).

6. Assemble lower column to upper column and secure with impact clamp (11 and 12) leaving attachment nuts loose at this stage (Fig.K.17).

7. Manipulate column into position through bulkhead grommet, attach cable trough clip (51) and assemble bottom halves of clamps (40) and (30), placing felt (29) in lower clamp. Position steering wheel at required height before tightening clamp bolts.

8. With steering wheel and road wheels in straight-ahead position, engage lower column in steering coupling and secure with pinch bolt (Fig.K.7).

9. Tighten bolts (13) on impact clamp, and friction screw (9). Secure with locknut (10).

NOTE:- If column is adjusted to lowest position, telescoping will not be possible.

10. Connect electrical leads under fascia.

11. Connect battery.

Technical Data

Type	Rack-and-pinion (Limited collapsible column)
Lubricant	Energrease L2 or equivalent
Pinion end-float	0.25 mm (0.010 in.) maximum
Pinion pressure pad end-float	0.1 mm (0.004 in.) nominal

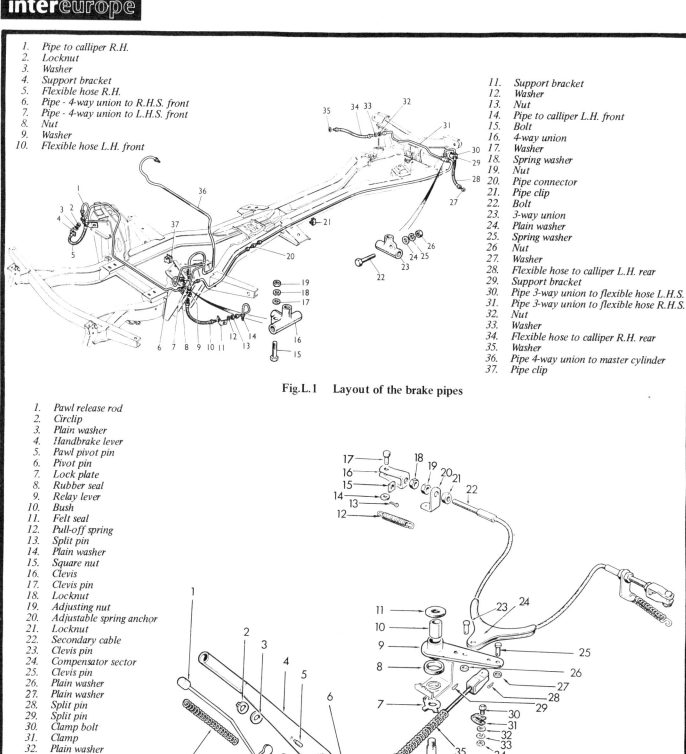

1. Pipe to calliper R.H.
2. Locknut
3. Washer
4. Support bracket
5. Flexible hose R.H.
6. Pipe - 4-way union to R.H.S. front
7. Pipe - 4-way union to L.H.S. front
8. Nut
9. Washer
10. Flexible hose L.H. front

11. Support bracket
12. Washer
13. Nut
14. Pipe to calliper L.H. front
15. Bolt
16. 4-way union
17. Washer
18. Spring washer
19. Nut
20. Pipe connector
21. Pipe clip
22. Bolt
23. 3-way union
24. Plain washer
25. Spring washer
26. Nut
27. Washer
28. Flexible hose to calliper L.H. rear
29. Support bracket
30. Pipe 3-way union to flexible hose L.H.S.
31. Pipe 3-way union to flexible hose R.H.S.
32. Nut
33. Washer
34. Flexible hose to calliper R.H. rear
35. Washer
36. Pipe 4-way union to master cylinder
37. Pipe clip

Fig.L.1   Layout of the brake pipes

1. Pawl release rod
2. Circlip
3. Plain washer
4. Handbrake lever
5. Pawl pivot pin
6. Pivot pin
7. Lock plate
8. Rubber seal
9. Relay lever
10. Bush
11. Felt seal
12. Pull-off spring
13. Split pin
14. Plain washer
15. Square nut
16. Clevis
17. Clevis pin
18. Locknut
19. Adjusting nut
20. Adjustable spring anchor
21. Locknut
22. Secondary cable
23. Clevis pin
24. Compensator sector
25. Clevis pin
26. Plain washer
27. Plain washer
28. Split pin
29. Split pin
30. Clamp bolt
31. Clamp
32. Plain washer
33. Spring washer
34. Nut
35. Spring
36. Pivot bolt
37. Primary cable
38. Square nut
39. Locknut
40. Clevis
41. Clevis pin
42. Plain washer
43. Split pin
44. Ratchet
45. Pawl
46. Pawl spring

Fig.L.2   Details of the handbrake assembly

Braking System

GENERAL
ROUTINE MAINTENANCE
BRAKE ADJUSTMENT
FRONT BRAKE PADS - Replacement
FRONT BRAKE CALLIPER - Removal and Installation
- Overhaul
BRAKE DISCS
REAR BRAKE SHOES - Replacement

REAR WHEEL CYLINDER - Removal and Installation
PISTON SEALS - Replacement
MASTER CYLINDER - Removal and Installation
- Overhaul
BLEEDING THE HYDRAULIC SYSTEM
BLEEDING THE HYDRAULIC
SYSTEM
TANDEM BRAKE SYSTEM
TECHNICAL DATA

GENERAL

The foot brake operates hydraulically through a conventional, single-line system on all four wheels with disc-type brakes at the front and drum-type at the rear on all models. The handbrake operates mechanically on rear wheels only.

The front brake callipers are of the twin opposed piston-type and are self-adjusting.

The rear drum brakes are of the leading and trailing shoe type with one double-acting wheel cylinder and one adjuster.

The handbrake is floor-mounted and operates through a two cable linkage.

The brake master cylinder with integral hydraulic fluid reservoir is mounted on the engine compartment rear bulkhead, immediately over the brake pedal.

On the GT6-Plus, model for the U.S.A. market, a tandem-braking hydraulic system is installed in which pressure is transmitted to separate front and rear hydraulic circuits from the master cylinder. A pressure differential valve between the two circuits operates a warning light if pressure drops in one of the circuits.

ROUTINE MAINTENANCE
Every Month

Check the fluid level in the brake master cylinder and top-up to the bottom of the filler neck if required. If fluid loss is excessive, this should be investigated.

Every 6,000 miles (10,000 km)

Check the front brake pads for wear and renew if reduced to 3.0 mm (0.125 in.) or less in thickness. Adjust the drum brake shoes if necessary as described in brake adjustment section. Check all pipes and hoses for damage, deterioration, leakage or chafing, and renew as necessary.

Every 12,000 miles (20,000 km)

Smear the handbrake compensator and cable guides with grease.

BRAKE ADJUSTMENT
Rear Brakes

1. With wheel clear of ground, fully release handbrake and check wheel is free to rotate.

2. Screw in adjuster as far as possible then release one notch at a time until it is just free to turn (Fig.L.3).

3. Lower vehicle to ground.

Handbrake

Adjustment of the handbrake is normally effected automatically by shoe adjustment at the rear wheels. However after considerable mileage, stretched cables may necessitate adjustment as follows: (Fig.L.4).

1. Raise rear wheels, release handbrake and turn adjuster on rear wheel backplates fully in.

2. Disconnect pull-off spring (12) and remove clevis pin (17) at each wheel.

3. Release locknuts (18) and turn each forkend (16) by equal amounts until cable slack is taken up yet pin (17) can be easily inserted. Tighten locknuts.

4. Secure clevis pins with split pins, connect springs and adjust spring bracket (20) on cables to provide a light spring tension.

5. Turn each brake adjuster back one notch at a time until wheels are free to rotate.

6. Lower vehicle and remove jack.

FRONT BRAKE PADS - Replacement (Fig.L.5)

1. Remove front wheel, withdraw spring clips (8) and remove retaining pins (9).

2. Remove friction pads (4) and damping shims (12).

   CAUTION: Do not depress pedal while pads are removed.

3. Clean exposed faces of pistons and pad recesses and force pistons back into cylinders.

Fig.L.3   Adjusting the rear brakes

Fig.L.4   Details of handbrake assembly
secondary cable attachment at the rear
wheel (see Fig.L.2 for key)

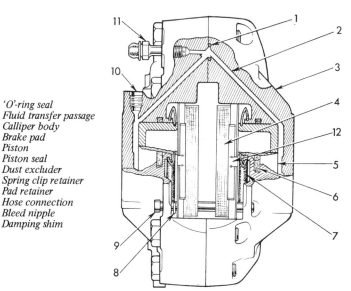

1.   'O'-ring seal
2.   Fluid transfer passage
3.   Calliper body
4.   Brake pad
5.   Piston
6.   Piston seal
7.   Dust excluder
8.   Spring clip retainer
9.   Pad retainer
10. Hose connection
11. Bleed nipple
12. Damping shim

Fig.L.5   Sectional view of the brake
calliper

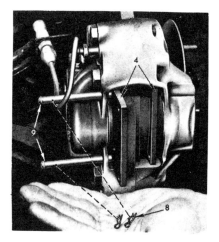

Fig.L.6   Removing the brake pads

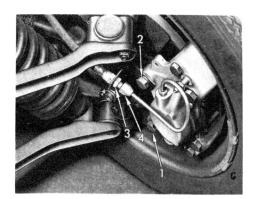

Fig.L.7   Brake calliper and hose attachments

1.   Calliper mounting bolt - lower
2.   Calliper mounting bolt - upper
3.   Brake hose locknut
4.   Pipe union nut

Fig.L.8   Measuring the brake disc run-out

NOTE:- This will displace fluid back to master cylinder. Avoid overflowing by temporarily opening bleed screw.

4. Install new friction pads and shims, insert pins (9) and secure with clips (8).

NOTE:- Shims must be fitted with arrow pointing in direction of wheel forward rotation.

5. Pump brake pedal several times to bed-down pads and spin discs to ensure brakes do not drag.

6. Refit wheel, check fluid level and road test vehicle.

FRONT BRAKE CALLIPER - Removal and Installation (Fig.L.7)
Removal

1. Drain system and remove road wheels.

2. Remove friction pads.

3. Hold hose locknut (3) at bracket and disconnect pipe connection (4).

   NOTE:- Do not twist pipe.

4. Remove two bolts (1 and 2) and calliper unit.

   NOTE:- If calliper is being removed to gain access to another component only, the hydraulic pipe need not to be disconnected and unit should be suspended from frame with string or wire. In this case, bleeding after installation is not necessary.

Installation

1. Assemble to hub and connect pipe from calliper to bracket.

2. Install friction pads and refit road wheels.

3. Fill and bleed system. Check for leaks.

4. Road test vehicle.

FRONT BRAKE CALLIPER - Overhaul (Fig.L.5)
Dismantling

1. Clean unit with brake fluid or methylated spirits. Do NOT use paraffin or other mineral based solvents.

2. Remove pistons (5) and bleed screw (11)

3. Lever dust seal and retainer (7) from mouth of cylinder and with blunt-ended wire pick seal (6) from inner groove in cylinder wall.

   NOTE:- Do not separate calliper halves.

Inspection

Clean and dry all parts and examine for cracks and damage. Renew seals.

Assembly

1. Apply brake fluid or methylated spirits to seal (6) and work into inner groove in cylinder, with fingers.

2. Locate lip of dust seal and retainer (7) in its recess in the cylinder.

3. Square piston at mouth of cylinder with closed end leading and press into cylinder. Push cylinder fully home and engage outer lip of dust excluder with recess in piston.

4. Refit bleed screw.

BRAKE DISCS

Normally the front discs require no maintenance but should be checked for scores and distortion on overhaul. With dial indicator set up as shown in Fig.L.8, the maximum permissible run-out on the friction faces is 0.152 mm (0.006 in.) taken at 12.7 mm (0.50 in.) from edge of disc.

Removal and Installation

1. Remove front hub (see FRONT SUSPENSION section)

2. Remove four bolts (8) (Fig.L.8) and separate discs.

3. Install by reversing removal procedure.

REAR BRAKE SHOES - Replacement (Figs. L.10 and L.11)
Removal

1. Remove wheel and brake drum and turn adjuster fully anti-clockwise.

2. Remove split pin (2) and release steady pins (8), cups (12 and 14) and springs (13).

3. Pull one shoe out of slots in adjuster (31) and piston (15), move shoe away from backplate and release towards other shoe. Release springs and remove shoes.

Inspection

1. Wire brush shoes and examine for cracks. Renew shoes if linings are worn to below one third original thickness, contaminated with oil or are damaged.

2. Clean adjuster and ensure screw turns freely.

3. Renew springs if distorted or stretched.

Installation

1. Apply zinc base grease sparingly to adjuster and shoe abutment ends.

2. Assemble brake shoes and springs (18 and 25) with exposed position of each lining surface against direction of rotation. Locate one shoe in slots on adjuster and piston and pull other shoe to engage opposite slots. Ensure handbrake lever

Fig.L.9   Brake disc attachment bolts

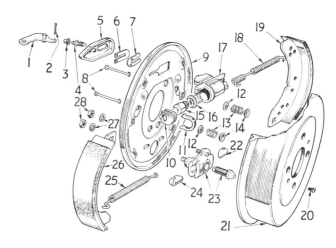

Fig.L.10   Exploded view of rear brake
assembly - L.H. shown

Fig.L.11   General view of the rear brake
assembly - R.H. shown

1.	Handbrake lever	15.	Piston
2.	Split pin	16.	Seal
3.	Dust cap	17.	Wheel cylinder
4.	Bleed nipple	18.	Return spring
5.	Dust excluder	19.	Brake shoe
6.	Retaining clip	20.	Countersunk screw
7.	Retaining clip	21.	Brake drum
8.	Steady pins	22.	Adjuster tappet
9.	Backplate	23.	Adjuster wedge and body
10.	Dust excluder	24.	Adjuster tappet
11.	Clip	25.	Return spring
12.	Steady pin cups	26.	Brake shoe
13.	Springs	27.	Shakeproof washers
14.	Steady pin cups	28.	Nuts

Fig.L.12   Removing retaining plate from the
rear wheel cylinder

Fig.L.13   Removing the rear wheel cylinder
and handbrake lever

enters slotted shoe web and fit split-pin to handbrake lever (Fig.L.11).

3. Fit anti-rattle springs (13) on shoes and secure with steady pins (8) passed through cups (12 and 14) and rotated 90° to engage groove in cup.

4. Fit brake drum and adjust brakes.

5. Mount road wheel and road test vehicle.

REAR WHEEL CYLINDER - Removal and Installation

1. Remove brake shoes as previously described.

2. Drain hydraulic system through bleed screw, disconnect hose from pipe and unscrew from cylinder.

3. Disconnect handbrake cable from lever.

4. Remove dust excluder and retaining plates (Fig.L.12).

5. Withdraw cylinder and handbrake lever from backplate (Fig.L.13).

Installation

Reverse removal procedure, adjust brakes and bleed hydraulic system.

PISTON SEALS - Replacement

1. Remove cylinder

2. Remove dust excluder and extract piston.

3. Remove old seal from piston

4. Clean cylinder and piston with methylated spirits or brake fluid. Examine contact surfaces for scores or pitting and renew if necessary.

5. Using fingers only, fit new seal on piston with lip towards bottom of cylinder.

6. Lubricate seal with brake fluid, insert piston in cylinder and fit dust excluder.

7. Install cylinder.

MASTER CYLINDER - Removal and Installation (Fig.L.14)
Removal

1. Drain system at any wheel unit, bleed screw.

2. Pull back rubber dust excluder (11) and remove clevis pin (14).

3. Disconnect pipe line at cylinder.

Installation

1. Secure master cylinder to mounting bracket.

2. Connect push rod to pedal with clevis pin and refit dust excluder.

3. Connect pipe line and fill and bleed system.

4. Road test vehicle.

MASTER CYLINDER - Overhaul (Fig.L.15)
Dismantling

1. Pull off dust cover (12), depress push rod (13), remove circlip (11) and push rod with stop plate (10).

2. Shake or gently blow out plunger (9) with attached parts.

3. Lift securing clip on spring retainer (7) and remove retainer with valve assembly from plunger.

4. Guide valve shank (5) through offset hole in retainer. Remove spring (6), distance piece (4) and spring (3) from valve shank.

5. Remove seal (2) from shank with finger and remove distance cup (4).

6. Remove seal (8) from plunger.

Inspection

1. Clean all parts in methylated spirits or brake fluid and inspect for damage. Renew all rubber parts.

Re-assembly

NOTE:- Observe strict cleanliness during assembly.

1. Lubricate all interior parts with brake fluid.

2. Fit seals (2 and 8) to valve shank (5) and plunger (9).

3. Fit disc spring (3), distance piece (4) and spring (6) to valve shank (5); attach spring retainer (7) and locate assembly on plunger (9).

NOTE: Disc spring (3) must be assembled as shown in Fig.L.15 with periphery against distance piece (4).

4. Insert plunger assembly in cylinder, fit push rod (13) with stop plate (10) and secure with circlip (11). Assemble dust cover (12).

BLEEDING THE HYDRAULIC SYSTEM

1. Attach hose to bleed nipple on brake unit nearest to master cylinder and immerse other end in brake fluid (Fig.L.16).

2. Unscrew nipple approximately one turn and have assistant slowly depress and hold down pedal.

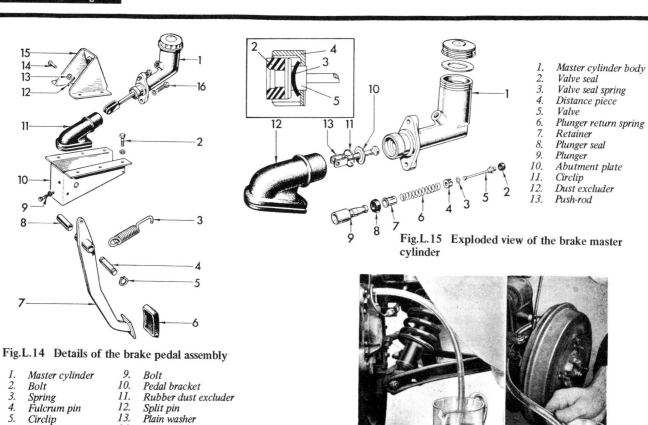

1. Master cylinder body
2. Valve seal
3. Valve seal spring
4. Distance piece
5. Valve
6. Plunger return spring
7. Retainer
8. Plunger seal
9. Plunger
10. Abutment plate
11. Circlip
12. Dust excluder
13. Push-rod

Fig.L.15 Exploded view of the brake master cylinder

Fig.L.14 Details of the brake pedal assembly

1.	Master cylinder	9.	Bolt
2.	Bolt	10.	Pedal bracket
3.	Spring	11.	Rubber dust excluder
4.	Fulcrum pin	12.	Split pin
5.	Circlip	13.	Plain washer
6.	Pedal rubber	14.	Clevis pin
7.	Pedal	15.	Master cylinder bracket
8.	Pivot bush	16.	Bolt

Fig.L.16 Bleeding the brakes

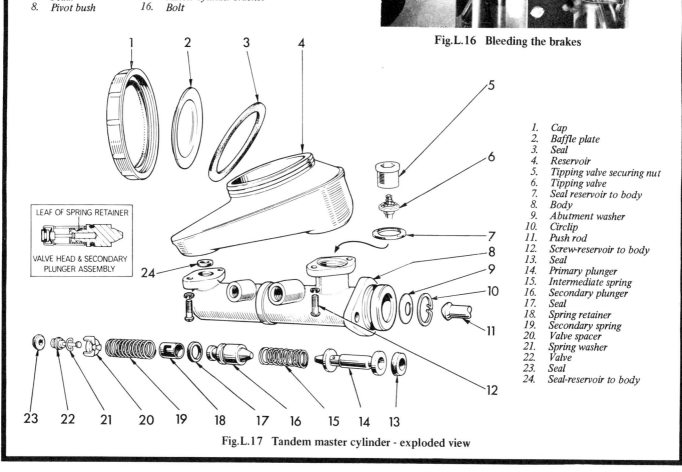

LEAF OF SPRING RETAINER

VALVE HEAD & SECONDARY PLUNGER ASSEMBLY

1. Cap
2. Baffle plate
3. Seal
4. Reservoir
5. Tipping valve securing nut
6. Tipping valve
7. Seal reservoir to body
8. Body
9. Abutment washer
10. Circlip
11. Push rod
12. Screw-reservoir to body
13. Seal
14. Primary plunger
15. Intermediate spring
16. Secondary plunger
17. Seal
18. Spring retainer
19. Secondary spring
20. Valve spacer
21. Spring washer
22. Valve
23. Seal
24. Seal-reservoir to body

Fig.L.17 Tandem master cylinder - exploded view

3. Repeat until fluid free from bubbles emerges from the hose.

4. Finally tighten nipple and remove hose.

5. Repeat for other three brake units working progressively away from the master cylinder.

6. When bleeding operation is completed, adjust rear brake shoes.

TANDEM BRAKE SYSTEM

On this system, pressure generated by the depression of the foot operated brake pedal is transmitted to independent front and rear braking systems. Both systems are connected to a pressure differential warning actuator (P.D.W.A.) fitted with an electrical switch contact. The master cylinder of this system is shown in Fig.L.17.

A brake failure warning light on the fascia glows brightly in the event of a malfunction occuring in the brake system.

The system operates as follows:- Pressure on the foot brake pedal causes the hydraulic brake fluid to be pressurised in both the independent front and rear brake pipes through the master cylinder Fig.L.18. Both the front brake and rear brake systems are connected to opposing sides of the P.D.W.A. unit fitted with the electrical contact. A shuttle in the P.D.W.A. unit remains in the midway position as long as the pressure in both systems is the same, and keeps the electrical contact in-operative. A fall in pressure in either system moves the shuttle in the P.D.W.A. unit, operates the electrical contact and illumi-nates the warning light on the fascia. The electrical circuit is arranged so that the brake warning light is in a series /parallel connexion with the oil pressure warning light. (See Fig.L.19). When the brake system is working correctly, both the brake warning light and the oil pressure warning light extinguish as engine speed is increased from idling. Should the brake system partially fail, the brake circuit is earthed so causing the brake warning light to glow brightly.

Bleeding the Tandem braking system

If air has entered either the front or rear braking system, it is only necessary to bleed the one affected, as the systems are independent of one another. Care must however be exercised in bleeding a tandem system in order not to move the shuttle in the P.D.W.A. from its midway position. In the event of the shuttle being moved, it must be centralised by following the instructions given later in this section.

Scrupulous cleanliness must be observed when dealing with hydraulic braking systems, and it is essential that mineral oil or grease should not be allowed to come into contact with those parts of the system contacted by brake fluid. Perform the operation with clean, non-greasy hands. Use only methylated spirit or brake fluid for cleaning parts. Clean all bleed nipples. Clean the fluid reservoir, remove the filler cap, ensuring that no dirt or foreign matter enters, and top-up the reservoir. The fluid must be kept above the dividing partition on the reservoir, during the bleeding operation. Fluid bled from the system must be discarded and not- re-used. Fresh fluid for the system should be obtained from sealed containers which should be closed again after use.

Start the bleeding operation on the brake of the pair being bled that is sited farthest from the master cylinder. If both systems are being bled, commence with the rear brake system. For the rear brakes, the handbrake must be released, and the adjusters turned to lock the shoes against the drums. After bleeding has been completed, the rear brakes must then be adjusted as detailed in the previous text. Proceed as follows:-

a) Push a bleed tube over the nipple, and submerge the other end in a glass container holding sufficient brake fluid to cover the end of the bleed tube.

b) Undo the bleed nipple by half a turn.

c) Engage the services of an assistant who should depress the brake pedal slowly and allow it to return slowly. Only LIGHT pedal pressure is required and the pedal must NOT be pushed through the end of its stroke. Do NOT test for pedal pressure until all air has been dispelled from the systems, as such action will move the shuttle and illuminate the fascia light. Pause between each pedal movement. When bubbles of air cease to be expelled through the bleed tube, with the pedal depressed, close the bleed nipple. Attend to the nipple of the other brake of the system.

Centralising the P.D.W.A. piston

If the P.D.W.A. shuttle has been moved from its midway position, it must be centralised in the following manner.

a) Fit a bleed tube as described in 'a' above to a brake bleed nipple at the opposite end of the car to that which has just been bled.

b) Undo the bleed nipple by half a turn.

c) Operate the ignition switch but do NOT start the engine. The brake warning light should glow but the oil pressure light should not come on.

d) A steady pressure should be applied to the foot brake pedal until the brake light dims and the oil light glows. On the pedal, a click should be felt as the shuttle returns to its midway position.

e) Tighten the bleed screw, and remove the bleed tube.

NOTE:- The shuttle will move to the other side of the valve if the pedal has been pushed too hard, necessitating the proce-dure to be repeated on the brake system on the opposite end of the car.

P.D.W.A. unit

The P.D.W.A. unit functions to indicate by a warning light on the fascia that there is a malfunction in either of the front of rear brake hydraulic systems. An exploded view of the unit is given in Fig.L.20. The shuttle valve assumes a midway position providing there is equal pressure in both fluid lines. The shuttle has a groove in its periphery, whose function is to permit the electrical switch to remain in the non-operative position. Unequal pressure in either line moves the shuttle so causing it to depress the plunger of the switch and close its contacts. Observe that the shuttle consists of two separate parts.

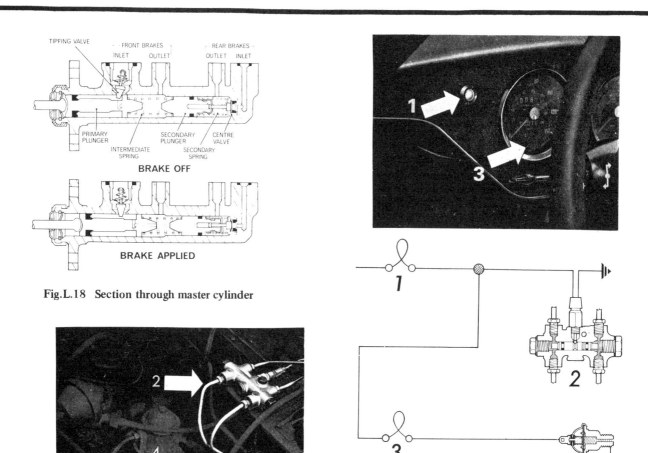

Fig.L.18   Section through master cylinder

1. Brake line failure warning light
2. Brake line failure switch
3. Oil pressure warning light
4. Oil pressure switch

Fig.L.19   General layout of system

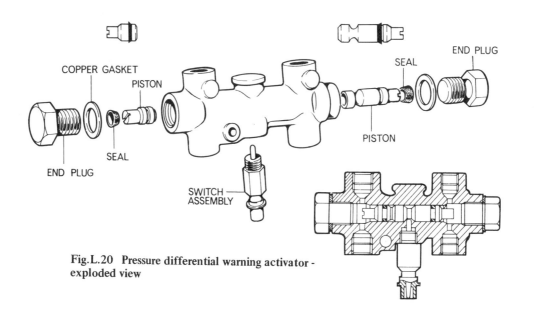

Fig.L.20   Pressure differential warning activator -
exploded view

Removal and Refitting

a) Remove the electrical connexion.

b) Take out the end plugs from the unit and discard the copper washers.

c) Unscrew the nylon switch.

d) Using care, push out the valves so as not to damage the bores.

e) Carefully remove the seals so as not to score the shuttle valves.

A Girling service kit is available and must be used. Using clean brake fluid, carefully clean all parts and dry them with lint free cloth. Inspect all parts for imperfections, especially the bore of the body and the shuttle valve sections. If imperfections are found, the unit should be replaced entirely. The nylon switch may be tested separately by reconnecting the warning light circuit, depressing the plunger and pressing the switch in contact with the earthed portion of the chassis.

To reassemble the unit proceed as follows:-

a) Using clean brake fluid, smear the valve pistons, seals, and bore.

b) With the fingers, fit the new oil seals to the pistons. The lips of the seals must point towards the slots in the ends of the pistons. (See Fig.L.20).

c) Push the longer piston into the bore until the groove in its periphery aligns with the switch plunger hole. Insert the switch, tightening to a torque of 2 to 2.5 lb.ft. Take care that the piston seals do not move past the central hole in the valve body, as this will damage them so making it necessary to replace.

d) Insert the shorter piston, and push up against the longer piston.

e) Fit new copper washers to the plugs and screw them into position, tightening to a torque of 16 to 20 lb.ft.

f) Refit the unit to the vehicle.

MASTER CYLINDER

An exploded view of the master cylinder is given in Fig. L.17. The GT6 model has a tandem master cylinder consisting of two independent hydraulic cylinders in series, one for the front brakes and the other for the rear brakes. The common reservoir supplies both cylinders, but it is divided by a partition. It is important, when replacing parts, to identify the exact type of master cylinder fitted to a car as those with varying volume have been fitted in the past.

The T.V.C.V. master cylinder (Fig.L.18) operates in the following manner:-

Pedal pressure onto the push rod moves the primary plunger up the cylinder bore, and allows a spring-loaded tipping valve to return to centre. The primary inlet port (the supply port) is closed as the tipping valve moves to centre, and further movement of the primary plunger creates hydraulic pressure which is transmitted through the outlet ports to the wheel cylinders of the front brakes. At the same time the pressure created acts in conjunction with the increasing force of the intermediate spring so as to overcome the stronger secondary spring, so causing the secondary plunger to move. As the secondary plunger moves, it closes the inlet port of the rear brake supply so that the pressure is transmitted to the rear wheel cylinders. Should failure occur in either chamber or circuit, mechanical contact between the plungers takes place and the remaining chamber builds up the normal pressure required to operate the brakes that it controls.

Maintenance

Under normal circumstances, very little maintenance is required for the master cylinder but the fluid level should be inspected every week. A translucent container permits the fluid level to be ascertained without removing the filler cap. Gradual lowering of the fluid level over a long period will occur due to wear of the brake pads. This is normal and topping-up will not be required. A sudden appreciable drop in the fluid level should be investigated immediately, and the trouble found and rectified. A danger line is marked on the side of the casing, and the level of the fluid must not be allowed to fall below this (Fig.L.21). If it is necessary to top-up the reservoir, clean it externally and ensure that no dirt enters as the cap is removed. Only new fluid from a sealed container should be used for topping-up.

Removal

a) Be careful not to allow the fluid to come into contact with paintwork. Take off both fluid pipes from the cylinder body, plug the open ports of the master cylinder.

b) Withdraw the rubber dust cover to expose the master cylinder push rod and clevis pin.

c) Take out the split pin, and remove the clevis pin attaching the push rod to the brake pedal.

d) Undo the bolts which attach the master cylinder to the bulkhead and lift off the unit.

Dismantling and inspection

It is emphasised that scrupulous cleanliness is essential when dealing with the brake system. The entry of mineral oil, foreign matter or dirt will cause premature brake failure.

a) Drain off and discard the fluid from the master cylinder.

b) Take out the four screws (Fig.L.17) (12) which attach the reservoir to the cylinder body.

c) Depress the push rod (11), remove the circlip (10), and withdraw the push rod together with abutment plate (9) and circlip (10).

d) Using an Allen key, unscrew the tipping valve securing nut (5) and remove the seal (7).

e) Depress the primary plunger and remove the tipping valve (6).

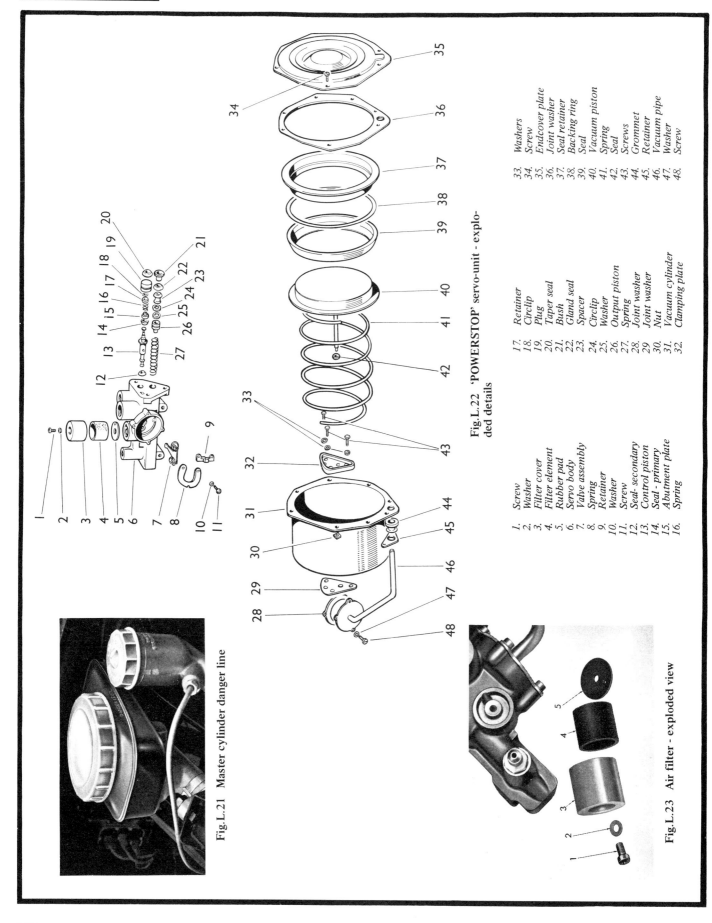

Fig.L.21 Master cylinder danger line

1.	Screw
2.	Washer
3.	Filter cover
4.	Filter element
5.	Rubber pad
6.	Servo body
7.	Valve assembly
8.	Spring
9.	Retainer
10.	Washer
11.	Screw
12.	Seal- secondary
13.	Control piston
14.	Seal - primary
15.	Abutment plate
16.	Spring
17.	Retainer
18.	Circlip
19.	Plug
20.	Taper seal
21.	Bush
22.	Gland seal
23.	Spacer
24.	Circlip
25.	Washer
26.	Output piston
27.	Spring
28.	Joint washer
29.	Joint washer
30.	Nut
31.	Vacuum cylinder
32.	Clamping plate
33.	Washers
34.	Screw
35.	Endcover plate
36.	Joint washer
37.	Seal retainer
38.	Backing ring
39.	Seal
40.	Vacuum piston
41.	Spring
42.	Seal
43.	Screws
44.	Grommet
45.	Retainer
46.	Vacuum pipe
47.	Washer
48.	Screw

Fig.L.22 'POWERSTOP' servo-unit - exploded details

Fig.L.23 Air filter - exploded view

f) Either by shaking, or applying low pressure air remove the internal parts.

g) Separate the plunger and intermediate spring.

h) Lift the leaf spring of the spring retainer and remove the spring and centre valve sub-assembly from the secondary plunger. (See inset of Fig.L.17)

i) Remove the spring (19), valve spacer (20), and spring washer (21) from the valve stem (22), and remove the valve seal (23) from the valve head.

j) Remove the seals from the primary (14) and secondary (16) plungers.

k) Lever out the baffle (2), and remove the cap washer (3) from the filler cap.

Clean all parts thoroughly with Girling cleaning fluid or methylated spirit. Examine the cylinder bore and the plunger for scoring, ridge or burrs. If these are present, a new master cylinder must be fitted. A service kit is available from Girling and this contains all parts needing to be replaced.

Re-assembly

All moving parts and seals must be smeared with new clean hydraulic fluid.

a) Fit the seals to the primary and secondary plungers.

b) Fit the valve seal (23) smallest diameter leading, on the valve head (22).

c) Locate the spring washer (21) on the valve stem so that it flares away from the valve stem shoulder, and follow with the valve spacer (20), legs first.

d) Attach the spring retainer (18) to the valve stem, keyhole first.

e) Slide the secondary spring (19) over the spring retainer, then position the sub-assembly on the secondary plunger (16).

f) The spring must now be compressed whilst the leaf of the spring retainer is pressed down behind the head of the plunger. The best way to do this is to use a vice with two pieces of clean paper placed between the jaws to prevent contamination of the component. Place the assembly in the vice and close the jaws of the vice until the spring is almost coil bound. Using a small screwdriver, press the spring retainer right back against the secondary plunger. With a pair of small pointed nose pliers, depress the leaf of the spring retainer behind the head of the plunger. Ensure that the retainer leaf is straight and firmly located behind the plunger head as shown in Fig.L.17 inset.

g) Fit the intermediate spring (19) into position between the primary and secondary plunger.

h) Using clean brake fluid, lubricate the cylinder bore and the plunger seals.

i) Insert the plunger assemblies into the bore with the valve

end leading. As you do so, ease the entrance of the plunger seals.

j) Press the primary plunger down the bore and fit the tipping valve, securing nut and seal. Tighten to a torque of 35 to 40 lb.ft..

k) Fit the cap washer and baffle to the filler cap, then screw the cap on to the reservoir.

l) Fit the reservoir seals (24 and 7), position the reservoir on the cylinder and secure with the retaining screws.

m) Fit the push rod (11) with the abutment plate (9) and circlip.

n) Reverse the removal process to fit the unit in the car. Bleed the system as described previously. Use only new hydraulic fluid from sealed containers.

POWERSTOP SERVO UNIT

The Girling Powerstop unit utilises the vacuum of the inlet manifold to assist in applying the brakes. It is fitted to later models, and as an option on others. Matters are so arranged that if the system becomes inoperative the brakes can still be applied, but greater pressure on the foot brake pedal will be required. The unit is shown in exploded view in Fig.L.22.

Servicing

All seals should be changed at 36,000 miles (60,000 km) or three years whichever comes sooner. The Girling company recommend that the unit be returned to them for service or replacement, but where this is not possible, a service kit is provided for use by skilled and trained personnel. Use of the service kit will enable the seals to be replaced providing the internal working surfaces of the unit are in good order. The work should not be undertaken by amateurs.

Scrupulous cleanliness is essential when working on the component. The hands should be washed and dried to remove all oil and grease, and a clean surface provided on which to lay out the parts. Only Girling cleaning fluid, alcohol, or Castrol Girling brake and clutch fluid should be used to wash and clean parts. Special care is necessary when removing and refitting the circlip in the hydraulic output cylinder, and when assembling the vacuum cylinder to the body.

The unit may be dealt with under five headings as follows:-

1. The air filter

2. The vacuum cylinder

3. The valve chest

4. The valve control piston

5. The hydraulic ouput cylinder

Changing Air filter (Fig.L.23)

This element which is of moulded cellular construction,

Fig.L.24   Details of valve chest

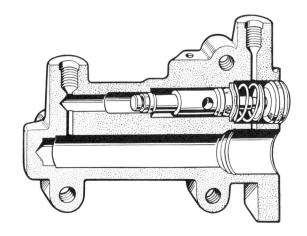

Fig.L.25   Section through control cylinder

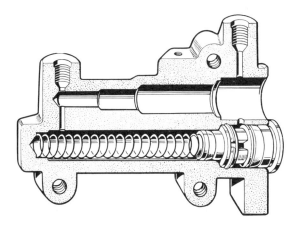

Fig.L.27   Section through output cylinder

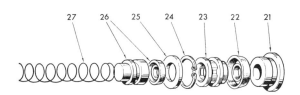

Fig.L.26   Control piston - exploded view

(See Fig. L.22 for key)

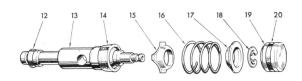

Fig.L.28   Output piston - exploded view

(See Fig. L.22 for key)

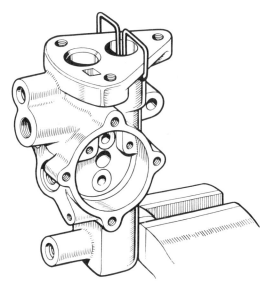

Fig.L.29   Output piston - removal

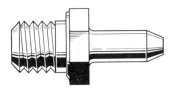

Fig.L.30   Special adaptor

should be changed whenever the brake shoes are replaced, or the servo unit is serviced. Having obtained a new rubber pad and element, proceed as follows:-

a) Referring to Fig.L.23 take out the screw (1), and lift off the cover (3), filter element (4), and rubber pad (5).

b) Clean the base plate, fit a new rubber pad and element, replace the cover and secure with the screw.

Dismantling servo unit (Fig.L.22)

To dismantle the vacuum cylinder, hold the unit in a vice by its mounting legs.

a) Take out the bolts (34) and the nuts(30).

b) Gradually apply pressure to the end cover (35) so as to allow the spring (41) to push out the piston assembly.

c) Remove the end cover and piston assembly. Take out the bolts (43) and separate the clamp plate (32), vacuum cylinder (31), and the joint washer (29) from the servo body.

To dismantle the valve chest (Figs. L.22 and L.24)

d) Remove screws (48) and lift off the cover, tube assembly (46) and joint washer (28).

e) Remove the screws (11), spring (8), and valve retainer (9). Depress the plug (19), and carefully lift out the rocking lever and valve assembly (7).

f) Clean all parts. Examine, and if necessary, lap the nylon air valves on a sheet of glass using fine lapping paste.

To dismantle the control cylinder (Figs.L.22,L.25 & L.26)

g) Use a wooden surface on which to tap the face of the body, so as to remove the plug (19). Withdraw the control piston assembly from the bore.

h) To dismantle the control piston assembly - Compress the spring (16) and push off the circlip (18). Take off the retainer (17), spring (16), and abutment plate (15). Remove the seals (12,14 and 20) from the piston (13) and plug (19). Fig.L.22.

i) Clean all parts, and lubricate with clean brake fluid.

j) Fit new seals (12 and 14) to the piston (13) - lips of seals must face away from the centre hole. Refit the abutment plate (15), spring (16), retainer (17), and circlip (18) to the piston. Fit a new seal (20) to the plug (19).

To dismantle the output cylinder (Figs.L.22,L.27 & L.28)

k) Withdraw the piston rod bush (21) from the bore, then remove the gland seal (22) by using a suitable piece of bent wire. Shake out the nylon spacer (23).

l) Depress the piston (26) (special tool is available), clip the ends of the tool under the body as shown in Fig.L.29.

m) Using a pair of circlip pliers, insert them in the circlip holes (24) and when the circlip is fully compressed, lift it out carefully so as not to scratch the bore.

n) Release the compression tool so that the spring (27) will push out the washer (25) and the piston (26). Discard the piston.

o) Clean all parts, and lubricate the bores with Castrol-Girling red rubber grease. Examine all bores for defects.

Assembly (Fig.L.22)
Output cylinder

Because the seal fitted to the piston during manufacture cannot be replaced, a new output piston (26) must be fitted if the unit is being overhauled. Make sure that the outer seal is fitted with the lip towards the smaller end of the piston (26). Smear the piston with Castrol-Girling red rubber grease, and then fit it into the end of the spring (27). Place the washer (25) on the piston, and fit the compression tool into the end of the piston. Feed the spring into the bore and gently enter the piston. With the piston kept square in the bore, gradually depress it until it is possible to clip the compression tool over the edge of the body. Now fit the circlip (24) around the compression tool, and using the circlip pliers compress the circlip and insert it into the bore. The circlip must be resting on the washer (25) before the pliers are released. Make sure that the circlip is correctly located in its groove before removing the compression tool.

NOTE:- It cannot be too strongly emphasised that great care not to scratch the bore must be used, if subsequent brake failure is to be avoided.

Fit the spacer (23) - large end first - gland seal (22) - lipped edge first - and bush (21) into the bore.

Valve control cylinder

Lubricate the bore with Castrol-Girling red rubber grease, and insert the control piston assembly. Align the hole in the piston with the hole in the valve chest. Press the sealing plug (19) into the end of the bore.

Valve chest

Depress the plug (19) to align the hole in the control piston (13) with the hole in the valve chest. Insert the rocking lever and valve assembly with the spring location away from the retaining screws. Fit the spring (8) and valve retainer (9) and secure with the screws (11) and washers. Fit a new joint washer (28) and replace the cover and pipe (46). Fit the screws (48) and washers, but do not tighten them.

Vacuum cylinder

Hold the body mounting face uppermost, in a vice. Position a new joint washer (29) and fit a new grommet (44) in the flange of the vacuum cylinder (31). Locate the vacuum cylinder over the projecting flange of the bush (21) and place the clamp plate (32) into position. Secure it loosely, leaving the bolts (43) finger tight.

Place the piston (40) and spring (42) in position, and push the piston through the full stroke several times so as to align the bush (21). The piston and spring should now be carefully removed, and the three bolts (43) tightened. Now tighten the three screws (48) which secure the valve cover.

Using the new ring supplied with the kit, replace the rubber backing ring (28). Smear the piston with Castrol-Girling red rubber grease; and using the special lubricant supplied with the kit apply it to the leather seal (39). Fit the spring (41) and piston assembly, and place a new joint washer (36) on the vacuum cylinder flange. Locate the cover plate (35) on top of the piston and depress the cover plate. Fit the nuts (30) and bolts (34) around the flange and tighten them. Unless the unit is to be fitted at once to the car, plug or tape the ports to prevent the ingress of foreign matter.

SERVO UNIT TESTING

The following tests can be made, once the brake system has been re-installed in the car. (It is assumed that all faults in connexion with the system have been eliminated, and the brakes have been adjusted). The adaptor shown in Fig.L.30 will be required, and this can be made from a suitable pipe union ¾" x 24 UNF. Five tests are involved as follows:-

TEST 1. Before connecting the pipes, fit a bleed screw in the hydraulic outlet port and an adpator into the hydraulic inlet port. Connect the vacuum hose to the adaptor and remove the filter element. With the engine idling, place the fingers over the air inlet and vacuum ports to ascertain if there is any suction at either orifice. Should suction be found, it indicates that the bores are scored or the parts have been incorrectly assembled.

TEST 2. Connect up the hydraulic and vacuum pipes and bleed the system. With the engine running, apply the brake. It should be possible to hear the hiss made by the air at the inlet of the unit, and with the hand placed on the vacuum cylinder feel the movement of the unit as it operates. Unsatisfactory results indicate that the unit is not working. The malfunction could be caused by a faulty non return valve, or a fault within the unit.

TEST 3. Run the engine for a minute, and then switch off. Pause for two minutes, then apply the brakes; the Servo unit should operate and can be detected by using the method described in Test 2. Unsatisfactory results indicate leaking gaskets. air valve or rubber grommet. Clamp the vacuum hose and repeat the test. If now satisfactory, the non return valve is faulty. To test for a leaking air valve, run the engine, and place the finger over the air inlet. If the suction is only slight, the air valve is satisfactory, and the leak is elsewhere.

TEST 4. Run the engine and apply hard pressure to the foot pedal, holding it down hard for twenty seconds. No perceptible creep on the pedal should be detected. If creep is present it indicates there are leaks or scored bores in the components. The source of the trouble can only be detected by elimination. Check for leaks in the system. If no leak is evident, each hose must be clamped in succession (a service tool is available) and the test repeated to locate the fault. Plug the master cylinder outlet and test again. If creeping is evident when the hoses are clamped and the pedal is solid when the master cylinder is plugged, the Servo unit is faulty.

TEST 5. Jack up the front of the car to free the wheels. With the engine running, apply the brakes and release them. The wheels should be free to move half a second after the release of the pedal. If the brakes remain on, disconnect the vacuum pipes, operate the brakes to eliminate all vacuum in the Servo unit and repeat the test; if the brakes remain on, the fault is not in the Servo unit. If the brakes release normally, the fault lies in the Servo unit, and the vacuum piston alignment is suspect.

FAULT DIAGNOSIS CHART

Fault	Cause	Action
Hard pedal - apparent lack of assistance with engine running.	Lack of vacuum. Restricted hose. Blocked air inlet. Rubber grommet swollen Faulty output piston. Major fault in the unit.	Check vacuum connections. Check hose and replace - Examine filter and air inlet. Overhaul, using Service kit. Fit new unit.
Brakes hanging on.	Misaligned vacuum piston. Swollen rubber grommet or backing ring. Piston return stop incorrectly adjusted.	Apply Test No. 5. Replace parts, as necessary. Reset piston stop.
Servo unit operates	Swollen rubber grommet. Blocked filter or restricted air inlet.	Check and replace as necessary. Tighten vacuum connections. Replace hose.
Poor assistance on heavy braking.	Air leak in servo low vacuum.	Dismantle and fit all parts in service kit.
Servo only operates when engine is running	Air leaks in gasket or air valve.	Tighten vacuum connexions. Replace vacuum hose or non return valve
Poor slow running of engine.	Vacuum hoses faulty, or non return valve faulty.	Replace vacuum hose, or non return valve.
Loss of fluid	Failure of seals or scored bores	Replace unit. Overhaul using Service kit.

Technical Data

System	Girling Hydraulic
Brakes -	Disc front, drum rear

Front brakes:

Vitesse 6	Disc 228.6 mm (9 in.) dia.
Vitesse 2 litre/GT6	Disc 246 mm (9.7 in.) dia.

Rear brakes	Drum 203 x 31.75 mm (8 x 1.25 in.)

Total swept area:

Vitesse 6	1339.63 sq.cm (207 sq. in.)
Vitesse 2 Litre/GT6	1677.42 sq. cm (260 sq. in.)

Max. permissible disc run-out	0.102 mm (0.004 in.)
Recommended hydraulic fluid	Castrol-Girling Brake Fluid Crimson or similar to SAE 70 R3 spec.

P.D.W.A. assembly Manufacturer	Girling
Stanpart number. Early unit with single pin - assembly	213990
- switch	148159
Later unit with twin pins - assembly	215104
- switch	149971
Pressure differential need to actuate switch	200 psi (Approx.)
Switch plunger load - with plunger contact surface 0.522 in. below seat flange	5.2 to 6.4 lb.
Switch thread	3/8 " 24 UNF 2A
Torque load - fitting switch to pressure differential warning actuator body	2 to 2.5 lb.ft.

Oil pressure switch:- Manufacturer	A.C. or Smiths
Stanpart number	121398
Operating pressure. Early unit	4.5 to 7.5 psi
Later unit	3 to 5 psi
Thread	1/8" 27 NPTF

Repair of all units is by replacement	No maintenance is required.

Operational indications.

Condition	BRAKE warning light	OIL warning light
Ignition ON-		
Engine not running	On faintly	On faintly
Engine running	Off	Off
Engine running - Front or rear brake line pressure low	On brightly	Off
Engine running Oil pressure low	On faintly	On faintly

Fig.M.1   Lubricating the generator rear bearing

Fig.M.2   Checking specific gravity of the battery electrolyte

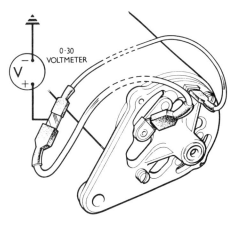

Fig.M.3   Generator output test

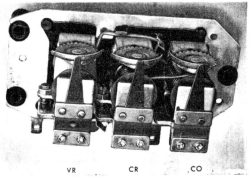

Fig.M.4   Control box with the cover removed

VR   Voltage regulator
CR   Current regulator
CU   Cut-out

Fig.M.5   Adjusting the voltage setting

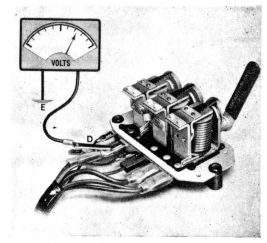

Fig.M.6   Adjusting the cut-out,cut-in voltage

Electrical Equipment

GENERAL

This section deals primarily with the charging and starting systems, the ignition system having been dealt with previously in the IGNITION SYSTEM section. The 12 volt electrical system is of negative ground polarity, except on the Vitesse Six which has positive ground polarity, and care should be taken, therefore, when reconnecting the battery to ensure the correct polarity is observed.

The charging system comprises the battery, generator (or alternator on the G.T.6 Mk 2) and the charging system control unit. The lead-acid type battery has a capacity of 43 ampere-hour on the Vitesse Six, 39 ampere-hour on the Vitesse 2 Litre and 56 ampere-hour on the G.T.6, all at the 20 hour rate. Battery output is controlled by a three bobbin unit, voltage regulator, current regulator and cut-out.

The G.T.6 Mk 2 is equipped with an alternator with the control unit incorporated and has an output of 28 amps. Only the charging circuit voltage is regulated by the alternator control unit as the inherent self-regulating properties of the alternator limit the output current, obviating the need for a current regulator. The need for a cut-out is also eliminated by the effect of the diodes incorporated in the alternator which prevent reverse current from flowing.

The starter motor is an inertia-engagement type, operated by a separate solenoid switch.

Front lighting comprises sealed beam headlamps and left and right-hand light assemblies incorporating the parking and direction indicator lights. At the rear, the tail/stop and direction indicator lights are also incorporated in a single assembly at each side.

ROUTINE MAINTENANCE
Monthly

Check the level of the electrolyte in the battery and if required, add distilled water to bring the level above the tops of the separators.

Every 6,000 miles (10,000 km)

Check the operation of all the electrical circuits.

Every 12,000 miles (20,000 km)

Apply a few drops of engine oil to the generator rear bearing (Fig.M.1). Clean the exterior of the battery, remove any corrosion from the battery terminal posts and coat the posts with petroleum jelly before securing the leads. Check the earth lead for security and condition.

BATTERY

Check and maintain the battery at regular intervals as quick-starting of the engine depends to a great extent on the state of charge of the battery.

Electrolyte Level

The level of the electrolyte in the battery should be checked periodically and replenished with distilled water as required. In an emergency, it is permissible to use melted snow, rain water or plain drinking water free of high mineral content. Add water as required to each cell so that the electrolyte level is approx. 6.0 mm (0.25 in.) above the separators. DO NOT OVERFILL. The engine should be operated immediately after adding water, particularly in cold weather, to assure proper mixing of the water and acid.

Sulphuric acid of the correct concentration should be added if the specific gravity of the electrolyte needs to be corrected as a result of drainage or leakage from the battery.

Exterior

The external condition of the battery, terminal posts and cable terminal should be checked periodically. If the top of the battery is contaminated by acid film or dirt between the terminal posts, wash with a diluted ammonia or soda solution to neutralise any acid present and then flush with water. Care must be taken to keep the vent plugs tight so that the neutralising solution does not enter the cells.

To ensure good contact, the battery cables should be tight on the terminal posts. If the battery posts or cable terminals are corroded, the cables should be disconnected and terminals and posts cleaned with a soda solution and wire brush. Apply a thin film of petroleum jelly to the posts before reconnecting the cables. The ground battery cable and engine unit ground strap should also be inspected for proper connection and condition.

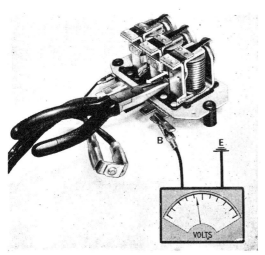

Fig.M.7   Adjusting the drop-off voltage setting

Fig.M.8   Adjusting the current setting

Fig.M.9   Voltage regulator air gap

Fig.M.10 Cut-out air gap

Fig.M.11 Generator adjusting and mounting
points

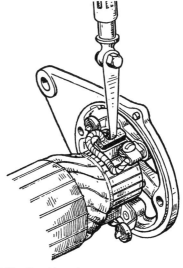

Fig.M.13 Checking the generator brush tension

Specific Gravity

The specific gravity of the electrolyte is a good indication of the state of charge of the battery. Prior to testing, inspect the battery for any damage, such as a broken casing or cover, loose terminal posts, etc., which would make the battery unserviceable. Check the specific gravity of each cell with a hydrometer, drawing enough electrolyte into the hydrometer to make the scale float (Fig.M.2). If the electrolyte level is less than 6.0 mm (0.025 in.) above the separators, distilled water should be added and the battery charged for at least one hour before carrying out the check.

The following table relates the specific gravity to the battery condition at 16ºC (60ºF).

HYDROMETER READING	BATTERY CONDITION
1.280	Fully charged
1.240	75% charged
1.200	50% charged
1.160	25% charged
1.120	Discharged

If the electrolyte temperature varies from 16ºC (60ºF), adjust the reading obtained by adding 0.004 for every 5.5ºC (10ºF) above 16ºC and by subtracting the same amount for every 5.5ºC below 16ºC.

If the readings are reasonably uniform, the battery is probably healthy, although low readings indicate that charging is required. If one cell is about 0.030 lower than the rest, it is probably failing. An extended charge may revive it. If the readings are irregular, with one or more cells 0.050 lower than the rest, the battery is not fit for further use and should be replaced.

Charging

Slow charging is the preferred method of re-charging a battery as it may safely be used regardless of the condition of the battery provided that the electrolyte is at the proper level in all the cells. The normal charging rate is 1 amp per positive plate per cell (i.e. 3.5 amps for 40 amp/hr battery with 7 plates per cell, since there is always one more negative plate per cell than positive). A minimum of 24 hours is required when using this method. The vent plugs must be removed while charging takes place as the electrolyte boils due to the decomposition of the water. Where an auto-fill type cover is fitted, the cover should be left on as this displaces the vent hole ball plugs. A battery is in a fully charged condition when all cells are gassing freely and three corrected specific gravity readings, taken at hourly intervals, indicate no increase in specific gravity.

If fast-charging the battery, the precautions given above for slow-charging are even more important. A battery may be charged at any rate which does not cause the electrolyte temperature to exceed 52ºC (125ºF) and which does not cause excessive gassing and loss of electrolyte.

DO NOT ATTEMPT TO CHARGE A BATTERY WITH FROZEN ELECTROLYTE AS IT MAY CAUSE THE BATTERY TO EXPLODE.

FAULTS IN THE CHARGING SYSTEM

The ignition warning light on the instrument panel can give a reasonable indication of the operation of the charging system and it may be of general interest to name a few of the faults which can be indicated by the functioning of the lamp.

When the charging system is operating correctly, the lamp should be 'OUT' when the ignition is switched off, 'ON' when the ignition is switched 'ON' and should go 'OUT' again once the engine is running at speed.

Should the warning light still be illuminated with the engine running at speed (above the cut-in speed of the generator/alternator) this indicates the generator/alternator is not supplying current to the battery.

First check the condition and adjustment of the generator/alternator drive belt and, if satisfactory, check all wiring connections between the generator/alternator, control unit (where separate) and the ignition switch. If the warning light now functions correctly, test the state of the battery and recharge as required. However, persistent illuminations of the light indicates a fault in the generator/alternator or the control unit and the tests described below should be carried out on the individual components to isolate the fault.

If the warning light glows slightly with the engine at speed, a high resistance in the circuit is indicated. Check for loose or corroded terminals or damaged wires.

If the warning light does not illuminate under any conditions, a blown bulb or broken connection to the warning light are indicated. Check the wiring or replace the bulb as necessary.

GENERATOR OUTPUT TEST

Disconnect the leads from the "D" and "F" terminals at the control unit and join the leads together. Connect a 0-20 voltmeter between their junction and a good earthing point. Run the engine at approximately 750 rev/min, restricting voltmeter reading to not more than 20 volts.

NOTE:- Do not exceed this speed otherwise the generator may be damaged.

The voltmeter reading should rise rapidly without fluctuation. Should the reading be incorrect, connect a jumper lead between the "D" and "F" terminals on the generator and connect the voltmeter between this wire and a good earthing point (Fig.M.3). If the reading is still incorrect, there is a fault in the generator. A cure may be effected by replacing the generator brushes.

GENERATOR CONTROL UNIT

NOTE:- Before disturbing the electrical or mechanical settings of the control unit, ensure that any suspected fault is not to a defective battery, slack generator drive belt, defective wiring or connections, or poor earth. Fig.M.4 indicates voltage regulator, current regulator and cut-out positions in control box.

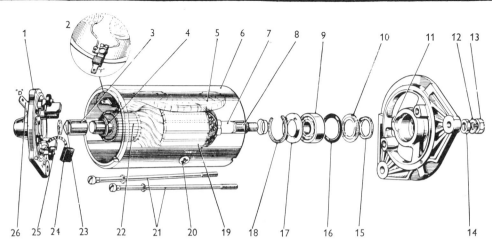

1. Commutator end bracket
2. Field connector and field winding earth lead
3. Porous bronze bearing bush
4. Fibre thrust washer
5. Field winding
6. Yoke
7. Shaft
8. Key
9. Ballrace
10. Pressure ring and felt ring retaining plate
11. Drive end bracket
12. Washer
13. Shaft nut
14. Pulley spacer
15. Felt ring
16. Pressure ring
17. Bearing retaining plate
18. Circlip
19. Armature
20. Pole shoe screw
21. Through-bolts
22. Commutator
23. Felt ring retainer
24. Brush
25. Felt ring
26. Output connector

Fig.M.12 Exploded view of the generator

Fig.M.14 Commutator end bracket and brushes.

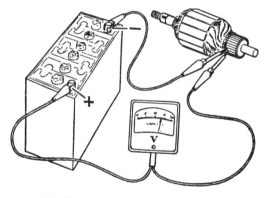

Fig.M.16 Armature open-circuit test

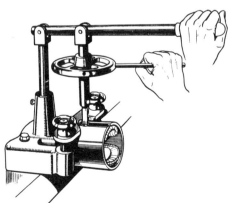

Fig.M.15 Removing/tightening the pole shoe retaining screws.

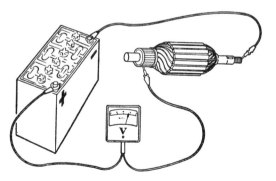

Fig.M.17 Armature insulation test

Clean regulator contacts with carborundum stone or silicon carbide paper followed by methylated spirits and cut-out contacts with fine glass paper followed by methylated spirits.

Voltage regulator open-circuit setting (Fig.M.5)

1. Disconnect cables from terminal "B" at control box and join together with jumper lead. Connect 0-20 voltmeter between "D" and a good earth.

2. Run engine at 2,200 rpm. Check voltmeter reading against following table.

Ambient Temperature	Voltage Setting
10°C (50°F)	14.9 - 15.5
20°C (68°F)	14.7 - 15.3
30°C (86°F)	14.5 - 15.1
40°C (104°F)	14.3 - 14.9

NOTE:- A reading fluctuation of more than $\pm$ 0.3 volt may be due to dirty contacts.

3. To bring a steady reading inside limits when necessary, rotate the voltage regulator cam with the special tool counter-clockwise to raise setting or clockwise to lower it. Check the setting by stopping the engine then again bringing the engine speed to 2,200 rpm.

4. Remove voltmeter and jumper lead and restore connections. Replace cover.

Cut-out, Cut-in Voltage Setting (Fig.M.6)

1. Connect a moving coil voltmeter between terminal "D" and earth.

2. Switch on headlamps.

3. Start engine and slowly increase speed. Voltage should raise steadily then drop slightly when voltage is 12.7 to 13.3 volts and contacts close.

4. If necessary, bring cut-in within limits by turning the cut-out relay adjustment cam counter clockwise to raise setting and clockwise to lower it.

5. Remove voltmeter, restore connections and refit cover.

Cut-out Drop-off Voltage Setting (Fig.M.7)

1. Disconnect cables from terminal "B" at control box and connect together with jumper lead. Connect a moving coil voltmeter between terminal "B" and earth.

2. Start engine and run-up to 2,200 rpm. Slowly decelerate and check that voltmeter pointer drops to zero (contacts open) between 9.5 and 11.0 volts.

3. If drop-off is outside limits, stop engine and adjust cut-out contact gap by bending fixed contact. Reducing gap increases voltage and increasing gap decreases voltage.

4. Repeat test until correct result is obtained.

5. Remove voltmeter, restore connections and refit cover.

Current Regulator On-Load Setting (Fig.M.8)

1. Disconnect cables from terminals "B" at control box and join together with jumper lead. Short out voltage regulator contacts with bulldog clip and connect ammeter between "B" and jumper lead.

NOTE:- Ensure terminal "B" carries only this connection.

2. Switch on all lights, run engine at about 3,300 rpm and check current setting is 24-26 amps on ammeter. A reading fluctuating more than one amp indicates possible dirty contacts.

CAUTION:- Do not switch on lights after engine has been started.

3. If necessary bring output within limits by rotating current adjustment cam with special tool as shown.

4. Switch off engine, remove ammeter, bulldog clip and jumper lead and restore connections. Replace cover.

Air Gap Settings (Fig.M.9 or M.10)

NOTE:- The air gaps should normally require no attention. If setting has been lost, reset as described.

1. On voltage or current regulator turn cam to minimum lift using special tool. Slacken contact screw and insert 0.054 in. feeler gauge as far as the two rivet heads. Press down on armature and set adjustable contact to just touch armature contact. Remove feeler and adjust voltage or current setting.

2. On cut-out relay insert 0.015 in. feeler gauge between armature and core, press down armature, bend cut-out fixed contact release armature and remove feeler gauge Adjust armature back-stop to give core gap of 0.9 to 1.14 mm (0.035 to 0.045 in.). Check cut-in and drop-off voltage settings.

GENERATOR - Removal and Installation (Fig.M.11)
Removal

1. Isolate battery and disconnect leads from the generator terminals.

2. Slacken bolts (1) and (2), pivot generator towards engine and remove fan belt.

3. Remove bolts and remove generator.

Installation

1. Reverse the removal procedure, tensioning the fan belt to give 19.00 - 25.00 mm (0.75 - 1.00 in.) side movement at the mid-point on the longest run.

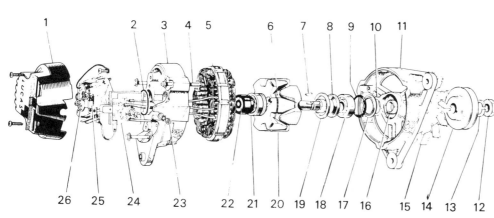

Fig.M.19 Exploded view of the Lucas 15 ACR
alternator

1. Moulded cover
2. Rubber 'O' ring
3. Slip ring end bracket
4. Through-bolt
5. Stator windings
6. Field winding
7. Key
8. Bearing retaining plate
9. Pressure ring
10. Felt ring
11. Drive end bracket
12. Nut
13. Spring washer
14. Pulley
15. Fan
16. Spacer
17. Pressure ring and felt ring
   retaining plate
18. Drive end bearing
19. Circlip
20. Rotor
21. Slip ring end bearing
22. Slip ring moulding
23. Nut
24. Rectifier pack
25. Brushbox assembly
26. Control unit

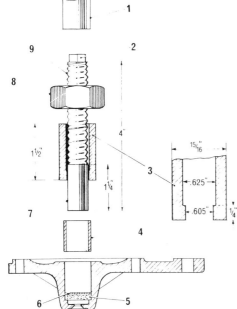

Fig.M.18 Pressing a new bush into the commutator
end bracket

1. Press
2. Squared end
3. Sleeve
4. Porous bronze bearing bush
5. Felt ring
6. Felt ring retainer
7. Fitting pin - 0.5924" diameter
8. Extracting nut
9. Thread - 0.625" B.S.F. truncated 0.614"

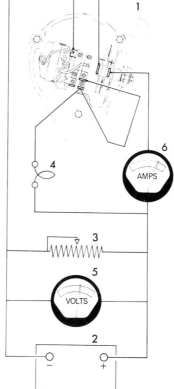

Fig.M.20 Alternator output test circuit

1. Alternator
2. 12 Volt battery
3. 0 - 15 ohm, 35 amp variable
   resistor
4. 12 volt, 2.2 watt bulb
5. 0 - 20 Voltmeter
6. 0 - 40 Ammeter

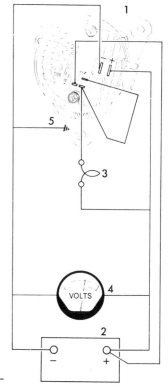

Fig.M.21 Control unit test circuit

1. Alternator
2. 12 Volt battery
3. 12 Volt, 2.2 watt bulb
4. 0 - 20 Voltmeter
5. Earth connection to alternator body

GENERATOR BRUSHES - Inspection and/or Replacement
(Fig.M.14)

1. Remove generator from car as described above.

2. Remove two through-bolts at rear of generator and withdraw commutator end bracket.

3. Lift up brush springs and withdraw brushes from holders.

4. Check brushes for wear. Renew if less than 7.1 mm (0.28 in.) in length.

5. Check commutator for oil contamination; if present, brushes must be renewed. Clean commutator surface with cloth moistened with white spirit, drying carefully afterwards. Contact surface of commutator should be smooth and dark grey in colour.

6. To renew brushes, remove screw and lock washer securing each brush lead to holder and detach brushes. Ensure replacement brushes are of correct length and type. Use special carbon grade H100 brushes only. Secure leads of new brushes to holders.

7. Check brushes for freedom of movement in holders. If necessary, clean brush and holder with cloth moistened in white spirit or petrol, drying carefully.

8. Check brush spring tension, using spring scale (Fig.M.13). If tension is below 17 oz., fit new springs.

9. Locate brush springs on side of brush, ensure fibre washer is fitted on armature shaft and assemble end bracket. Fit and secure through-bolts.

10. Insert thin screwdriver through ventilation hole in commutator bracket adjacent to brush holders. Gently lever up spring ends, press down brush onto commutator and position spring end on top of brush. Repeat for other brush.

11. Install generator on car as described above.

GENERATOR - Overhaul (Fig.M.12)
Disassembly

1. Remove shaft nut (13) and washer and draw off drive pulley. Remove spacer (14) and fan.

2. Remove two through-bolts together with key (21) at rear of generator and withdraw commutator end bracket (1). Remove fibre thrust washer (4) from armature shaft and retain.

3. Withdraw armature complete with drive end bracket (II) from generator yoke (6).

4. If required, press armature shaft out of drive end bracket.

5. Clean yoke, field coils, armature end brackets with a brush or air line. Wash all other parts in solvent and dry thoroughly.

Field Coils

Inspect field coils for burned or broken insulation and for broken or loose connections. With field coils still installed in yoke, measure resistance by connecting an ohmmeter between field terminal post and yoke. Field resistance should be 5.9 ± 0.3 ohms. If an ohmmeter is not available, a 12 volt D.C. supply with an ammeter in series can be used instead. Ammeter reading should be approx. 2 amps. Zero reading on ammeter or "infinity" reading on ohmmeter indicates open-circuit in field coils. If current reading is much more than 2 amps or ohmmeter reading is much below 6 ohms, this indicates insulation of one coil has broken down. In either case coils must be renewed. Replace coils as follows:

1. Drill out rivet securing field terminal assembly (2) to yoke. Unsolder field coil connections from terminal post, marking relative positions of wires. Inner wire (yellow) is insulated and outer wire (red) connects to earth.

2. If original field coils are to be refitted, mark yoke and pole pieces to ensure each pole piece is refitted in exactly the same position, otherwise residual magnetic polarity of the generator will be altered.

3. Remove insulation piece.

4. Remove pole shoe screws (Fig.M.15), remove pole shoes and withdraw field coils.

5. Fit new field coils to shoes. If original shoes are being refitted, ensure they are installed in exactly the same positions as before.

6. Fully tighten pole screws (Fig.M.15) and centre punch into screw slots to lock.

7. Fit insulation piece.

8. Solder field coil connections to terminal post, ensuring that wires are correctly fitted.

9. Before finally peening over rivet end to secure field terminal assembly to yoke, temporarily fit commutator end bracket to ensure correct alignment of post.

Armature

Clean armature with petrol soaked rag. Inspect commutator surface for pits or burned spots. If commutator is in good condition, the surface will be smooth and dark-grey in colour. If pits or burned spots are present, carefully polish the surface of the commutator with strip of glass paper while rotating armature. NEVER use emery cloth. If commutator is badly worn or scored, it may be reskimmed to a minimum skimming diameter of 36.5 mm (1.43 in.). The re-skimming operation should be entrusted to an electrical specialist.

NOTE:- As the commutator is of the moulded type, the segments do NOT require undercutting. However, the insulation slots should be kept clear of copper and carbon residue.

Fig.M.22 Unsoldering the stator leads on the rectifier pack

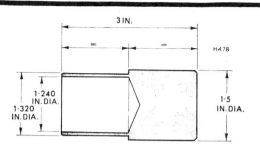

Fig.M.23 Dimensions of slip ring bearing extractor tool

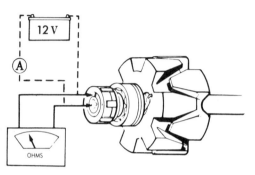

Fig.M.24 Checking the resistance of the rotor windings

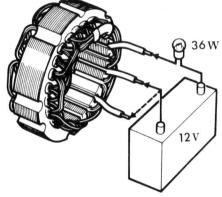

Fig.M.25 Testing the stator windings for continuity

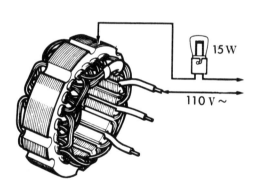

Fig.M.26 Testing the stator winding insulation

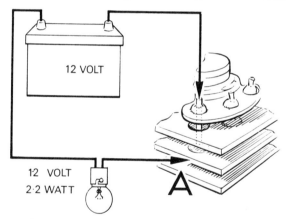

Fig.M.27 Checking the alternator diodes

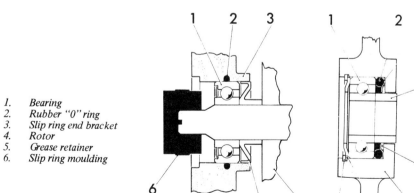

1. Bearing
2. Rubber "0" ring
3. Slip ring end bracket
4. Rotor
5. Grease retainer
6. Slip ring moulding

Fig.M.28 Sectional view of the slip-ring end bearing

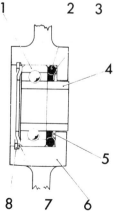

1. Bearing
2. Pressure ring
3. Pressure ring and felt ring retaining plate
4. Spacer
5. Felt ring
6. Drive end bracket
7. Bearing retaining plate
8. Circlip

Fig.M.29 Sectional view of the drive end bearing

Indications of a short-circuit are discolouration of any one or two coils and a blackening of two or more commutator segments. An open-circuit will cause burned spots between the commutator segments.

To test for open circuits in the commutator segments or in the armature windings, connect a 12 volt battery and voltmeter in series with a pair of test prods. Place prods on each pair of adjacent segments in turn and note voltmeter readings. If armature is in good order, all readings will be similar. If a low zero reading is obtained between any pair of segments, one or more adjacent coils are open-circuited (Fig.M.16).

To check if armature is grounded, using same circuit as above, place one of prods in contact with end of armature shaft. and other on each commutator segment in turn (Fig.M.17). There should be no voltmeter readings. If reading is obtained, one of the armature coils is grounded. A test lamp may be used instead of voltmeter, in which case lamp will glow if there is a ground.

Bearings

If worn or damaged, the armature shaft bearings can be replaced as follows:-

Commutator end bracket

a). Remove old brush from bracket by screwing 0.625 tap a few turns squarely into bush and withdrawing.

b). Remove felt ring and retainer and clean housing. Renew felt washer if necessary.

c). Install felt ring and retainer in bore and press in bush until flush (Fig.M.18). New bush should be soaked in engine oil for 24 hours before fitting and must not be reamed.

Drive end bracket

a). Remove circlip and plate (17). Press bearing (9) from bracket and remove pressure ring (16) retainer (10) and felt washer (15).

b). Clean all items. Check ball race for cracks and wear and renew if necessary.

c). Install items in reverse order of removal. Pack bearing with high melting point grease before installation.

Re-assembly

Support inner journal of drive end bracket bearing and press bracket onto armature shaft.

Assemble armature and end bracket to yoke, ensure that locating dowel on bracket correctly engages groove in yoke.

3. Fit thrust washer (4) to end of armature shaft and refit commutator end bracket as described in "GENERATOR BRUSHES - Inspection and/or Replacement".

4. Fit pulley spacer and key to shaft, assemble fan with blades towards end bracket and pulley with boss towards fan. Fit washer and secure with nut.

5. It may be necessary to provide residual magnetism in the field coils after the generator has been installed in the car. With the leads disconnected from the "D" and "F" terminals on the generator, connect a jumper lead to the battery negative terminal and flick the other end of the jumper lead several times against the "F" terminal on the generator.

ALTERNATOR - PRECAUTIONARY SERVICE NOTES
(G.T.6 Mk. 2 only)

It is essential that the following notes be observed when carrying out and maintenance or repairs on a charging system which includes an alternator.

1. Never remove alternator without first disconnecting battery.

2. Never disconnect or reconnect battery while alternator is running, otherwise damage to control box may occur.

3. Never run alternator with battery disconnected and field windings energised, otherwise control unit may be damaged.

4. When installing battery or reconnecting battery leads, always ensure that correct polarity is observed. Reversal of battery connections may damage alternator diodes.

5. Never allow alternator output cable to ground if disconnected at alternator. If this cable grounds with ignition switched on, control unit and associated wiring may be damaged.

6. Never allow alternator output cable or terminal to ground as damage to alternator and/or alternator circuit may result, even when ignition is switched off.

7. Never allow field terminal of alternator or connecting lead to ground.

8. No attempt should be made to polarise alternator. This is not necessary and any attempt to do so may result in damage to alternator, control unit or associated wiring.

9. Never use regulator terminal on alternator as a source for running lights or other accessories otherwise the control unit will be adversely affected.

10. Never use an ohmmeter of the type incorporating a hand-driven generator to check the alternator diodes. Only . D.C. not exceeding 24 volts, should be used when testing.

11. If arc welding is to be carried out on vehicle, disconnect alternator and control unit to avoid possible damage.

12. Always disconnect positive lead from battery before using a fast charger. Charger must always be connected in parallel with battery, positive-to-positive, negative-to-negative.

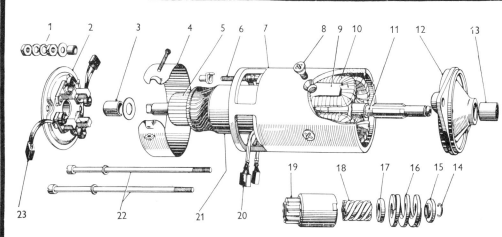

1. Terminal post nuts and washers
2. Commutator end bracket
3. Commutator end bracket bearing bush
4. Cover band
5. Commutator
6. Terminal post
7. Yoke
8. Pole shoe screw
9. Pole shoe
10. Field winding
11. Shaft
12. Drive end bracket
13. Drive end bracket bearing bush
14. Jump ring
15. Shaft collar
16. Main spring
17. Buffer washer
18. Screwed sleeve
19. Pinion and barrel
20. Field winding brush
21. Armature
22. Through-bolts
23. Earth brush

Fig.M.31 Exploded view of the starter motor

Fig.M.30 Starter motor installation

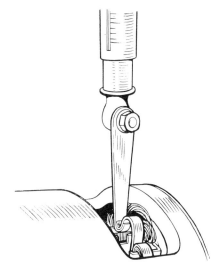

Fig.M.32 Checking the brush spring tension

Fig.M.33 Commutator end bracket and brushes

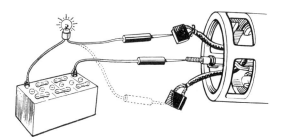

Fig.M.34 Testing the field coils for continuity

13. When using a starting unit, voltage must not exceed charging system voltage or damage to battery, alternator and starter may result. Fast charger must never be used as a booster unit for starting because of accompanying high voltage. After engine has started, always disconnect negative cable.

14. To avoid damaging alternator bearings when adjusting drive belt tension, apply leverage only on drive end bracket of alternator, not on any other part.

ALTERNATOR OUTPUT TEST (Fig.M.20)

SPECIAL NOTE: Polarity sensitive components in the alternator may be damaged if subjected to incorrect polarity. Check polarity of alternator and battery terminals.

NOTE:- When the alternator is cold, the stated output may be exceeded slightly. To avoid misleading results, the check should be performed with the unit as near to its normal operating temperature as possible.

Disconnect the multi-socket connector from the rear of the alternator. Remove the moulded cover from the rear of the unit. Connect a test circuit as shown in illustrations.

NOTE:- The variable resistor should only be connected across the battery for as long as is necessary to carry out the check.

Start engine and gradually increase the speed. The test light should go out at 720 rev/min.

Further increase the engine speed to 2,870 rpm. With the engine held at this speed, adjust the variable resistor until the voltmeter reads 14 volts. The ammeter reading should now be approx. 28 amps.

If the ammeter reading is incorrect, the alterantor should be overhauled or exchanged.

TESTING THE ALTERNATOR CONTROL UNIT (Fig.M.21)

CAUTION: DO NOT SUBJECT UNIT TO INCORRECT POLARITY.

1. Disconnect leads at alterantor and provide test circuit as shown in illustration.

2. Run engine at gradually increasing speed. At 720 engine RPM, light should go out.

3. Hold speed at 2,870 engine RPM. Voltmeter should now read a steady 14.0 - 14.4 volts.

4. If a steady 14.0 - 14.4 volts is not obtained and alternator functional check is satisfactory, the control unit should be replaced.

ALTERNATOR - Removal and Installation

Refer to ALTERNATOR - PRECAUTIONARY SERVICE NOTES before attempting removal of the alternator.

Disconnect the battery. Disconnect the multi-socket connector from the rear of the alternator. Slacken alternator mounting bolts of the tensioning strap. Push the alternator towards the engine and lift off the drive belt. Completely remove the mounting bolts and detach the alternator from the engine.

Installation is the reverse of the removal procedure.

Tighten the mounting bolts so that the drive belt has a total free movement of 19.0-25.0 mm (0.75-1.00 in.) at the mid-point on the longest run.

If the alternator has been overhauled or an exchange unit fitted, check the alternator output when installed.

ALTERNATOR - Overhaul (Fig.M.19)
Dismantling

1. Remove moulded cover.

2. Disconnect brushbox connector, using long-nosed pliers if necessary, remove three screws and brushbox (25).

3. Identify three stator wires on rectifier pack (24) and unsolder wire connections as quickly as possible using long-nosed pliers as a heat sink. (Fig.M.22). Slacken nut and remove rectifier pack.

4. Remove through-bolts (4).

5. Using tool detailed on Fig.M.23 against bearing (21) outer journal, support slip ring end bracket (3) by hand and tap out bearing. Carefully file out surplus solder on slip ring moulding if necessary to accommodate tool. Remove "O"-ring (2) from bearing housing.

6. Remove stator (5) from end bracket.

7. Remove pulley and fan. Retain key.

8. Press rotor from drive end bracket.

Inspection
Brushes

Clean the brushes with a cloth moistened in petrol or white spirit. Check brushes for wear. Renew if less than 5 mm (0.2 in.) protrudes from the brushbox when free. Check brushes for freedom of movement in the brushbox. If necessary, lightly polish the brush sides with a fine file. Check the brush spring pressure, using a push type spring scale. The specified tension is 7 - 10 oz.. If the tension is low, renew the brushbox assembly.

Slip Rings

Clean the slip rings with a cloth moistened in petrol or white spirit. Inspect the contact faces of the rings. These should be smooth and clean. If necessary, polish the faces with very fine glass paper. Never attempt to machine the rings.

Rotor

Check the resistance of the rotor windings by connecting an ohmmeter between the slip rings (Fig.M.24). The resistance

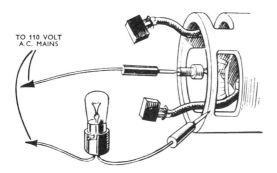

Fig.M.35 Testing the field coil insulation

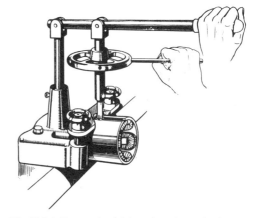

Fig.M.36 Removing/tightening the pole shoe retaining screws.

Fig.M.37 Wiper motor installation - Vitesse

Fig.M.38 Wiper motor installation - GT6 Mk 1

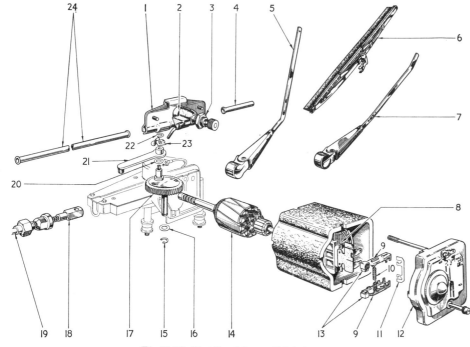

1. Wheel box
2. Jet and bush assembly
3. Nut
4. Rigid tubing - right hand side
5. Wiper arm
6. Blade
7. Wiper arm
8. Field coil assembly
9. Brushgear
10. Tension spring and retainers
11. Brush gear retainer
12. End cover
13. Brushes
14. Armature
15. Circlip
16. Washer
17. Final drive wheel
18. Cable rack
19. Rigid tubing - left-hand side
20. Spacer
21. Connecting rod
22. Circlip
23. Parking switch contact
24. Rigid tubing - centre section

Fig.M.39 Details of Lucas DR3 A windscreen wiper meschanism - Vitesse and GT6 Mk 1

should be 4.3 ohms. If an ohmmeter is not available, an ammeter and a 12 volt battery can be used instead. The ammeter reading should be 2.8 amps.

Test the rotor insulation, using a 110 volts A.C. power supply and a 15 watt test lamp. Connect the lamp between one of the slip rings and one of the rotor poles. The lamp must not light up. If it does, the rotor should be replaced.

The stator leads must be disconnected before carrying out the following tests.

Test the stator windings for continuity, using a 12 volt battery and a test lamp of at least 36 watts. Connect the lamp and battery in series with any two of the three stator leads (Fig.M.25). Repeat the test with the two other combinations of leads. The test lamp must light during all three tests. Replace the stator if this is not the case.

Using a 110 volt A.C. power supply and a 15 watt test lamp connected in series, connect one lead to one of the stator cables and the other to the stator casing (Fig.M.26). If the lamp lights up, the stator windings are grounded and the stator must be replaced.

Diodes

The diode leads must be completely detached from the phase terminals before performing the following tests. Use a pair of long-nose pliers as a heat sink when unsoldering the connections, as the diodes are heat sensitive and can be easily damaged (Fig.M.22). Release the connections quickly with a hot soldering iron.

Connect each of the diodes in turn in series with a 2.2 watt test lamp and a 12 volt battery. Connect one of the test leads to one of the diode leads and the other test lead to the diode heat sink (Fig.M.27). Note the behaviour of the test lamp. Reverse the connections and repeat the test. The test lamp should light up in one direction only. A diode that passes current in both directions has probably been subjected to excessive voltage and the rectifier pack must be replaced.

Rotor Bearings

The rotor bearings are "unit-life" items and it is therefore unlikely that replacement will become necessary. However, if replacement is required proceed as follows:

Slip Ring End Bearing (Fig.M.18)

1. Unsolder the two field winding connections from the slip ring moulding (6) and pull the moulding from the shaft. Extract bearing and remove grease retainer (5).

2. Pack bearing with Shell Alvania R.A. grease or equivalent, fit serviceable grease retainer to shaft, press bearing onto shaft with shielded face outwards and also fit slip ring mouldings. Solder two connections to slip ring moulding.

Drive End Bearing (Fig.M.29)

1. Remove circlip (8) and retaining plate (7), push out the bearing and remove the "O" ring (2), retaining plate (3), felt ring (5) and spacer (4).

2. Fit the retaining plate, felt ring, pressure ring and serviceable "O"-ring. Pack bearing with Shell Alvania R.A. grease or equivalent and press bearing into the housing. Fit the retainer and circlip.

Re-assembly

1. Using spacer (16) and suitably-sized tube against bearing inner journal, press rotor into drive end bracket.

2. Locate key and fit fan and pulley.

3. Position stator windings in correct attitude to drive end bracket.

4. Fit serviceable "O"-ring (2) in bearing housing and carefully press slip ring end bracket over bearing.

5. Fit through-bolts.

6. Position rectifier pack with rubber locating piece and secure with nut.

7. Correctly position three stator wires on rectifier pack and quickly solder with "M" grade 45-55 tin lead solder (Fig. M.22). Do not overheat or bend diode pins.

8. With brushes correctly entered, secure brushbox to rectifier pack with connector and three screws.

9. Fit moulded cover.

STARTER MOTOR - Removal and Installation (Fig.M.30).

The starter motor is mounted on the rear right-hand side of the engine.

Removal

1. Disconnect cable from battery and starter motor.

2. Remove two attachment bolts and remove starter motor upwards.

Installation

1. Reverse removal procedure ensuring that the mounting face shoulder correctly registers on the engine bearer plate face.

2. Reconnect cables.

NOTE:- A clearance of 2.39 - 3.96 mm (0.094-0.156 in.) is required between end of pinion and starter ring gear. Packing pieces and shims in thickness of 10.16, 12.70 and 0.406 mm (0.4 in, 0.5 in and 0.016 in.) are available.

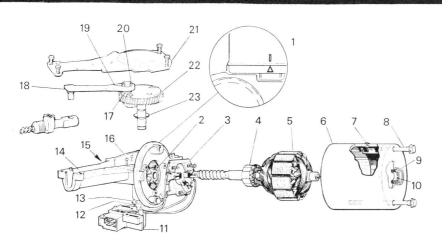

Fig.M.41 Details of Lucas 14W windscreen wiper motor - GT6 Mk 2

1. Aligning marks
2. Self-aligning bearing
3. Brush assembly
4. Commutator
5. Armature
6. Cover
7. Permanent magnet
8. Through bolt
9. Cover bearing
10. Felt washer
11. Limit switch unit
12. Final gear shaft spring clip
13. Washer
14. Crosshead guide channel
15. Thrust screw (non-adjustable)
   or
   Thrust screw and lock nut (adjustable)
16. Gearbox
17. Washer
18. Connecting rod
19. Washer
20. Crank pin spring clip
21. Gearbox cover
22. Final gear
23. Dished washer

Fig.M.40 Wiper motor - GT6 Mk 2

Fig.M.43 Removing the headlamp cover panel - Vitesse

1. Seal
2. Housing
3. Pivot
4. Adjuster
5. Bush
6. Clip
7. Adaptor
8. Locknut
9. Clip
10. Light unit
11. Rim
12. Screws

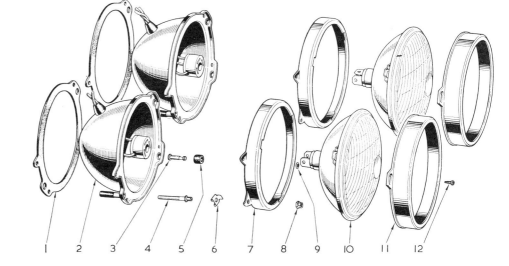

Fig.M.42. Exploded view of headlamp assembly - Vitesse

1 - 3 Retaining screws
4 Rubber pivot
A Horizontal adjustment screw
B Vertical adjustment screw

**Fig.M.44 Headlamp with cover panel removed -
Vitesse**

**Fig.M.45 Replacing sealed beam light unit -
Vitesse**

**Fig.M.46 Front parking/flasher lamp -
Vitesse**

Fig.M.47 Rear flasher/stop/tail lamp - Vitesse

**Fig.M.48 License plate illumination and
reverse lamp - Vitesse**

**Fig.M.50 Replacing sealed beam light unit -
GT6**

Fig.M.49 Headlamp with rim removed - GT6

1 - 3 Retaining screws
A Horizontal adjustment screw
B Vertical adjustment screw

Fig.M.51 Front parking lamp (inner) and
flasher lamp (outer) - GT6

Fig.M.52 Rear flasher lamp (outer) and
reverse lamp (inner) - GT6

Fig.M.53 Tail/stop lamp - GT6

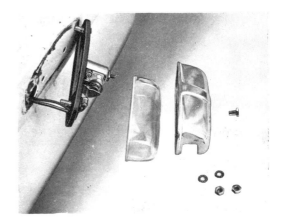

Fig.M.54 License plate illumination lamp -
GT6

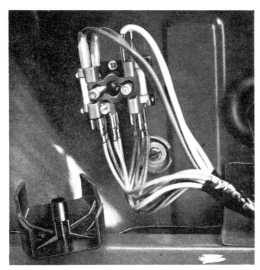

Fig.M.55 Fuse box location on bulkhead
Vitesse

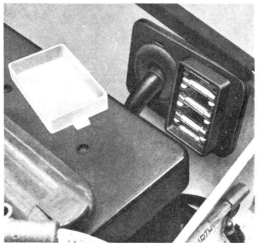

Fig.M.56 Fuse box location on bulkead
GT6

STARTER MOTOR (Fig.M.31)
Inspection and/or Replacement of Brushes

1. Remove starter motor from car.

2. Slacken clamp screw and slide brush cover (8) away from brush apertures. Lift brush springs using piece of hooked wire and withdraw brushes from holders.

NOTE:- If the original brushes are to be re- used, they MUST be refitted in their ORIGINAL positions.

3. Check brushes for wear. If brushes are so worn that they do not bear on the commutator, or if the flexible lead is visible on the brush contact face, new brushes must be fitted. Minimum brush length is 8 mm (0.31 in.)

4. Check brush spring tension, using a spring scale (Fig.M.32). If tension is below 32 oz, fit new springs.

5. If brushes are to be renewed, remove nuts and washers, insulating washer and insulating bush (1) from field terminal post. Unscrew two through-bolts (22) and withdraw end plate (2) from starter yoke (Fig.33).

6. Check commutator for oil contamination. If present, brushes must be renewed. If commutator is blackened or dirty, clean with cloth moistened in white spirit or petrol, drying thoroughly, or clean with very fine glass paper. Never use emery cloth and never attempt to under-cut the mica insulation between the segments.

7. To renew earthed brushes (23) on end plate, unsolder brush leads from clip beneath brush box. Open clip, insert replace-ment brush lead, squeeze clip and resolder.

8. To renew insulated brushes (20) on field coils, cut off brush leads 3 mm (0.125 in.) from aluminium. Clean and tin original brazed joint at field coil connection. Open loop of replacement brush lead and tin loop, taking care not to allow solder to run towards brush. Place brazed joint within loop, squeeze loop and resolder.

9. Check brushes for freedom of movement in holders. If necessary, clean brush and holder with cloth moistened in white spirit or petrol, drying carefully. Sides of brushes can be eased by lightly polishing with a fine file.

10. Check that insulator band is fitted between yoke and end of field coils, and insulating bush is fitted to field terminal post.

11. Pass insulated brushes out through apertures in yoke.

12. Check thrust washer is fitted on armature shaft.

13. Fit earthed brushes in their holders and assemble end plate to starter yoke, ensuring that dowel on plate correctly engages notch in yoke. Fit through-bolts and tighten securely.

14. Refit insulating bush, insulating washer and nuts and washers on field terminal post. Tighten inner nut securely.

15. Fit insulated brushes in insulated holders.

16. Press brushes down onto commutator and lift brush springs into position on top of brushes.

17. Refit brush cover (4) over brush apertures and tighten clamp screw.

18. Refit starter on car.

Replacement of the Drive Pinion

NOTE:- If difficulty is experienced with the starter motor not meshing correctly with the ring gear, it may be that the drive assembly requires cleaning. The pinion and barrel assembly should move freely on the screwed sleeves. If there is any dirt or other foreign matter on the sleeve, it must be washed off with paraffin.

Do NOT use grease on the drive assembly as this would attract dirt.

1. Remove starter motor from car.

2. Compress drive spring (16) and retainer (15), using a suitable clamping device, and release jump ring (14). Re-move clamping device and withdraw retainer drive spring, thrust washer (17), screwed sleeve (18) and pinion and barrel assembly (19).

NOTE:- The pinion and barrel assembly cannot be dismantled it is supplied as a complete assembly with the screwed sleeve.

3. Assemble in the reverse order of removal.

Overhaul
Disassembly

1. Remove end plate as described above for replacing brushes.

2. Withdraw armature and end bracket assembly.

3. Remove drive pinion assembly as described above and withdraw front plate armature shaft.

4. Clean yoke, field coils, armature, drive assembly and end plate with a brush or air line. Wash all other parts in solvent and dry thoroughly.

Field Coils

Inspect the field coils for burned or broken insulation and for broken or loose connections. Check the field brush connec-tions and brush lead insulation.

Test the field coils for continuity by connecting a 12-volt battery and test lamp between the brush tappings on the field coils (Fig.M.34). If the lamp fails to light, an open-circuit in the field coils in indicated and the coils must be replaced. Lighting of the lamp does not necessarily indicate that the field coils are in order. It is possible that a field coil may be grounded to a pole shoe or the starter yoke.

Test the insulation of the field coils by connecting a 110 volt. A.C. supply and a test lamp between the field terminal and the starter yoke (Fig.M.35). If the lamp lights, this indicates that the field coils are grounded to the starter yoke and must be replaced. Replace the coils as follows.

Fig.M.57 Flasher unit, located behind fascia on the L.H. side - Vitesse

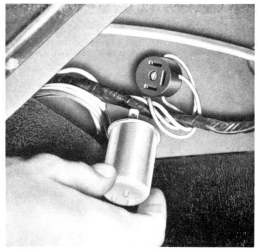

Fig.M.58 Replacing flasher unit, located behind fascia on the R.H. side - GT/ Mk 1

Fig.M.59 Flasher unit, located behind fascia on the R.H. side - GT6 Mk 2

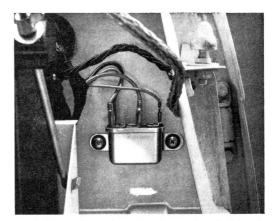

Fig.M.60 Overdrive relay, located on bulkhead Vitesse

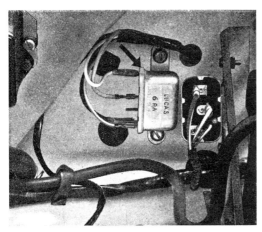

Fig.M.61 Overdrive relay, located on bulkhead GT6

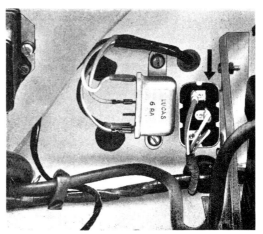

Fig.M.62 Horn relay, located on bulkhead - GT6

1. If original field coils are to be refitted, mark yoke and pole pieces to ensure each pole piece is fitted in exactly the same position as before.

2. Fit pole expander and remove pole screws (Fig.M.39). Remove pole pieces and withdraw field coils.

3. Unsolder coil tappings from terminal post.

4. If required, new insulated brushes should be soldered to field coil tappings before installing coils in the starter yoke. See brush replacement for details.

5. Fit pole pieces and field coils in starter yoke, ensuring that the pole pieces are installed in exactly the same positions as before.

6. Fit pole shoe expander and fully tighten pole screws (Fig.M.39). Centre-punch into screw slots to lock.

7. Fit insulator band between yoke and end of field coils (Fig.M.35).

8. If a new field terminal post is being fitted, temporarily fit end plate to ensure correct alignment of the post before finally soldering.

Armature

The armature and commutator should be inspected and tested as described previously for the generator.

NOTE:- The mica insulation between the commutator segments must NOT be undercut on the starter armature.

Bearings

Bearings worn to such an extent that they allow excessive side play of the armature shaft, must be renewed.

NOTE: New brushes must be soaked in engine oil for 24 hours prior to fitting.

1. Press old bearing bush out of end bracket.

2. Using a shouldered mandrel diameter as armature shaft, press new bush into end bracket.

NOTE:- Bush is made of porous bronze and must NOT be reamed out after fitting as this may impair the porosity of the bush.

Re-assembly

Assemble in the reverse order of dismantling.

Technical Data

BATTERY

Type	Lead acid
Voltage	12 - volts
Capacity at 20 hour rate	43 ampere-hours
Plates per cell	9

GENERATOR

Make and Model	Lucas C40 - 1
Type	Two brush, two pole compensated voltage control.
Rotation	Clockwise
Max output at 13.5 volts	25 amperes at 2.275 rpm (connected to load at 0.54 ohms)

CONTROL BOX

Make and Model	Lucas RB 340

Cut-in voltage	12.7 - 13.3
Drop-off voltage	11.0 - 9.5

ALTERNATOR (G.T.6Mk. 2)

Make and Model	Lucas 15 ACR
Rectifier pack-output	6 diodes (3 live side-3 earth side)
- field winding supply	3 diodes
Stator windings	3 phase - star connected.
Drive ratio - engine rpm. alternator rpm	11 : 18
Output	28 amp

CONTROL UNIT
STARTER MOTOR

Make and Model	Lucas M35G
Type	Four pole, four bush, series-wound.

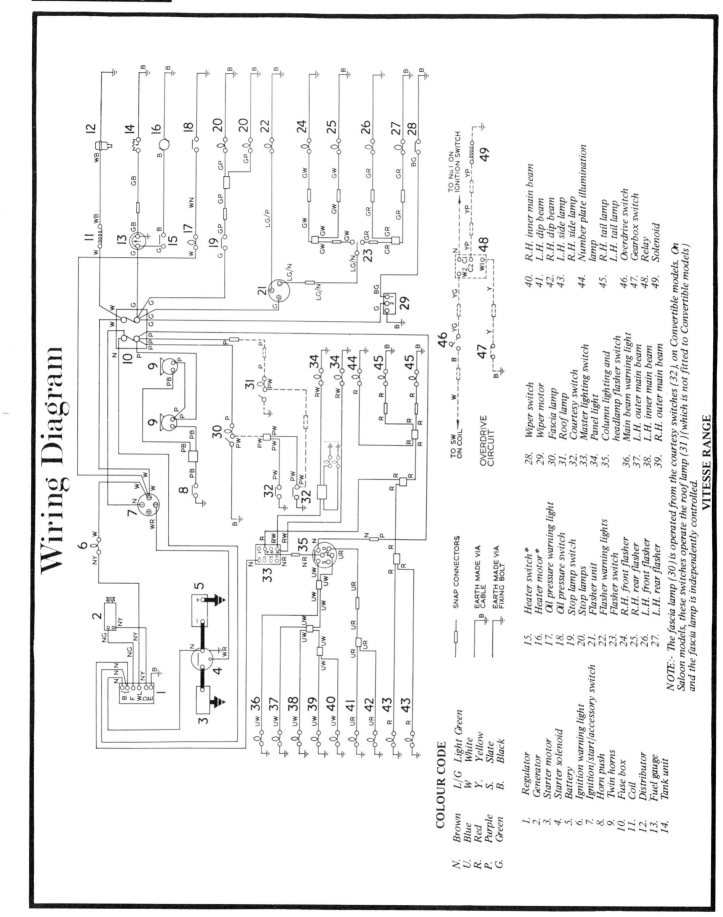

Wiring Diagram

COLOUR CODE

N.	Brown	L/G	Light Green
U.	Blue	W	White
R.	Red	Y.	Yellow
P.	Purple	S.	Slate
G.	Green	B.	Black

1. Regulator
2. Generator
3. Starter motor
4. Starter solenoid
5. Battery
6. Ignition warning light
7. Ignition/start/accessory switch
8. Horn push
9. Twin horns
10. Fuse box
11. Coil
12. Distributor
13. Fuel gauge
14. Tank unit

15. Heater switch*
16. Heater motor*
17. Oil pressure warning light
18. Oil pressure switch
19. Stop lamp switch
20. Stop lamps
21. Flasher unit
22. Flasher warning lights
23. Flasher switch
24. R.H. front flasher
25. R.H. rear flasher
26. L.H. front flasher
27. L.H. rear flasher

28. Wiper switch
29. Wiper motor
30. Fascia lamp
31. Roof lamp
32. Courtesy switch
33. Master lighting switch
34. Panel light
35. Column lighting and headlamp flasher switch
36. Main beam warning light
37. L.H. outer main beam
38. L.H. inner main beam
39. R.H. outer main beam

40. R.H. inner main beam
41. L.H. dip beam
42. R.H. dip beam
43. L.H. side lamp
44. Number plate illumination lamp
45. R.H. tail lamp
46. Overdrive switch
47. Gearbox switch
48. Relay
49. Solenoid

43. R.H. side lamp
45. L.H. tail lamp

— SNAP CONNECTORS

⊥ EARTH MADE VIA CABLE

⊥ EARTH MADE VIA FIXING BOLT

OVERDRIVE CIRCUIT

TO SW ON COIL — W — W

VITESSE RANGE

NOTE:- The fascia lamp (30) is operated from the courtesy switches (32) on Convertible models. On Saloon models, these switches operate the roof lamp (31) (which is not fitted to Convertible models) and the fascia lamp is independently controlled.

166

Wiring Diagram

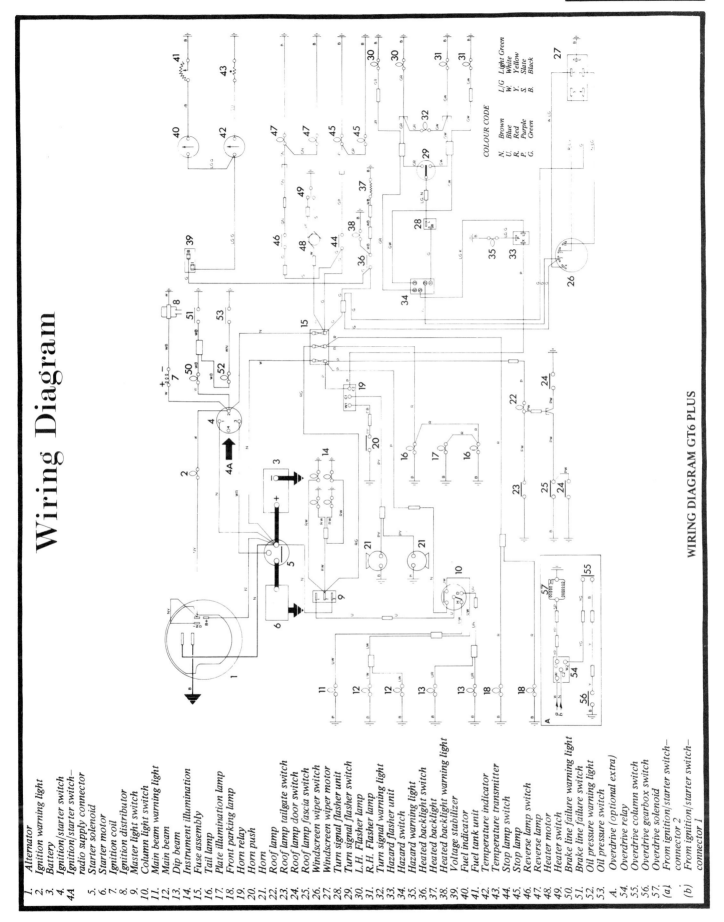

1. Alternator
2. Ignition warning light
3. Battery
4. Ignition/starter switch
4A. Ignition/starter switch–radio supply connector
5. Starter solenoid
6. Starter motor
7. Ignition coil
8. Ignition distributor
9. Master light switch
10. Column light switch
11. Main beam warning light
12. Main beam
13. Dip beam
14. Instrument illumination
15. Fuse assembly
16. Tail lamp
17. Plate illumination lamp
18. Front parking lamp
19. Horn relay
20. Horn push
21. Horn
22. Roof lamp
23. Roof lamp tailgate switch
24. Roof lamp door switch
25. Roof lamp fascia switch
26. Windscreen wiper switch
27. Windscreen wiper motor
28. Turn signal flasher unit
29. Turn signal flasher switch
30. L.H. Flasher lamp
31. R.H. Flasher lamp
32. Turn signal warning light
33. Hazard flasher unit
34. Hazard switch
35. Hazard warning light
36. Heated backlight switch
37. Heated backlight
38. Heated backlight warning light
39. Voltage stabilizer
40. Fuel indicator
41. Fuel tank unit
42. Temperature indicator
43. Temperature transmitter
44. Stop lamp switch
45. Stop lamp
46. Reverse lamp switch
47. Reverse lamp
48. Heater motor
49. Heater switch
50. Brake line failure warning light
51. Brake line failure switch
52. Oil pressure warning light
53. Oil pressure switch
54. Overdrive solenoid
A. Overdrive (optional extra)
54. Overdrive relay
55. Overdrive column switch
56. Overdrive gearbox switch
57. Overdrive solenoid
(a) From ignition/starter switch–connector 2
(b) From ignition/starter switch–connector 1

COLOUR CODE

N. Brown
U. Blue
R. Red
P. Purple
G. Green

L/G Light Green
W. White
Y. Yellow
S. Slate
B. Black

WIRING DIAGRAM GT6 PLUS

167

Engine

SYMPTOMS

	a	b	c	d	e	f	g	h	i	j	k	l	m	n	o	p	q	r	s	t	u	v
ENGINE WILL NOT CRANK	*	*	*	*																		
ENGINE CRANKS SLOWLY	*	*	*																			
ENGINE CRANKS BUT DOES NOT START					*	*	*	*			*											
ENGINE STARTS BUT RUNS FOR SHORT PERIODS ONLY					*	*																
ENGINE MISFIRES AT LOW SPEED					*	*																*
ENGINE MISFIRES AT HIGH SPEED					*	*																*
ENGINE MISFIRES AT ALL SPEEDS					*	*					*	*	*	*	*							*
ENGINE MISFIRES ON ACCELERATION AND FAILS TO REV.					*	*																*
ROUGH IDLE					*	*					*	*			*							*
RUNS ROUGH AT HIGH SPEED					*	*	*	*	*	*	*	*	*	*	*							*
LACK OF POWER							*	*	*	*	*	*	*	*	*					*		*
POOR ACCELERATION					*	*	*	*	*	*	*	*	*	*	*					*		*
LACK OF TOP SPEED					*	*	*	*	*	*	*	*	*	*	*							*
EXCESSIVE FUEL CONSUMPTION					*	*					*			*	*							
EXCESSIVE OIL CONSUMPTION															*	*	*	*	*			
PINKING					*	*																
COMPRESSION LEAK								*			*	*		*		*					*	*

PROBABLE CAUSE

a. Fault in the starting system – Refer to the ELECTRICAL EQUIPMENT section for diagnosis.
b. Engine oil too thick.
c. Stiff engine.
d. Mechanical seizure.
e. Fault in the ignition system – Refer to the IGNITION SYSTEM section for diagnosis.
f. Fault in the fuel system – Refer to the FUEL SYSTEM section for diagnosis.
g. Incorrect valve timing.
h. Compression leak.
i. Air leak at inlet manifold.
j. Restriction in exhaust system.
k. Poor valve seating.
l. Sticking valves.
m. Leaking cylinder head gasket.
n. Worn camshaft lobes.
o. Incorrect tappet clearance.
p. Worn or damaged cylinder bores, pistons and/or piston rings.
q. Worn valve guides.
r. Damaged valve stem seals.
s. Leaking oil seal or gasket.
t. Incorrectly installed spark plug.
u. Cracked cylinder.
v. Broken or weak valve springs.

REMEDIES

b. Drain oil and replace with correct oil.
c. Add small quantity of oil to the fuel and run engine gently.
d. Strip engine and renew parts as necessary.
g. Retime engine.
h. Trace and seal.
i. Trace and seal.
j. Remove restriction.
k. Regrind seats.
l. Free and trace cause.
m. Renew gasket.
n. Fit new camshaft.
o. Adjust tappets.
p. Exchange engine.
q. Replace valve guides.
r. Replace seals.
s. Replace gasket.
t. Replace plug with correct one.
u. Renew cylinder block.
v. Replace springs.

Lubrication System

SYMPTOMS

	a	b	c	d	e	f	g	h	i	j	k	l	m	n
EXCESSIVE OIL CONSUMPTION	*	*	*	*										
LOW OIL PRESSURE					*	*	*	*	*	*	*	*	*	*

PROBABLE CAUSE

a. Worn or damaged cylinder bores, pistons and/or piston rings.
b. Worn valve guides.
c. Damaged valve stem seals.
d. Leaking oil seal or gasket.
e. Faulty oil pressure gauge, switch or wiring.
f. Relief valve defective.
g. Oil pick-up pipe strainer blocked.
h. Oil filter over-flow valve defective.
i. Worn oil pump.
j. Damaged or worn main and/or big-end bearings.
k. Incorrect grade of engine oil.
l. Oil level low.
m. Oil level too high.
n. Oil leak or the pressurised side of the lubrication system.

REMEDIES

a. Regrind cylinder bores and fit new oversize pistons and rings.
b. Replace valves and guides.
c. Replace seals.
d. Seal leak or replace gasket.
e. Trace and rectify.
f. Check and replace if necessary.
g. Remove blockage.
h. Check and replace if necessary.
i. Replace pump or parts.
j. Renew bearings.
k. Replace oil with correct grade.
l. Top up oil.
m. Drain off surplus oil.
n. Trace and remedy.

Cooling System

SYMPTOMS

	a	b	c	d	e	f	g	h	i	j	k	l	m	n	o
OVERHEATING	*	*	*	*	*	*		*	*	*	*	*	*	*	
ENGINE FAILS TO REACH NORMAL OPERATING TEMPERATURE							*								*

PROBABLE CAUSE

a. Insufficient coolant.
b. Drive belt slipping or broken.
c. Radiator fins clogged.
d. Cooling fan defective.
e. Water pump defective.
f. Thermostat jammed shut.
g. Thermostat jammed open.
h. Ignition timing too far retarded.
i. Excessive vehicle load or dragging brakes.
j. Internal passage in the engine and/or radiator blocked.
k. Hoses blocked.
l. Carburetter mal-adjustment.
m. Excessive carbon deposit in the cylinders.
n. Insufficient engine oil or use of inferior grade of oil.
o. Excessive radiator area.

REMEDIES

a. Top up radiator.
b. Tighten belt or renew.
c. Unclog fins.
d. Trace fault, rectify or renew.
e. Replace water pump.
f. Replace thermostat.
g. Replace thermostat.
h. Retime ignition.
i. Unload car, check brakes.
j. Trace and clear.
k. Trace clear blockage.
l. Adjust correctly.
m. Decarbonise engine, top overhaul.
n. Top up with correct grade. Drain if necessary.
o. Partially blank off in winter only.

Trouble Shooting

Ignition System

SYMPTOMS

	a	b	c	d	e	f	g	h	i	j	k	l	m	n	o	p	q	r
ENGINE CRANKS BUT DOES NOT START	*	*	*						*	*		*	*	*	*	*		
ENGINE STARTS BUT RUNS FOR SHORT PERIODS ONLY	*	*	*						*	*		*	*	*	*			
ENGINE MISFIRES AT LOW SPEED	*				*	*	*											
ENGINE MISFIRES AT HIGH SPEED			*	*	*	*			*	*	*	*				*		
ENGINE MISFIRES AT ALL SPEEDS			*	*	*	*	*		*	*	*	*				*		
ENGINE MISFIRES ON ACCELERATION AND FAILS TO REV.			*	*	*	*	*		*	*						*		
ROUGH IDLE	*	*	*		*	*	*	*	*	*	*	*	*				*	
ENGINE RUNS ROUGH AT HIGH SPEED	*	*	*		*	*	*	*	*	*			*	*			*	
LACK OF POWER	*	*	*	*	*	*	*	*	*	*	*	*	*				*	
POOR ACCELERATION	*	*	*	*	*	*	*	*	*	*	*						*	
LACK OF TOP SPEED	*	*	*	*	*	*	*	*	*	*	*						*	
EXCESSIVE FUEL CONSUMPTION	*	*	*	*	*	*	*	*	*	*				*	*	*		
PINKING	*	*			*	*	*							*	*	*	*	*

	a	b	c	d	e	f	g	h	i	j	k	l	m	n	o	p	q	r

PROBABLE CAUSE

a. Battery discharged or defective.
b. Contact breaker points need cleaning or renewing.
c. Incorrect contact breaker points.
d. Contact breaker spring weak.
e. Spark plugs need cleaning or renewing.
f. Incorrect spark plug gaps.
g. Wrong type of spark plug fitted.
h. Static ignition timing incorrect.
i. Coil or capacitor defective.
j. Open circuit or loose connection in the L.T. circuit.
k. Open circuit, short to earth or loose connection on the coil H.T. lead.
l. Open circuit, short to earth or loose connection on the spark plug leads.
m. Plug leads incorrectly connected.
n. H.T. leak on coil, distributor cap or rotor, due to oil, dirt, moisture or damage.
o. Centrifugal advance not functioning correctly.
p. Vacuum advance not functioning correctly.
q. Worn distributor cam or distributor shaft bush.
r. Using wrong grade of fuel.

REMEDIES

a. Recharge or replace battery.
b. Clean or renew.
c. Fit correct points.
d. Renew contact breaker set.
e. Clean or renew spark plugs.
f. Adjust gaps.
g. Fit correct plugs.
h. Retime ignition.
i. Replace as necessary.
j. Trace and rectify.
k. Trace and rectify.
l. Trace and rectify.
m. Connect correctly.
n. Clean with dry lint free rag.
o. Examine and oil sparingly.
p. Check and rectify.
q. Replace defective parts.
r. Change to correct grade of fuel.

Fuel System

SYMPTOMS

	a	b	c	d	e	f	g	h	i	j	k	l	m	n	o	p	q	r	s	t	u	v
ENGINE CRANKS BUT DOES NOT START	*	*	*	*	*	*	*															
ENGINE STARTS BUT RUNS FOR SHORT PERIODS ONLY	*	*	*	*	*	*	*						*	*								
ENGINE MISFIRES AT LOW SPEED				*	*					*												
ENGINE MISFIRES AT HIGH SPEED			*	*					*			*										
ENGINE MISFIRES AT ALL SPEEDS	*	*	*	*	*	*	*					*										
ENGINE MISFIRES ON ACCELERATION AND FAILS TO REV.		*		*					*			*				*						
ROUGH IDLE				*						*	*	*						*				
ENGINE RUNS ROUGH AT HIGH SPEED			*	*					*			*							*		*	
LACK OF POWER			*						*			*		*					*		*	
POOR ACCELERATION			*						*			*					*		*		*	
LACK OF TOP SPEED			*						*			*							*		*	*
EXCESSIVE FUEL CONSUMPTION		*									*	*				*			*	*		
PINKING																*				*		
BACKFIRE											*							*		*		

	a	b	c	d	e	f	g	h	i	j	k	l	m	n	o	p	q	r	s	t	u	v

PROBABLE CAUSE

a. Fuel tank empty.
b. Fuel line blocked.
c. Fuel pump defective.
d. Blockage in carburetter.
e. Air lock in fuel line.
f. Fuel filter blocked.
g. Carburetter needle valve jammed.
h. Water in carburetter.
i. Erratic fuel flow due to blockage.
j. Idling speed too low.
k. Incorrect setting of choke control.
l. Incorrect carburetter fuel/float level.
m. Carburetter icing.
n. Air leak at inlet manifold.
o. Incorrect grade of fuel.
p. Carburetter accelerator pump defective.
q. Throttle linkage mal-adjusted.
r. Incorrect adjustment of idling mixture.
s. Air filter clogged.
t. Incorrect ignition timing.
u. Carburetter piston sticking.
v. Wrong carburetter jets fitted.

REMEDIES

a. Fill tank.
b. Blow out obstruction with compressed air.
c. Replace pump.
d. Remove blockage.
e. Trace and bleed out.
f. Clean filter.
g. Free needle.
h. Drain out water, dry out.
i. Remove blockage.
j. Adjust throttle stop screw.
k. Reset control.
l. Adjust level.
m. Wait for ice to melt. If persistent, trace cause.
n. Trace leak and seal.
o. Dilute fuel with highest octane rating obtainable.
p. Trace fault and rectify.
q. Adjust correctly.
r. Adjust mixture control.
s. Clean filter.
t. Retime ignition.
u. Oil carburetter.
v. Replace with correct jets.

Trouble Shooting

Braking System

SYMPTOMS

PROBABLE CAUSE →	a	b	c	d	e	f	g	h	i	j	k	l	m	n	o	p	q	r	s	t	u	v	w
BRAKE FAILURE					*		*	*												*			*
BRAKES INEFFECTIVE	*	*	*	*	*	*	*	*															
BRAKES GRAB OR PULL TO ONE SIDE	*	*	*	*							*			*		*		*					
BRAKES BIND									*						*		*	*	*		*		*
PEDAL SPONGY					*	*	*	*															
PEDAL TRAVEL EXCESSIVE	*				*												*			*			*
EXCESSIVE PEDAL PRESSURE REQUIRED	*	*	*																			*	
HYDRAULIC SYSTEM WILL NOT MAINTAIN PRESSURE								*												*			*
BRAKE SQUEAL DEVELOPS	*	*	*	*												*							
BRAKE SHUDDER DEVELOPS				*								*	*	*									
HANDBRAKE INEFFECTIVE OR REQUIRES EXCESSIVE MOVEMENT	*									*							*		*				

PROBABLE CAUSE

a. Brake shoe linings or friction pads excessively worn.
b. Incorrect brake shoe linings or friction pads.
c. Brake shoe linings or friction pads contaminated.
d. Brake drums or discs scored.
e. Insufficient brake fluid.
f. Incorrect brake fluid.
g. Air in the hydraulic system.
h. Fluid leak in the hydraulic system.
i. Fluid line blocked.
j. Mal-function in the brake pedal linkage.
k. Unequal tyre pressures.
l. Brake disc or drum distorted or cracked.
m. Brake back plate or calliper mounting bolts loose or looseness in the suspension.
n. Wheel bearings incorrectly adjusted.
o. Weak, broken or improperly installed shoe return springs.
p. Uneven brake lining contact.
q. Incorrect brake lining adjustment.
r. Pistons in wheel cylinder or calliper seized.
s. Weak or broken brake pedal return spring.
t. Master cylinder defective.
u. Fluid reservoir overfilled or reservoir air vent restricted.
v. Servo vacuum hose disconnected or restricted, or servo unit defective.
w. Wheel cylinder or calliper defective.

REMEDIES

a. Replace linings or pads.
b. Replace with correct linings or pads.
c. Clean thoroughly.
d. Renew drums or discs.
e. Bleed out old fluid and replace with correct type.
f. Top up reservoir.
g. Bleed brake system.
h. Trace and seal.
i. Trace and clear blockage.
j. Correct as necessary.
k. Adjust and balance tyre pressures.
l. Renew disc or drum.
m. Tighten as necessary to correct torque.
n. Adjust wheel bearings.
o. Renew or install correctly.
p. Trace cause and remedy.
q. Adjust correctly.
r. Free and clean.
s. Renew spring.
t. Replace master cylinder and seals.
u. Lower fluid level. Clear air vent.
v. Check and replace hose. Renew servo unit if defective.
w. Replace as necessary.

Electrical Equipment

SYMPTOMS

PROBABLE CAUSE →	a	b	c	d	e	f	g	h	i	j	k	l	m	n	o	p	q	r
STARTER FAILS TO OPERATE		*	*		*			*	*									
STARTER OPERATES BUT DOES NOT CRANK ENGINE				*		*	*											
STARTER CRANKS ENGINE SLOWLY	*	*	*															
STARTER NOISY IN OPERATION				*			*											
IGNITION WARNING LIGHT REMAINS ILLUMINATED WITH ENGINE AT SPEED										*	*	*						
IGNITION WARNING LIGHT FAILS TO ILLUMINATE WHEN IGN. IS SWITCHED ON										*	*	*						
IGNITION WARNING LIGHT STAYS ON WHEN IGN. IS SWITCHED										*	*	*						
LIGHTS DIM OR WILL NOT ILLUMINATE		*											*			*		
BULBS BLOW FREQUENTLY AND BATTERY REQUIRES FREQUENT TOPPING-UP											*							
DIRECTION INDICATORS NOT FUNCTIONING PROPERLY															*			*

PROBABLE CAUSE

a. Stiff engine.
b. Battery discharged or defective.
c. Broken or loose connection in circuit.
d. Starter pinion jammed in mesh with flywheel ring gear.
e. Starter motor defective.
f. Starter pinion does not engage with flywheel ring gear due to dirt on screwed pinion barrel.
g. Starter drive pinion defective or flywheel ring gear worn.
h. Starter solenoid switch defective.
i. Ignition/starter switch defective.
j. Broken or loose drive belt.
k. Regulator defective.
l. Generator/alternator defective.
m. Bulb burned out.
n. Mounting bolts loose.
o. Fuse blown.
p. Light switch defective.
q. Short circuit.
r. Flasher unit defective.

REMEDIES

a. Add a small quantity of oil to the fuel and run the engine carefully.
b. Recharge or replace battery.
c. Trace and rectify.
d. Release pinion.
e. Rectify fault or replace starter motor.
f. Clean and spray with penetrating oil.
g. Replace defective parts.
h. Trace fault, renew if necessary.
i. Renew switch.
j. Replace belt.
k. Adjust or replace.
l. Adjust or replace.
m. Renew bulb.
n. Tighten bolts to correct torque.
o. Replace fuse after ascertaining cause of blowing.
p. Renew switch.
q. Trace and rectify.
r. Replace unit.

Tightening Torques

ENGINE

Air cleaner attachment	0.8-1.1 kg/m	6-8 lb/ft
Alternator attachment	2.49-2.77 kg/m	(18-20 lb/ft)
Camshaft keeper plate	2.49-2.77 kg/m	(18-20 lb/ft)
Carburettor attachment	1.6-1.9 kg/m	(12-14 lb/ft)
Connecting rod bolts	5.25-5.81 kg/m	(38-42 lb/ft)
Crankshaft pulley attachment	12.44-13.83 kg/m	(90-100 lb/ft)
Cylinder head bolts	5.81-6.36 kg/m	(42-46 lb/ft)
Distributor attachment	1.11-1.38 kg/m	(8-10 lb/ft)
Distributor clamp bolt	0.42-0.56 kg/m	(3-4 lb/ft)
Distributor pedestal attachment	1.66-1.94 kg/m	(12-14 lb/ft)
Engine plate bolts	2.49-2.77 kg/m	(18-20 lb/ft)
Exhaust pipe to manifold	1.9-2.2 kg/m	(14-16 lb/ft)
Fan attachment	1.94-2.2 kg/m	(12-14 lb/ft)
Flywheel attachment	5.81-6.36 kg/m	(42-46 lb/ft)
Fuel pump attachment	1.6-1.9 kg/m	(12-14 lb/ft)
Generator bracket to block	2.49-2.77 kg/m	(18-20 lb/ft)
Generator bracket engine plate	6.22-6.91 kg/m	(45-50 lb/ft)
Generator attachment	2.77-3.05 kg/m	(16-18 lb/ft)
Generator pulley attachment	1.40-1.70 kg/m	(10-12 lb/ft)
Main bearing caps	7.60-8.30 kg/m	(55-50 lb/ft)
Manifold to cylinder head	2.8-3.0 kg/m	(20-22 lb/ft)
Oil filter	2.07-2.49 kg/m	(15-18 lb/ft)
Oil pump attachment	0.83-1.11 kg/m	(6-8 lb/ft)
Rocker pedestals	3.32-3.60 kg/m	(26-28 lb/ft)
Sparking plug	1.94-2.2 kg/m	(14-16 lb/ft)
Starter motor attachment	3.60-4.40 kg/m	(26-32 lb/ft)
Sump attachment	2.21-2.49 kg/m	(16-18 lb/ft)
Sump drain plug	2.49-2.77 kg/m	(20-22 lb/ft)
Timing cover attachment	1.94-2.21 kg/m	(14-16 lb/ft)
Timing cover setscrews (slotted)	1.11-1.38 kg/m	(8-10 lb/ft)
Water elbow attachment	2.2-2.5 kg/m	(16-18 lb/ft)
Water pump pulley attachment	2.0-2.2 kg/m	(14-16 lb/ft)
Water pump attachment	2.5-2.8 kg/m	(18-20 lb/ft)

CLUTCH

Clutch unit to flywheel	2.77 kg/m	(20 lb/ft)
Clutch housing to engine	3 87-4.15 kg/m	(28-30 lb/ft)
Clutch master and operating cylinders	2.49-2.77 kg/m	(18-20 lb/ft)

GEARBOX

Clutch housing to gearbox	3.32-3.60 kg/m	(24-26 lb/ft)
Countershaft location	1.93-2.21 kg/m	(14-16 lb/ft)
Drain and filler plugs	2.77-3.00 kg/m	(20-22 lb/ft)
Driving flange	12.40-13.80 kg/m	(90-100 lb/ft)
Gear lever shaft	0.83-1.11 kg/m	(6-8 lb/ft)
Mounting bracket	2.49-2.77 kg/m	(18-20 lb/ft)
Operating shaft attachment	0.83-1.11 kg/m	(6-8 lb/ft)
Rear extension	1.93-2.21 kg/m	(14-16 lb/ft)
Reverse idler shaft	1.93-2.21 kg/m	(14-16 lb/ft)
Reverse lever fulcrum	1.93-2.21 kg/m	(14-16 lb/ft)
Selector fork	1.11-1.38 kg/m	(8-10 lb/ft)
Speedometer sleeve	1.93-2.21 kg/m	(14-16 lb/ft)
Top cover	1.10-1.40 kg/m	(8-10 lb/ft)
Top extension	1.66-1.94 kg/m	(12-14 lb/ft)

REAR AXLE

Bearing cap to housing	4.5-4.7 kg/m	(32-34 lb/ft)
Crown wheel attachment	5.8-6.4 kg/m	(42-46 lb/ft)
Front mounting plate to axle	3.6-3.9 kg/m	(26-28 lb/ft)
Front mounting plate to chassis	3.6-3.9 kg/m	(26-28 lb/ft)
Hypoid front casing to rear	2.5-2.8 kg/m	(18-20 lb/ft)
Inner axle flange	4.4-5.0 kg/m	(32-36 lb/ft)
Pinion flange	12.4-13.8 kg/m	(90-100 lb/ft)
Road spring plate studs	3.9-4.2 kg/m	(28-30 lb/ft)
Rear axle mounting	5.3-5.5 kg/m	(38-40 lb/ft)

REAR SUSPENSION

Axle shaft coupling	3.32-3.60 kg/m	(24-28 lb/ft)
Damper lower attachment	4.15-4.42 kg/m	(30-32 lb/ft)
Damper upper attachment	5.81-6.36 kg/m	(42-46 lb/ft)
Hub nut	13.85-15.21 kg/m	(100-110 lb/ft)
Radius arm brackets to frame	3.32-3.60 kg/m	(24-26 lb/ft)
Road spring to axle unit	3.87-4.18 kg/m	(28-30 lb/ft)
Spring end to vertical link	5.81-6.36 kg/m	(42-46 lb/ft)
Top wishbone attachment	3.87-4.15 kg/m	(28-30 lb/ft)
Trunnion to wishbone	4.84-5.25 kg/m	(35.38 lb/ft)
Vertical link to hub	5.81-6.36 kg/m	(42-46 lb/ft)
Wishbone assembly to frame	3.04-3.32 kg/m	(22-24 lb/ft)
Wheel attachment	5.25-5.81 kg/m	(38-42 lb/ft)

FRONT SUSPENSION

Anti-roll bar link attachment	5.25-5.81 kg/m	(38-42 lb/ft)
Anti-roll bar link stud	1.66-1.94 kg/m	(12-14 lb/ft)
Anti-roll bar "U"-bolts	0.42-0.28 kg/m	(3-4 lb/ft)
Ball assembly to upper wishbone	2.49-2.77 kg/m	(18-20 lb/ft)
Ball assembly to vertical link	5.25-5.81 kg/m	(38-42 lb/ft)
Damper top attachment	1.12-1.38 kg/m	(8-10 lb/ft)
Damper bottom attachment	7.60-8.30 kg/m	(55-60 lb/ft)
Suspension unit sub-frame	3.60-3.87 kg/m	(26-28 lb/ft)
Fulcrum bracket to lower wishbone	3.60-3.87 kg/m	(26-28 lb/ft)
Stub axle to vertical link	12.44-15.82 kg/m	(90-100 lb/ft)
Steering tie-rod ball joint	3.60-3.87 kg/m	(26-28 lb/ft)
Vertical link, calliper plate and steering lever	4.24-4.84 kg/m	(32-35 lb/ft)
Vertical link and calliper plate	2.49-2.77 kg/m	(18-20 lb/ft)

STEERING

Coupling pinch bolt	2.49-2.77 kg/m	(18-20 lb/ft)
Column clamps	0.83-1.11 kg/m	(6-8 lb/ft)
Safety clamp friction screw	2.49-2.77 kg/m	(18-20 lb/ft)
Safety clamp attachments	0.83-1.11 kg/m	(6-8 lb/ft)
Steering unit to frame	2.49-2.77 kg/m	(18-20 lb/ft)

BRAKES

Brake calliper attachment	6.91-7.60 kg/m	(50-55 lb/ft)
Brake disc to hub	4.24-4.84 kg/m	(32-35 lb/ft)
Master cylinder attachment	2.21-2.77 kg/m	(16-20 lb/ft)
Pipe connections	0.83-1.11 kg/m	(6-8 lb/ft)
Rear backplate attachment	2.21-2.49 kg/m	(16-18 lb/ft)

1962> VITESSE 6 & 2 LITRE

Lubricate and Clean

		MO 6 12 36 / MI 6 12 36 / KM 10 20 60
CAR UP		
ENGINE	Drain oil	1 ● ● ● *
Filter	Change element	2 ● ●
	Clean element	3
GEARBOX	Check oil/top up	4 ● ● ●
	Change oil	5
Overdrive Filter	Clean element	6
AUTOMATIC TRANSM.	Drain fluid	7
Filter	Clean element	8
DIFFERENTIAL	Check oil/top up	9 ● ● ●
	Change oil	10
Limited Slip Differential	Check oil/top up	11
	Change oil	12
Sliding Joints(Drive Shaft)	Check oil/top up	13
	Change oil	14
SHOCK ABSORBERS	Check oil/top up	15
PROP./DRIVE SHAFT(S)	Lubricate	16
GREASE GUN POINTS	Lubricate	17 ● ● ● *
PEDAL SHAFT(S)	Lubricate	18 ● ● ●
HANDBRAKE	Lubricate	19 ● ●
GEAR LINKAGE	Lubricate	20
CAR LOWERED – WHEELS FREE		
WHEEL BEARINGS-Front	Repack	21 ● ● *
WHEEL BEARINGS-Rear	Repack	22 ● ●
BRAKE FLUID	Renew/bleed syst.	23
CAR DOWN – BONNET OPEN		
ENGINE	Refill with oil	24 ● ● ●
	Check oil level	25
Breather Cap	Clean	26
Air Cleaner	Service element(s)	27 ●
	Replace element(s)	28
PCV-System	Clean filter	29
	Clean valve/hose(s)	30 ● ● *
	Replace valve	31
Carburettor(s)	Clean jets/bowl	32
	Top up pist. damper	33 ● ● ● *
	Lubricate linkages	34
Fuel Bowl/Filter(s)	Clean/replace	35 ● ●
Fuel Injection Pump	Check oil level	36
Filter(s)	Clean/replace	37
AUTOMATIC TRANSM.	Refill with fluid	38
	Check fluid level	39
DISTRIBUTOR	Clean cap & ign.coil	40 ● ● ●
Spindle/Cam	Lubricate	41 ● ● ●
COOLING SYSTEM	Check/top up	42 ● ● ●
	Flush system	43
Corrosion Inhibitor	Check solution	44
Anti-Freeze	Check	45
Water Pump	Lubricate	46 ● ●
SCREENWASHER	Check/top up	47 ● ● ●
BATTERY	Check/top up	48 ● ● ●
	Check spec. gravity	49
Connections	Clean, grease	50
GENERATOR	Lubricate	51 ● ●
STEERING	Check/top up	52 ● ● *
Power Steering	Check/top up fluid	53
	Grease ram	54
	Clean filter	55
CLUTCH/BRAKE	Check/top up fluid	56 ● ● ●
BRAKE SERVO	Clean filter	57
	Renew filter	58
HYDR. SUSPENSION	Check/top up fluid	59
	Renew fluid	60
	Clean filter	61
CAR DOWN – EXTERNAL		
LOCKS, HINGES, ETC.	Lubricate	62 ● ● ●
Door Drain Holes	Clean	63
WIPER SPINDLES	Lubricate	64

EVERY

MOnths / MIles (1000) / KMs (1000) — whichever comes first

Service, Check, Adjust

		MO 6 12 36 / MI 6 12 36 / KM 10 20 60
CAR UP		
ENGINE	Check sump bolt torq.	65
Engine Mountings	Check torque	66
Engine Flame Trap	Service and clean	67
AUTOMATIC TRANSM.	Adjust brake bands	68
	Renew sump gasket	69
	Check sump bolt torq.	70
PROP./DRIVE SHAFT(S)	Check for wear	71 ● ●
	Tighten bolts	72 ● ●
SUSP., FRONT/REAR	Check for wear	73 ● ●
	Tighten bolts	74 ● ●
	Check boot gaiters	75
Shock Absorbers	Check operation	76
STEERING	Ch. compon. f. wear	77 ● ●
	Tighten bolts	78 ● ●
	Check boot gaiters	79
U-BOLTS	Check torque	80
HANDBRAKE	Check/adjust	81
CLUTCH	Check/adjust	82
GEAR LINKAGE	Check/adjust	83
EXHAUST SYSTEM	Check/tighten bolts	84 ● ●
CHECK FOR OIL, FUEL, WATER, etc. LEAKS		85 ● ●
CAR LOWERED – WHEELS FREE		
WHEEL BEARINGS	Check/adjust	86 ● ●
BRAKES	Check/adjust	87 ● ●
	Overhaul compl.syst.	88
Linings/Drums	Clean/check wear	89 ● ●
Pads/Discs	Check for wear	90 ● ●
Self-adj. Mechanism	Check	91
Cylinders, Hoses	Check for wear	92 ● ●
ROAD WHEELS	Inspect tyres	93
	Interch. & balance	94
	Adjust pressure	95 ● ●
Wheel Nuts	Check torque	96 ● ●
CAR DOWN – BONNET OPEN		
ENGINE	Check compression	97
Cylinder Head	Check torque	98
Valves	Adjust clearance	99 ● ●
Choke	Check operation	100
Mixture/Idling	Check/adjust	101 ● ●
Linkages	Adjust	102
Timing Chain	Check/adj. tension	103
V-Belt (s)	Check/adj. tension	104 ● ● ●
	Renew	105
SPARK PLUGS	Clean/set gap	106 ● ●
	Renew	107 ● ●
DISTRIBUTOR	Check/set point gap	108 ● ● ●
	Renew points	109
Dwell Angle	Check/adjust	110 ● ● ●
Ignition Timing	Check/adjust	111 ● ● ●
COOLING SYSTEM	Tighten hose clips	112
	Replace hoses	113
	Pressure test	114
STEERING	Check play, adjust	115
	Tighten bolts	116
Geometry	Check	117 ● ●
CHECK FOR OIL, FUEL, WATER, etc. LEAKS		118 ● ● ●
CAR DOWN – EXTERNAL		
LIGHTS, INSTRUMENTS	Check function	119 ● ● ●
Headlights	Check alignment	120
WIPERS	Check blades	121
SEAT BELTS	Check security, wear	122
ROAD OR DYNAMOMETER TEST		
BRAKES	Check efficiency	123 ● ● ●
AUTOMATIC TRANSM.	Check operation	124
ENGINE	Adjust, if required	125 ● ● ●
DEFECTS	Report	126

CAPACITIES

	Engine	Oil Filter	Gearbox	Automatic	Differential	Cooling inc. Heater Anti freeze	Hydr./Brake Fluid	Fuel Tank Octane	Grease	Oil can Steering box
	Ltr.Imp.Pts.USQu.	Ltr.Imp.Pts.USPts.	Ltr.Imp.Pts.USPts.	Ltr.Imp.Pts.USQu.	Ltr.Imp.Pts.USQu.	Ltr.Imp.Pts.USQu.	Ltr.Imp.Pts.USPts.	Ltr.Imp.Gls.US Gls.	Ref. No.	Ref. No.
VITESSE 2 Litre	4,5 8 4,8		0,85 1,5 1,8		0,57 1 1,2	6,2 11 6,7		38,5 8,75 11	19, 21, 22, 46, 52,	17,
VITESSE 6	4 7 4,2		OVERDRIVE: 1,35 2,3 2,8			8 14 8,4				18, 33, 34, 41, 51, 62,

LUBRICANTS

	Engine		Gearbox		Differential	Cooling inc. Heater Anti freeze	Hydr./Brake Fluid	Fuel Tank Octane	Grease	Oil can Steering box
	SAE 10W/30 SAE 10W/40 SAE 20W/50	> 0°C < 0°C	SAE 90 EP		SAE 90 EP	35 % −33°C	SAE 70 3R	97	MP	SAE 90 EP SAE 10

AUTOSERVICE DATA CHART